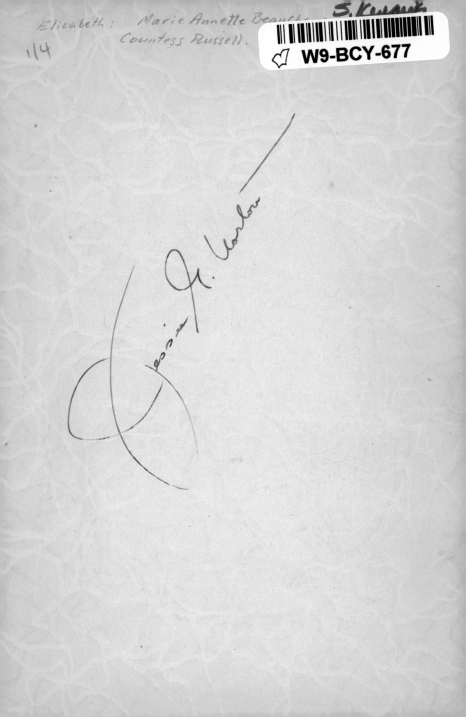

EXPIATION

BOOKS BY
ELIZABETH

*

EXPIATION

BY

E*lizabeth*

GARDEN CITY, N. Y.

DOUBLEDAY, DORAN & COMPANY, INC.

MCMXXIX

EXPIATION

EXPIATION

MILLY sat in her chair without moving. Her round, pale face was empty of expression. Her eyes were fixed on her hands, lying as if they didn't belong to her, folded, plump and passive, on her black lap. She had been like that, sitting quiet, looking at her hands, ever since it happened.

"Rouse her," the doctor had said, when poor Ernest's relations drew his attention to this conduct. But in vain did the clustered sisters-in-law try to; she remained silent, motionless, looking down at her hands folded on her black lap.

"If only she would cry," the Botts said to each other.

"A good cry would make all the difference," they agreed.

But Milly didn't cry; nor did she speak, except to murmur in her gentle voice, each time a sympathetic and condoling relative stroked her arm, or, from behind her chair, patted her bowed head, "How kind you all are."

Who wouldn't be kind to poor little Milly in her sorrow? Not only were the Botts kind, but the whole of Titford was kind. That important south London suburb appreciated the Botts, so financially sound, so continually increasing in prosperity. They were its backbone. They

subscribed, presided, spoke, opened. Titford was full of
Botts, and every one of them a credit to it. Whenever
they married, which they did punctually on arriving at
the proper age, or gave birth, which they also did
punctually, once married—except Ernest, who had
been childless,—Titford genuinely rejoiced; and whenever they died, which they did on achieving ripeness and
not before—except Ernest, who had been cut off
in a street accident,—Titford genuinely mourned, and
genuinely sympathized with the survivor; usually, by
that strange law of nature which makes the frailer
vessel to begin with yet ultimately the tougher, a
widow.

In this case the sympathy was particularly warm,
for Milly had always been popular. Long ago Titford
had decided that Mrs. Ernest Bott was a very ladylike
woman, and had taken her to its heart. Twenty-five
years almost to a month, it recollected, since poor
Ernest Bott brought his bride to the handsome red
brick house in Mandeville Park Road,—a slip of a girl
she was then, hardly more than a flapper, and looking
absurdly young to be the wife of a man nearing middle-
age, but from the very beginning behaving as a lady in
her position should, and going on behaving as she
should, in spite of what her sister did from that very
house only three months later. And so she had gone on
behaving ever since. The years rolled along, round,
comfortable, blameless years, the sister didn't reappear
and was forgotten, except deep down in the heart of the
Botts, who were slow to forget disgrace, and of all the
men in that numerous family Ernest was held to have
been the most fortunate in his marriage. Long since had
Mrs. Ernest ceased to be a slip. Long since had the
increasingly solid comfort Ernest was able to provide
had its way with her. And here she was at forty-five,

a little cushiony woman, fair-skinned and dove-eyed,
with dimples on her plump hands where other people
have knuckles, and a smooth head, sleekly covered
with agreeable hair the colour of respectability. Her
life, except for that one scandal of her sister—and who
can be responsible for what sisters do?—had been
blameless. Gossip had nothing to say about her;
criticism let her alone. She was just simply a credit to
the family and the place,—normal, well mannered,
never saying anything particular or much, ready at any
time to do a kindness, pleasantly smiling, nicely dressed,
abundantly nourished, returning calls punctually, at
first in a neat brougham with one horse which presently
developed into a pair, and later on in a car that kept on
becoming bigger, going to dinners in her velvets, going
to church in her furs or feathers, having an At Home day
once a month, amiably receiving visitors in her handsome drawing-room, listening nicely, never contradict-
ing, never being clever, never asserting, at the most
gently suggesting, and ready smilingly to withdraw her
suggestion if it seemed to be in the least degree unwel-
come.

What a wife. What a nice place the world would be
if all wives were more like Milly, the male Botts had
frequently thought—whispering it to themselves, for it
wouldn't do to say it out loud—when they had been
having trouble with their own. Ernest hadn't had a
day's trouble, an hour's bother, with Milly. Sweet little
Milly. Dear, easy-going little woman. One would do
anything for a woman like that. And so pleasant to
look at, too—so round and soft. All wives should be
round and soft, if only because one had to sleep with
them. As well ask at Whiteley's or Shoolbred's, thought
the Bott brothers, for a bony bed and expect to be
comfortable in it, as expect to be comfortable, lastingly

comfortable, with a bony wife. The bones of wives got into their characters, thought those upset Botts whose wives were thin and had recently been angry. But only secretly were they upset. Outwardly, each was an affectionate and contented husband. One has to be.

§

And here was Milly a widow, and a rich widow, and not one of the brothers a widower at the same moment and able to marry her, and keep her and poor old Ernest's money in the family. She would be snapped up at once—on the very day year. Bound to be. What man in his senses wouldn't wish to snap up Milly, even if she were poor? What man wouldn't wish, wouldn't most earnestly wish, to be gathered for the rest of his life to that soft, kind, pillowy bosom, and remain for ever safe in it from quarrels and angry words?

But the sisters-in-law, thinking of all the good Bott money, said, "Of course she won't dream of marrying again. Why should she, now that she will be so well off, and can do as she pleases?"

And that one of the sisters-in-law who had a temperament, and prided herself on it, and told her husband, when he remonstrated, that he ought to thank God on his knees that he had married a real woman and not the usual fish, said, "It isn't as if she had any sort of *go* in her. What does poor Milly, of all women, want with a man?"

And the old lady in whose house these things were being talked of, the oldest of anybody, the original old Mrs. Bott, who was many times a grandmother and a great-grandmother, and had even begun to be a great-great-grandmother, and who lived benignly on the top of Denmark Hill so as to be within easy reach, as she often said, of all her dear children in case they needed her, and yet not so close as to oppress them—the old lady recalled in silence, as she sat slowly shaking her head because of this speech of George's wife, who was more of a gipsy than a gentlewoman, old Mrs. Bott sometimes thought, but refrained from saying because she long had known that in families the more you refrain from saying the better,—the old lady recalled in silence an odd scene ten years before in that very room, when Milly, so quiet and well-behaved till then, had walked in one warm spring morning (it must have been spring and warm, for she remembered the French window was wide open and the gardener was mowing the lawn, which had suddenly become a field of daisies), and then had gone to the window and watched what was being done for a time, and then had turned round with a jerk, looking queer and different and very hot, too, poor child, after her walk, and said that she was feeling as if she might soon be rather tired of everything.

"Everything, *everything!*" she had then cried quite loud, as if she couldn't hold herself in a moment longer, flinging out both hands in a funny gesture, and crimson in the face from climbing the hill in the heat; and she had added, with tears in her eyes, "I can't any longer— I've come to the end——"

The end? thought old Mrs. Bott. Which end? There were so many ends to life, and in one's younger years one was always coming to them, and then finding that they weren't ends at all.

Well, well. She had given her a nice cup of tea. Poor Milly. There was a man in *that*, for dead certain, she decided; either Ernest and tiffs, or some new man and what these poor, eager, tormented children called love.

Whatever it was, however, it passed. Milly never said any more, and soon was her own gentle, contented self again; indeed, a few weeks after this little outburst she had become much sweeter, if possible, and more contented than ever before. Learning wisdom, thought the old lady. Settling down. One does.

Poor children, old Mrs. Bott often thought, contemplating her posterity,—so hard for them sometimes. And they didn't know, and nobody could tell them, because they wouldn't believe, how quiet and comfortable everything was going to be at last, and how little their troubles in the long run would really have mattered. No need to have worried so much, and eaten out their poor hot hearts,—no need, no need at all.

And now ten years later here was Milly bereaved, and so much overwhelmed that nothing roused her from the silent contemplation of her lap. There in the bedroom she sat, the bedroom from which Ernest had issued that last morning, never dreaming he wouldn't come back to it again, and old Mrs. Bott, brought over from Denmark Hill for the funeral, and sitting upstairs with Milly while the Will was being read in the dining-room, vainly tried to comfort her, laying her shaky hand at intervals on the motionless crape-clad shoulder, and saying such words as seemed most likely to be the right ones.

If only the shoulder would heave, thought old Mrs. Bott; if only poor Milly would cry. It was so much more like the very extremity of grief not to heave, not to cry, to sit pale and silent, with her head hanging like that. Who would have thought Milly had loved Ernest so much? The old lady dispassionately recalled her son, and wondered.

"You know, my dear," she quavered, for by this time she was extremely old, and everything about her quavered, "we shall all take such care of you, and see that you are never lonely."

Milly's head hung lower.

"The girls"—so old Mrs. Bott spoke of her daughters and daughters-in-law, by this time every one of them in the forties and fifties and sixties—"have made up their minds that you are to be their special care."

Milly's drooped eyelashes faintly quivered.

"And it isn't as if there were going to be any difference in your style of living, my dear, because Alec tells me"—Alec was the eldest son—"Ernest was even better off than we had been able to guess—I'm sure I don't know why men should be so secretive about what they're making—and you'll have all of it, and stay on in your nice house that you're so fond of."

"I—I don't deserve——" gasped Milly, faintly.

Was that a tear? Something dropped, surely, on her lap.

"There, there," quavered old Mrs. Bott, renewing her patting, her own eyes filling with tears. "There, there. Nobody ever deserved all we can any of us give you more than you, Milly, my dear. There, there. You'll be the better for a little cry—ever so better."

And she cried a little herself; only a little, for the years had dried up most of her tears. But a recollection of the days when Ernest was a baby had come into her mind, and all her hopes of him and all her pride, and how he had had tiny fair curls she used to twist into shape round her fingers—he who for so many, many years had been bald; and it seemed strange and sad to know that he was lying alone now under his wreaths—beautiful wreaths, too, and such a number of them—in the cemetery up the hill, and going to lie like that till kingdom-come, and nothing to show for having been alive at all, except his widow and his money. No children, that is. Ernest, in the matter of posterity, had been a blind alley, a *cul-de-sac*. Strange and sad not to go on in any way, to come to a dead stop. Old Mrs. Bott couldn't help crying a little to think of it. Poor Ernest;

all his tiny fair curls and pretty ways to end in nothing but a widow.

"It's only a dream," she said, drying her eyes and nodding her head wisely. "Life's just a dream." And she added, as through the open side window an unmistakable smell drifted from the house next door, "Curry, *I'll* be bound, at Glenmorgan to-day for lunch."

Then, laying her hand again on Milly's shoulder, and in her mind's eye gazing down the immense vistas of the years of her own life at all the little black dots strewn along them that were deaths, and seeing how small these dots had become, and how they dwindled smaller till the first ones were almost invisible, and it was quite difficult to sort them out and know which was which and whose was whose, she said, a second time wisely nodding her head, "It's all dreams, my dear. In the long run nothing, Milly my dear, but dreams." And her hand still shaking on Milly's shoulder, she stared with her red old eyes at the house opposite, and thought how queer it was the way the personalities those death-dots represented had disappeared out of her mind—her husband, for instance, dead these fifty years, only now came back with any clearness when she forgot at night to put the lid back on the vaseline. Every night throughout her grown-up life she had rubbed her eyelids with vaseline before going to sleep; and sometimes she had forgotten to cover the pot up again, and when that happened, and in the morning poor Alexander saw it, he used to scold her. He said, she recollected, that it was dirty and insanitary, and he talked of germs and dust getting in. And now, whenever she woke in the morning and saw the lid not on the pot, back he came as distinct and fresh as ever; never else. Queer, thought old Mrs. Bott, mechanically patting Milly's shoulder, and deep in contemplation of the strangeness of life, that there should be nothing left at all of poor Alexander except when a pot of vaseline had its lid off.

She blinked a little. The sun lay very brightly on the red house opposite, and dazzled her eyes. Life was certainly just a dream. From that house, too, came a smell of food; chiefly cauliflowers this time old Mrs. Bott opined, lifting an interested nose. Life was a dream, it was true, but a dream with waking moments. Right up to the very end meals were real and interesting. No doubt, she thought, her nose lifted, those were the people Ernest had complained of who had fads, he said, and wouldn't eat meat, and said rude things about England. "Poor creatures," she thought indulgently, "they've got to go through with it"—and she wished for their sakes they would go through with it quickly, for meanwhile they were missing a good many nice slices of mutton, and she supposed it would be difficult to like England or anything else if one were full of nothing but cauliflowers.

Then, as she was thinking this, the bedroom door opened a crack, and the head of her youngest son Bertie, a meat-fed man of fifty-two, was put through so carefully that it was evident the rest of him was on tiptoe.

"Come in, Bertie, and shut the door," quavered old Mrs. Bott. "No use making draughts."

"Do you," he asked in the half whisper of the occasion, looking at his sister-in-law, "feel equal to a talk?"

"Speak up, Bertie," quavered his mother. "No use standing there just making faces. Equal to a talk? Of course she is. Milly is always equal to anything—aren't you, my dear?" And again she patted the crape-clad shoulder, for of all her daughters-in-law she was fondest of this one. Much the fondest. She loved her.

Bertie took a neat, swift step into the room, and deftly

shut the door behind him, without making a sound; and there was such practice in the movement, such a completely noiseless dexterity, very surprising in one so big and heavy, that for the first time it occurred to old Mrs. Bott that perhaps he wasn't a faithful husband. So much skill in the silent shutting of doors. . . . Well, well; poor children; they had to fight it all out. She only hoped Bertie didn't worry too much about it, and make himself miserable with qualms. When he was as old as she was he would see that these things too were dreams, and to have qualms about what turned out afterwards to have been nothing but a dream was a sad waste of time.

"My poor Milly," began Bertie gravely, as one whose tidings were evil.

He seemed strangely moved. Quite upset, in fact, thought old Mrs. Bott, observing him with watery-eyed surprise; and crossing to where his sister-in-law sat he drew up a chair beside her, and put his hand on her arm with such an obvious desire to impart courage that old Mrs. Bott's surprise increased. Courage? What did Milly want with courage, when she was going to inherit several thousands a year?

"Has the Will been read?" she asked.

"He must have been ill," was Bertie's answer, as he cleared his throat.

"Ill?" echoed his mother. "Do you mean when he took that taxi?"

"When he made the Will," said Bertie, looking very uncomfortable. "Or rather, when he added the codicil."

It was evident to old Mrs. Bott now that there was to be a blow. "What codicil, my dear?" she quavered, across Milly's bowed head.

Bertie glanced at Milly. Fancy having to hit anything so gentle, so dove-like and patient, as the round black figure in the chair. Her feet were on a footstool because

her legs were so short, and it seemed to Bertie to make
his unpleasant job more difficult that poor Milly's legs
shouldn't reach the floor. Dear little legs too, he'd be
bound. He jerked back his thoughts. This wasn't the
moment to think of things like that.

"Poor old Milly," he said, taking her hand.

"Say what you've got to say, Bertie," quavered old
Mrs. Bott.

"I'm afraid it's a bad business—a very bad business,"
said Bertie, shaking his head and extremely reluctant to
go on.

"No good beating about the bush, then," said his
mother.

And then, holding Milly's hand so tight that it hurt,
he burst out that he couldn't understand Ernest—he
simply couldn't.

"Why?" quavered old Mrs. Bott, very anxious indeed.

"It's so *unfair*," said Bertie. "It isn't even com-
monly *decent*."

"But why, my son?" asked old Mrs. Bott, her mouth
quivering.

"Why?" repeated Bertie, dropping Milly's hand,
which lay inert where it fell, and getting up and going
to the window. He stood looking out. He couldn't look
at Milly—not while he hit her.

"Why?" he said again, his back to the two women.
"That's just what *I* want to know. He's only left Milly
a thousand pounds—one beggarly thousand, out of the
whole hundred thousand he'd got, and the rest is all to
go to a damned charity. Is that the way to behave to a
wife who has devoted herself for twenty-five years?
And to Milly, of all wives!"

The old lady sat staring at his back, her mouth
quivering so much that she could hardly speak.

"Whatever——" she began.

"And everything is to be sold—the house, furniture, every blessed thing—and given to this charity. Such a charity too!" He spun round in his indignation, and faced them. "He must have been stark mad. It's some Home of Rescue in Bloomsbury for fallen women. Why, none of us ever had anything to do with things like that. I didn't know Ernest had ever given such places a thought. It suggests—I'm blest if I know what it doesn't suggest. And for Milly, for the best wife a man ever had, nothing. Not a stick of furniture. Nothing but the bare thousand pounds. To keep her for a bit from starving, I suppose. To keep her out of the nearest gutter. It's the most scandalous——"

Old Mrs. Bott got up. She got up with difficulty, and Bertie had to go and help her. "I'm going downstairs," she said. "I don't believe a word of it. I shall ask Ernest's solicitor for myself."

"You won't get much out of *him*," said Bertie, helping her. "Of all the thin-lipped, cold-blooded——"

But he didn't try to keep her back; on the contrary, he encouraged her to go, leading her to the door by her elbow and assisting her carefully down to the dining-room.

Then he came back. Milly was sitting just as he had left her. He shut the door, swiftly and softly, and stood against it with his hands spread out behind him, as if to prevent anyone from coming in.

"Look here, Milly," he said, "there's something more. Mother'll hear that, too, before she sees you again. I only hope it won't get into the papers—you know how they put in whatever a man says in his Will that's at all out of the way. And what do you think Ernest put in his?"

Milly, her eyes bent on her hands, shook her patient head.

"He said, after leaving you the thousand pounds,

and expressly adding the word 'only,' which in itself is as good as a slap in the face—the whole thing beats me altogether—he said, 'My wife will know why.'"

§

For an instant Milly's mild eyes were veiled by some immediately suppressed emotion. Colour rushed across her face, and left it paler than ever. Her lips dropped apart. She raised her head and looked at Bertie, and her hands, so listless before, tightened in her lap.

Of course, thought Bertie. Naturally. Feeling the slur. What a damned mean thing to have done. Poor little Milly. Kind, sweet little woman, who wouldn't hurt a fly, to be served so. A wife in a thousand Milly had been, and now look at this. He had always supposed Ernest was a decent chap—a bit glum sometimes, when his liver was worrying him, but decent. How unpleasant, seeing that he was dead, to have to realize that he had been nothing but a cad. Some petty quarrel, some impulsive visit to his solicitor, some nursed resentment, and a life's devotion and affection wiped out with a smack in the face. A *post-mortem* smack, too,—of all smacks the meanest, thought Bertie. Not that Bertie for a moment believed Milly would or could ever quarrel. It must have been entirely on Ernest's side. The best one could say for him was that he was ill when he put in the codicil, having probably one of his worst liver attacks. But to let a liver attack turn a man permanently into a scoundrel!

"I've *done* with him—*done* with him," he vehemently declared; just as if there still was anything left of Ernest to be done with.

Milly, however, neither saw him nor heard him. Her eyes, wide open, were fixed now on the window, her hands tight together in her lap.

"How long?" her pale, astonished lips managed to get out, while she stared at the red wall of the house opposite.

"What, my dear? What, my poor little girl?" said Bertie, hurrying across and bending over her. A dear little woman. A dear, dear little woman. And with such pretty dark eyelashes too curling up at their tips. His wife hadn't got any. None visible, that is. Sandy.

"When?" whispered Milly, staring straight in front of her.

"When? Do you mean when he put it in? Two years ago. It's in a codidil. It beats me," said Bertie, his eyes moist with angry sympathy as he felt the warm roundness of the shoulder his hand was resting on, "how he could ever have quarrelled with you. And the worst of it is," he went on indignantly, "I can't let myself go about him because he's dead, and it wouldn't be decent. But I can tell you this, Milly——"

"Hush," she whispered, catching the hand on her shoulder quickly in hers, her eyes on the red wall opposite. So he had known. So Ernest had known. Two years ago. For two whole years he had known. Extraordinary. Incredible. . . .

"I can tell you this," persisted Bertie, refusing to hush, "that we're not going to let you suffer because Ernest chooses to behave like a damned——"

"Oh, don't," gasped Milly. "Please—I can't bear—you mustn't——"

And for the first time since Ernest's death she began really to cry. Laying her cheek in an abandonment of grief on the hand she held in hers, she cried so bitterly that her whole body shook. "Poor Ernest——" she sobbed. "Poor, poor Ernest——"

Bertie was profoundly moved. "Milly, you really are an *angel*," he said.

THE other Botts, however, didn't take it like that.

At first they too were indignant with Ernest, and ashamed of him, besides being very cold to the solicitor who had lent himself to the drawing up of such a scandalous codicil; but presently, after he had packed up his attaché case and gone, and they still all lingered there uncertain what to do next, there gradually spread among them an extremely unpleasant word, passed on somehow from one mouth to another, and whispered round till at last it got to George's wife, who said it out loud.

The word was *Fishy*.

The moment it had been said it was recognised as appropriate. There was no getting away from it—fishy was the word. A man didn't do what Ernest had done, and for two years allow it to remain unaltered, without some good, some tremendous reason.

﹒ "Oh, yes, he does, if he's a sneak and a coward," burst out Bertie.

"Bertie!" they cried, shocked; and suggested he should remember that Ernest was dead.

"I can't help that," said Bertie—as if anybody had supposed he could.

His wife looked at him with narrowed eyes. She had long suspected him of being more interested in Milly than brothers-in-law are supposed to be.

Old Mrs. Bott expressed a wish to be taken home. Poor children; they were going to quarrel. And all of

no use, if only they could be got to see it—just waste of
time and emotions, poor things. But nothing would
stop them once they began. She might, then, just as well
be at home. Better. Having tea.

"Alec, my dear, will you take me home?" she
quavered, trying to attract her eldest son's attention,
who was so much confounded and bewildered by what
had happened that he didn't hear.

All the Botts were confounded and bewildered, and
stood about in the dining-room in confused groups, taking no notice of the refreshments spread ready on the
side-table, and shutting the door—Fred thought of
that—on the maids who tried to bring in soup and
coffee. This wasn't the moment for having maids about,
nor for eating and drinking; though George's wife, the
one with the temperament, whose eyes were bright
with excitement and curiosity, and who after all wasn't
by blood a Bott, did furtively nibble chocolates.

"Fancy Milly," she whispered, being the first definitely to fasten the fishiness on her. "That quiet,
meek mouse. Just fancy!"

Yes—fancy Milly indeed, the other sisters-in-law
thought.

Nothing like this had ever happened to the family
before. They stood staring at each other. And there
was Titford looming in the background, unconscious
for the moment, but sure, unless the most minute precautions were taken, to know soon, as it always did
know soon on every occasion when there was anything
to know. What was to be done? Certainly, without any
doubt whatever, the thing was fishy.

"You remember her sister?" Bertie's wife whispered.

Remember? They remembered as if it were yesterday. The same blood, their eyes said, as they nodded
shocked heads, come out again. But blood that comes

out at forty-five is much worse, of course, than blood
that comes out at nineteen.

No, no, said the brothers and brothers-in-law, pulling
themselves together, it couldn't be. Too bad, too bad
to think for a moment that Milly . . . The truth was,
Ernest was a coward, with the deuce of a temper, which
he didn't dare let out because he knew nobody would
believe Milly could possibly give him any reason to be
angry. So he revenged himself like this, he played this
low-down trick on her. It was pretty unpleasant having
to regard him, now that he was dead and all that, as a
cad, but there it was.

Yes, yes, it must be, said the sisters and sisters-in-law
—and how could his brothers speak so of poor Ernest,
who was dead? Unpleasant as it was, they admitted, to
have to think of Milly, who had always been held up to
them as a pattern of what a wife should be—they looked
at their husbands—and what a daughter should be—
they looked at the old lady—unpleasant as it was to
have to think of her as deceiving them, it was much
worse to defame the dead. Clearly Milly had somehow
profoundly injured Ernest. She must have. She had.
That codicil could be explained in no other way. For
two whole years, and probably longer, she had been
taking them all in; she, at her age, and with her figure.

"Look here, you scrag women—you leave Milly's
figure alone," burst out Bertie.

What a thing to say, they thought, indignant and
shocked; what a thing to say on an occasion which had
only just left off being a funeral.

"Alec, my dear——" quavered old Mrs. Bott, again
trying to attract his attention.

"Shut up, Bertie," muttered his brother George, a
quiet, stout man in horn-rimmed spectacles.

He would have liked to say something of the sort

himself, but what was the use? After all, he and his
brothers had to sleep with their wives, and it made a
good deal of a hash up of one's business next day if there
hadn't been quiet in bed. That, thought George, who
was a plain, sensible man with plain, sensible thoughts,
was where wives got one: they could, and did, wear one
down in bed.

"Alec, my dear——"

"It's waste of time to squabble," said Fred, the rich-
est of the family, taking out his watch.

"I should say it's great waste of time forgetting that
one is supposed to be a gentleman," said Alec's wife,
usually of few words but stirred by Bertie's rudeness.

"The question surely is," said Alec, stroking his
beard nervously, "not what Milly has done or not done,
nor even"—he smiled propitiatingly at the assembled
wives—"what the poor little thing's figure is like, but
what steps we must take to keep this quiet. It seems to
me most important that we should keep it quiet."

Yes, they saw that; they were all agreed as to that.
And they shuddered as they pictured to themselves the
sorts of things Titford would say if it heard that Ernest
had disinherited his wife, and left everything, except
that one insulting thousand pounds, to a charity. It
mustn't hear. At all costs it must be prevented hearing.
That charity! The more they thought of it the more
ashamed they were. Indeed, no room had ever before
held so many people being so much ashamed as Ernest's
dining-room that afternoon. They were ashamed of
him, ashamed of the solicitor, ashamed of Milly, but
most of all, they discovered on thinking it over, were
they ashamed of the charity. A Home of Rescue for
Fallen Women? Extraordinary to have chosen such a
thing. Entirely unaccountable, this was, on Ernest's
part.

Then, somehow, it too was accounted for. No one knew who first accounted for it, but the explanation began to drift round among the sisters-in-law, passing from ear to ear in a whisper. A horrible explanation. It was, *He wished to provide for her future.*

There was a shiver, a silence, and then from somebody a faint giggle.

"Alec, my dear——" quavered old Mrs. Bott more insistently. Poor children; bent on being angry and unkind. So much better to have some nice hot soup and a sandwich, and then go quietly home and sleep it all off.

"I wish to *God*——" burst out Bertie a second time, bringing his fist down on the table with such a crash that the cups leapt in their saucers.

But what he wished he didn't say. He stopped, all red, looking as if his collar were going to choke him. No good; better hold on to oneself, he thought, remembering, he too, the importance of his night's rest. And there was that delicate business next day with Palliser and Leeds to fix up. He couldn't afford to go into that with his nerves all in rags.

Fred again looked at his watch. "We're wasting time," he observed.

"Quite," said Alec, nervously stroking his beard. He was the only Bott with a beard, and it was a very beautiful one—silvery, as became his years, and long, and always spotlessly clean, and a great comfort to him whenever he was worried or nervous, for then he stroked it and it soothed him.

"What line are we going to take about Milly?" asked Fred, shutting his watch, a gold hunter bequeathed him by his father, with a click.

"Much more important," said Bertie's wife, "is what line are we going to take about Titford."

"Isn't it the same thing?" one of the brothers-in-law,

a mild man, suggested; and surely, he thought, he hadn't said it aggressively? But Bertie's wife appeared to think he had, for she turned to him with some tartness, and said it wasn't. "At least," she said, "it doesn't seem so to me, but then I'm not as clever, perhaps, as you."

"Poor old Bertie," thought the brother-in-law.

"Poor little children," thought old Mrs. Bott. "Alec, my dear——" she said aloud.

"It *is* the same thing," said Fred. "The same thing to a T."

"I rather think so too," ventured Alec, his hand deep in his beard. How much he dreaded family conclaves. The women, when they got together, seemed to work each other up so. Separately, they were quite nice and good-natured. What was the matter with them, that they should be so unmanageable when they got together? Even Ruth, his quiet wife . . .

Then Walter Walker, of Shadwell and Walker, the great wool-brokers in Threadneedle Street, lifted up his voice and offered the suggestion for what it was worth— "For what it's worth, mind you," he repeated, anxious to show he knew he wasn't really a Bott but only connected, and therefore had little to say in this—that Milly should be taken into each of their homes in turn for three months at a time, perhaps six; taken in, and made much of, poor woman, he added, forcing himself to gaze round courageously through his spectacles at his sisters-in-law. Because, he affirmed, continuing courageous, this was not only the decent attitude, surely, to one who had always deserved well of them and had suddenly lost everything, husband, fortune, and home, and who was childless into the bargain——

"Whose fault is that?" interrupted his wife.

"My dear, you're not going to suggest that it was her fault she lost Ernest?" asked Walter mildly.

"Or that she's childless?" asked Bertie.

"Don't let's be *coarse*, please," said Bertie's wife, narrowing her eyes at him.

"You know perfectly well what I mean," said Walter's wife. "Whose fault is it that she lost her fortune?"

"Ernest's, of course," said Bertie.

"It's a pity, Bertie, that you will persist in taking that line about the dead," said Alec's wife.

Poor children; all so angry. And Ernest himself, over whom they were quarrelling, quite quiet up there on the hill, under his beautiful wreaths. "Alec, my dear——"

"Well, we won't go into that now," said Fred, looking at his watch a third time.

"Shall I finish my sentence?" asked Walter Walker mildly.

"By all means," said Alec, finding comfort in his beard.

"It's not only the decent attitude," continued Walter, clearing his throat, "but the best, quite the best way, of stopping criticism and gossip. In my opinion—I offer it, of course"—he glanced round deprecatingly—"for what it is worth—Milly should be taken in by the family in turn, and rather conspicuously made much of."

"Do you mean taken in for always?" asked his wife.

"Why not?" he said.

"Do you mean for the rest of her days she is to go round visiting us?" asked Bertie's wife incredulously.

"Why not?" said Walter Walker again.

There was a silence. The women looked at each

other. Putting aside the making much of Milly, which
was absurd of Walter, for why on earth should she,
who had brought such trouble and disgrace on them, be
made much of?—putting that aside, taking in was, they
felt, a delicate job. In the happiest of circumstances
they could imagine it would be a delicate job, unless the
person taken in was well enough off not to need it.
These weren't happy circumstances. These were most
doubtful ones, the Bott wives were sure, and the Bott
husbands uneasily suspected. It would be asking rather
a good deal of human nature, the wives thought—
except George's wife, who was excited and curious, and
would have liked to begin taking in Milly at once—to
have Milly in their homes, in their very bosoms, among
their innocent children and grandchildren, after whatever it was she had done. And to be asked to make much
of her into the bargain!

"Walter's quite right," said Fred.

"She certainly has got to live somewhere," said Alec.

"And you can't live on the interest of a thousand
pounds," Walter Walker pointed out deprecatingly.
"You can die on it, of course, but, even then, only in an
attic or a cellar. I'm sure none of us want Milly to die,
let alone in an attic or a cellar."

"I pay my typist a hundred and fifty a year," said
Fred. "Three times as much as the most we can get
safely for Milly. And it doesn't seem to stop her from
being a hungry-looking thing."

"Certainly we can't have one of our family either living or dying in an attic or a cellar," said Alec, shocked
at the picture Walter's words had conjured up.

No; they couldn't have that, of course, agreed the
wives and sisters. The family had always behaved well
and generously in regard to money, and it would never
do for Titford to suspect them of meanness. It did look

as if Milly might have to be taken in. But how unpleasant; how awkward; how certain to be painful.

"And the sooner the better," said Bertie.

"Beginning with us, I suppose," said his wife, narrowing her eyes at him.

"She's like a toothpick," thought Bertie, glowering at her. "She's got the figure of a toothpick." Aloud he said, forcing himself to speak calmly, "The house may be sold any day over Milly's head. I didn't like the look in that fellow's eye—that solicitor fellow of Ernest's. He's got a down on her."

"Perhaps he knows more than we do," said his wife.

Again Bertie glowered at her, and held on to himself.

"Why Ernest should leave us all out, and appoint as his executors this solicitor, whom none of us know, and the director of that very unpleasant charity——" began Alec, clutching his beard.

"Yes. I don't understand," said Walter Walker.

"There's something dashed queer about it," said Fred.

"Fishy," said George's wife.

Really, the more they considered it, fishy was the only word.

"But when you say, you men, that we're not only to take her in but to make much of her——" began Bertie's wife.

"She *is* a toothpick," thought Bertie, thrusting his hands into his pockets and walking over to a window and staring out, "boring away, boring away——"

"Only a man would have an idea like that," said Walter Walker's wife, looking severely at her husband, who also went to a window, another one, and gazed abstractedly at the view, which was a conifer.

"Well, hang it all," said Fred, who, being the most successful of a successful family, was also the boldest, "you can't not make much of her. It wouldn't be human. Petting's what she wants."

Petting?

There was a scandalised silence.

"No doubt you men will find it all quite easy," then said Fred's wife unexpectedly, for she usually kept pretty quiet.

"Yes—you've always been absurd, quite absurd about Milly," said the eldest Bott sister.

"You've bored us stiff with her virtues, and Milly this, and Milly that," said another sister.

"Rubbing her in till we got tired of her very name," said another.

"Actually admiring her for having lost her figure," said another; and the four wives of the four Bott brothers nodded their heads in agreement.

The men were amazed at this sudden flare of bitterness. The two at the windows turned round to stare. Why, they had always understood their wives were very fond of Milly, someone was heard to murmur.

"Fond of Milly? Of course we were fond of Milly," they cried. "But that never blinded us to——"

"Besides, you know quite well it's different now——"

"You yourselves admit what has happened is fishy——"

And the room, for the next ten minutes, was a babel of heated and disjointed conversation.

Poor children; poor children; all getting so hot and angry. The old lady could only sit and listen, her shaking hands clutching the top of her stick. No good trying to stop them. They had to go through with it. And presently the room would be quiet again, and the noise and anger have happened yesterday, last month, last year, twenty years ago, and be slid away for ever into silence. And then, before they could turn round, before they had had really time to think, these poor excited children would be quiet too, and asleep as Ernest was asleep. It seemed a pity they didn't realize, and that nobody could make them realize, that in the end it all wouldn't have mattered a bit what Ernest had meant or what Milly had done, and that they might just as well have been kind and happy together on this particular afternoon, as indeed on all their few afternoons, and together comfortably eaten the nice soup and sandwiches. Milly's cook made beautiful soup and sandwiches. Pity to waste everything like this, and all just so as to be angry and say unkind things.

She made a great effort, and by laying hold of the chimney-piece with one hand, and heavily leaning on her stick with the other, pulled herself up out of the chair.

They turned and looked at her, surprised. They had forgotten she was there.

"My dears," quavered the old lady, the stick shaking beneath her weight, "I want to go home."

"Why of course, mother," said Fred, who was nearest. "Tired?" he asked, drawing her arm through his and patting it.

"I'll send for the car," said Alec, ringing the bell.

"Never saw you, mother, you've been sitting so quiet," said George.

"And, my dears—" she looked round at them, "don't quarrel."

"We're discussing," said the eldest daughter, who had married late in life, and it had been a great relief to old Mrs. Bott when she did, because it seemed at one time as if she were never going to, and that would have been a pity; for till a woman had been through a husband, the old lady held, she didn't really know what God could do to her. "Mother," explained this daughter to the others, who were well acquainted with the theory, "always thinks we're quarrelling when we discuss anything."

"And so you usually are, my dears," said the old lady. "And it makes you so hot. Look at your poor hot faces. I wish you'd all have some nice soup. I can smell it through the door. It's waiting ready in the kitchen, I'm sure. It'll do you good."

"Mother," said the eldest daughter, again explaining to the others, who were well acquainted with this theory also, "invariably thinks everything can be settled by soup or a cup of tea."

"And so it usually can, my dear," said the old lady, holding on to Fred's arm.

"Not at all an unsound theory," said the youngest daughter's husband, a Mr. Noakes, of the Welsh Widowers' Life Assurance; and George's wife agreed with him. "Let's have in that soup, Alec—soup, and a glass of sherry, eh?"

"And my dears," the old lady continued, addressing them collectively from Fred's arm, "no need to worry your poor heads about Milly and taking her in, because I would like to take her in myself, please—take her in and make much of her, Walter my dear," she said, nodding her head at her Walker son-in-law.

"You, mother?"

The family stared.

"But you can't afford——" someone began.

"Can't I, my dears?" she interrupted. "Well, I daresay I can't—but you can. You can all subscribe. So much each. Whatever you think will be enough for poor Milly. She won't want much. She's a small eater."

The family now stared at each other. Why, of course; the real, the only solution. And so safe. Out of everybody's way, wrapped round, impenetrably to tongues,

in the mantle of the old lady's affection and respectability—how was it nobody had thought of it before? Fancy
mother, at her age, still being the one to think of things!
And it needn't cost much either, said the portion of the
family described by old Mrs. Bott as the girls, making
rapid calculations; there wouldn't be so very much to
subscribe. The interest on the thousand pounds would
go a long way, and there were nine brothers and sisters,
and if each paid, say, fifty pounds a year——

Fifty each? Oh, no—much too much. Fifty each
would make five hundred a year with her own fifty, and
nothing whatever for her to spend it on.

Thirty each, then.

George's wife said it ought to be fifty, and the other
wives said it was all very well for her, who had only one
child and accordingly hardly anything to spend George's
money on——

Twenty, said somebody. Twenty each would be
ample.

George's wife still persisted it ought to be fifty, and
Alec's wife said she thought perhaps thirty——

So they then decided that best of all would be simply
to pay mother's housekeeping books, and divide whatever they came to.

"Isn't she to have any clothes?" asked Fred.

Clothes? Why, she was a widow, and widows didn't
want clothes—not for at least a year, said the wives.
And after that there were all the clothes she had been
wearing before this happened. Not for years, as far as
they could see, would she need any more clothes.

"Considering that it's our money that's going to pay
for Milly——" began Bertie.

"Not altogether your money," said his eldest sister,
conscious that she and her sisters each had money of
their own; and the old lady, anxious there should be no

more arguing, interrupted again, and said, "I'll take
Milly now, if she'll come. Go up and fetch her, Alec
my dear. Then we'll be home in time for a nice cup of
tea."

§

But Alec brought the message down that Milly was
asleep, and had left word asking them to be so kind as
not to disturb her.

"Fancy being able to sleep," murmured Bertie's
wife.

"Poor child—sleeping it off," said old Mrs. Bott.
"To-morrow, then," she added, as she was led out and
carefully hoisted into the car by Alec and Fred. "You
can bring her over on your way to the City, Alec my
dear."

When to-morrow came, however, and a deputation of
the brothers went round to Mandeville Park Road to
tell Milly what had been arranged, and explain that it
was not merely the best but the only thing to do, and
that she couldn't possibly stay where she was, because
at any moment the house might be sold, they found
that she had left that morning before breakfast, and
no one knew where she had gone.

⁂(III)⁂

FOR Milly had sinned.

During the entire length of ten whole years she had
been sinning. The suspicions of her sisters-in-law, and
the uneasiness of her brothers-in-law, were only too
well justified: she had taken the Botts in, and for all
those years had been unfaithful to Ernest.

It had begun quite by chance. And what a chance,
thought Milly, looking back now with the horrified
clear vision which is the portion of the found out, at the
beginning. Such small things had made it begin. Five
minutes earlier, five minutes later, and she never
would have met Arthur. A missed train, a slower taxi,
even just a pause to watch the pigeons in the courtyard,
or, indeed, even a little decent reserve, and she would
have been saved. But the train was caught, the taxi
was swift, the pigeons didn't interest her, and in she
went; and there, in the British Museum, in the gallery
where the busts of the Roman emperors are, she met
Arthur Oswestry, and they sinned.

Ultimately, that is. For a long while they hadn't an
idea that they were going to. Sin creeps along towards
one, she discovered, looking quite good for quite a
long while. It had taken weeks of meetings before it
really began—meetings again at the British Museum,
then at the National Gallery, in tea-shops, in parks,
and even once in Westminster Abbey, which did seem
peculiarly wrong—weeks of talk, pleasant, comforting,
illuminating after the Titford talk, and presently weeks

29

of doubts, accompanied by tremors and flushing if
Ernest's unconscious eye happened to rest on her more
than usual when she got home, and by starting if he
suddenly spoke—ah, how base, how contemptible this
wretched love-business was, she saw now—and then
weeks of an increasing desire to avoid the Botts and
get out of her engagements, and then weeks of quivering
reluctances and stabbing yearnings, and then weeks of
agonized efforts to stick to her duty, of repeated attempts to keep away from Arthur, not to see him, to
forget him, wipe him out. In fact, it took a long while.
But it did begin ultimately; and they entered into that
condition of doubtful bliss, of continual looking forward
and continual unfulfilled expectation, of wonderful
dreams when they weren't together and acute, knife-
edged reactions when they were, and always terror,
terror, terror of being found out, which is passionate
love. Illicit passionate love, that is; passionate love
except for one's own husband. In other words, as Milly
well knew at the beginning, and now was once more
overwhelmed by knowing, Sin.

Who would ever have suspected, thought Milly at the
time, amazed at the upheaval in her entire nature, that
she should be capable of passionate love? It was the
very last thing she had suspected of herself. She was
thirty-five then, and Arthur was forty-five, and she had
never been in any sort of love before, least of all passionate; and neither, particularly, so he said, had he. As for
him, his kind sister who had lived with him had lately
died, and he was lonely and miserable and cold, and he
found Milly; his life had grown suddenly empty and
thin, and he found this soft, dear, loving little woman,
this sweet, pillowy little thing, with no children and
brimful, as he presently discovered, of thwarted ma-
ternalness. She was crying, too, that day, and he never

could bear to see anyone cry—standing glued, almost, to the cold bust of Marcus Aurelius so that she shouldn't be noticed, her own warm bust heaving. But he noticed. Halting along—he was slightly lame, and what a passion of tenderness this was presently to arouse in Milly—he noticed the heaving and the effort to hide. How did he find courage, who knew so few women, who had lived so much alone with his sister in his rooms in Oxford, where he was classical lecturer at Ebenezer—a cooling calling, and indeed until he met Milly he had never been very warm—how did he find courage to speak to her? But he did; and instantly, though he was unaware of that till later, was plunged up to his ears in a passionate love affair; a passionate love affair with someone else's wife; in other words, Sin.

Compared to herself, though, how much less was he a sinner, thought Milly, staring wide-eyed at the past. He wasn't married. He was betraying no one. Whereas she——

Too awful. Milly, on the night of Ernest's funeral, locked in her bedroom, supposed to be sleeping the sleep of exhausted grief, saw it all. For over nine years —their passion, and with it their fears and consciousness of guilt, had lasted only one year—she had been so much used to sinning that she hadn't thought about it any more, either one way or the other. Terrible, terrible, cried out Milly's heart, while her body walked up and down the room distractedly, to have got used to sinning. But there it was—a habit, and a completely regular one. Once a week she spent an afternoon with Arthur in Chelsea, where he had taken a studio—Ernest's office, and accordingly Ernest, was in the City—and was back in time for dinner, refreshed and happy. Refreshed and happy? Refreshed and happy because she had been betraying her husband? "Oh, what shall I *do?*" Milly cried, twisting her hands together; for, with Ernest dead, how was she ever to make it up to him, how was she ever to get forgiven?

There it was, however: she had come back refreshed and happy. Because, as soon as she and Arthur were out of the passionate stage of love, and therefore out of the stage of being sensitive and exacting and of feeling guilty, which spoilt things a good deal, because it made them go in deadly fear of being found out, they began to be quite happy. They settled down, that is; settled down to sin. Too awful, she now saw. But there it was.

That, she supposed, was what had helped to blind her to the real nature of those afternoons,—her coming back from them refreshed and happy. Could that be bad, she had sometimes in the second year asked herself, and decided that it couldn't, which made her be so good? Always after her afternoon with Arthur she was extra pleasant, extra amiable to Ernest, extra zealous in agreeing, in approving, in apologizing, in promising, with a kind of radiant good-nature about her that nothing could dim.

"What a wife," sighed the Bott brothers.

"There's no one like Milly," said old Mrs. Bott.

Titford loved her.

Besides, as time passed there were such numbers of these afternoons. Could that be wicked, she asked herself after Ernest's death and before the Will had opened her eyes, as she sat in the bedroom drooping over the remembrance of what she had done and seeking comfort, could that be wicked which went on steadily so long? Didn't time, if there were enough of it, end by transmuting everything? Did not the very slang of one generation—so did her thoughts anxiously wander in search of reassurance—become the polite language of the next? They had gone on and on, the afternoons had,

year in and year out, increasingly secure, increasingly
placid, at last indeed almost ordinary and mechanical,
with Arthur long since just a dear, very intimate friend
—really her only one—and the love-making, which had
notably quietened during the second and third years,
and by the fourth was mere affectionate routine, a
rather elaborate but sweet way of saying, How do you
do, after which they composed themselves to tea and
talk on calm things like excavations, which was what
Arthur in his off times was chiefly interested in—the
love-making latterly become quite unidentifiable as
such.

They were pleased to see each other; much pleased.
Arthur would say, when he opened the door on her
arriving, "Well, dear?" and kiss her affectionately, and
tell her about his cold. Generally he had a cold, for he
was delicate. And when she left, he would walk openly
with her to King's Road, and see her into a taxi for
Victoria, and remind her to keep her feet dry, and ask
her if she had enough change, just as if they were comfortably married.

It would have seemed to Milly fantastic, in these
later years, to regard such mild encounters as sin.

No, no—that wasn't sin, she had kept on assuring
herself during the days before the funeral, while the
kind, unconscious Botts patted her and said what they
could to comfort. Of that simple domestic happiness
Ernest, after all, had had the backwash. Because of it
she had been able to go on being a good wife to him.
Strange as it would seem to the Botts, to Titford, to the
whole world, she had been a very good wife to Ernest,
and entirely owing to her having been what the Botts,
and Titford, and the whole world would call a very bad
one. Those quiet afternoons with Arthur had created
a serenity in her that nothing could ruffle, a limitless

readiness to do everything Ernest wished. They had lit up the house in Mandeville Park Road like a lamp; they had warmed its hearth like a fire. Was not love, then, a good thing for a woman if it made her so much nicer all round? Had not her having had this dear, secret friend been for Ernest too sheer gain?

So she had thought, helped by Arthur, in the first weeks of their love, when she felt guilty and scared and was seeking justifications, and so she kept on telling herself she thought during the days before the funeral. Arthur had explained at the beginning the true wholesomeness of the situation to her, pointing out how three people were now content who before had all been unhappy——

"But Ernest wasn't unhappy," she remembered saying.

"In his heart he must have been," Arthur had insisted. "He must have felt you were only doing your duty, and that there wasn't any love in it. I think men must always know."

"Not husbands," Milly had said.

"I think they must," Arthur, who had never been a husband, gently persisted.

Well, perhaps; perhaps. Milly had doubtfully agreed. Ernest was so quiet, one never really knew what he thought about anything. Sometimes she had supposed he didn't think, except about his business; or hardly at all. He certainly never talked to her about anything except his business or the arrangements of his house, and when he was annoyed with her he didn't so much talk as smoulder. She got to know these smoulderings well. They were very punitive in their effect, much more so than a great blaze-up. Nor did he read anything, except newspapers and magazines, and disliked if she, in his presence, read. Their evenings were always the same—

two armchairs; a roaring fire, or, in summer, ferns; she
and he in the armchairs, he with a newspaper, she with
her crochet work, both doped with dinner. For fifteen
years it had been like that each evening, except when
they went to or gave parties; and every year she was a
little fatter, a little heavier, a little more expensively
dressed, and, because she had had another birthday,
with one more bracelet on arms which were thickening,
or one more brooch on a bosom grown rounder.

She was cooped round with comfort. "Will it be
enough," she sometimes anxiously used to wonder,
"when God, at the end, asks me what I have done with
my life, to point to Ernest and say, I saw to it that his
meals were good?"

No, it wouldn't be enough; she knew it wouldn't.
And she, having no children to keep her busy and give
her fresh interests as she grew older and new hopes,
after fifteen years of these evenings, and of days filled
with calling and callers, with visits to and from relations,
with hearing the same things said over and over
again, with smiling the same smiles and expressing the
same agreements, was becoming so intolerably lonely, so
much oppressed by the dreadful repetitions of life, that
she had been on the verge of throwing up the whole
thing, and scandalizing her world and making the Botts
acutely ashamed and miserable, by going off to her disgraced sister—for she was still only in the middle thir-
ties, and not nearly so heavy as she afterwards became—
when, on that aimless day of unhappiness, she met
Arthur, and he saved her.

Saved her? By adultery? Milly shuddered to think
that there had ever been a time when she thought of
adultery as salvation. To what depths of cynicism had
she not, with a light-heartedness that amazed her, de-
scended, and with what comfortable contentment had

she not, during the long quiet years before she was found out, remained in them! Only now did she see the whole thing as it really was; only now, in the awful light of Ernest's dead, accusing eyes.

Terrible what she had done—cheating and smiling while she cheated, being fed and clothed and trusted by the person she was cheating; trusted, that is, till two years ago when he found her out—so easy, seeing how careless she and Arthur had become, to find out—and yet went on clothing and feeding her, and letting her smile. Why, why didn't he stop everything, the clothing, the feeding, the ghastly cheat-smiling, and turn her out and have done with it? Perhaps he thought he might as well in his turn cheat and deceive. Perhaps he thought he might as well be as base as she was, and having discovered what she was doing not say a word, make no sign, behave as usual, and accept her eager attentions and devotions and panderings—all the things one pays back in, one makes up with—while in his heart he horribly laughed, as he watched and said nothing, hugging the knowledge of what he had put in his Will.

Ernest behaving like that—*Ernest*. And this too was her fault. She had made an incredible sneak of him who probably wouldn't have been a sneak at all if he had been let alone; she had made a cynical, sardonic, artful creature of somebody who was naturally, she had always supposed she knew, quite simple and easy to understand. And she who, during the days before the funeral, since the awful afternoon when he had slipped away from her for ever without recovering consciousness, without her even being able to get the word *Forgive* across to him, she who had been so much overwhelmed by the thought that he hadn't known, that all these years, however difficult he might sometimes be about details, he yet had loved her and believed in her.

and had died loving and believing in her, was appalled by the knowledge that for at least two years he had been doing nothing of the sort. While strangest and most terrible of all was it to Milly that she only now should see how wicked she had been, now that she had been found out.

§

She spent a dreadful night. She was paralyzed by knowing that the morning was rushing towards her, and with it, inevitably, the Botts. Essential, essential, that in the few hours left to her she should think clearly, decide quickly; and for the life of her she couldn't. The Botts would certainly flock round directly after breakfast, still full of affection and desire to help, for they wouldn't have had time, she thought, to put two and two together and guess what she had done, and what she still must have been doing as recently, obviously, as two years ago when Ernest added the codicil—she, well over forty then, whose figure alone made such conduct ridiculous and revolting; but it was only a question of hours before they did.

Her skin burned with shame. She saw the thing as the Botts and Titford would see it, who didn't know the miserable business had begun ten years ago, when she wasn't middle-aged and wasn't yet so fat, and that it had long become just friendship. How was she to meet that injured family, twice now disgraced because of her, for Agatha, who first disgraced them, couldn't have done so if she, Milly, had not brought her into the family by marrying Ernest, how face them knowing that before the next day was over they would be thinking things of her she didn't dare let her mind even look at—of her, when she was in reality every bit as decent, as settled down, as respectable as they till then had supposed?

She stood in the middle of the room wringing her hands. Had Arthur been worth it? Was anybody or anything in the world worth leaving off being good for? "I'm not the stuff sinners are made of," she cried to herself distractedly. "How, oh how, did I ever become one?" For she could no longer remember, in the turmoil of her spirit, the passion and the wonder of the beginning, and could only think of Arthur as an elderly man who talked of excavations and had a cold. Also, who had got her into this mess. If it hadn't been for him. . . .

No; Milly caught herself up. She wouldn't be unjust. Rather should she say, if it hadn't been for her. What could Arthur have done if she had declined to be a party to it? It is the woman who sets the tone, the Botts, and also their circle, which was the best in Titford, held; and no one can live for twenty-five years in the same atmosphere without soaking up at least a little of it. It is the woman, the Botts considered, on whom the duty has been laid of walking steadfastly along the straight path of virtue, thus persuading man, that natural deviator, to walk along it too. Sometimes he won't, the Botts admitted; and then the woman's duty is to continue along it alone. All she can do in that case is to pray for him; for she, having continued, is a good woman, and he, having deviated, is a bad man, and the good pray for the bad. Such was the creed, not often mentioned but always implicit, of the Bott wives and sisters. What would happen if the bad began to pray for the good, Milly had sometimes wondered but hadn't dared ask.

Ah, but they were right, right, the Botts were. She walked up and down in an agony of acknowledgment and self-accusation. She saw now how right they were. Her life was in ruins because she had departed from their standards. How easy it would have been to induce Arthur to follow her in the way of virtue and honour.

He was a delicate creature; he wasn't one of your charging sheiks; she only needed to keep herself to herself for a little, and not blush, and not quiver, and not be so obviously glad each time to see him again. She knew her face had lit up, for she had seen the swift reflection of it on his, and if hers hadn't his wouldn't have. The guilt had been hers. It was she who had led, and he who had followed. The Botts were right when they said, commenting on such rare cases of scandal as illuminated Titford, "That woman must have led him on." And though she had secretly rebelled against this invariable verdict, and though she had kept, beneath the acquiescent smiles marriage to Ernest had taught her, her heart inviolate from it and kindred condemnations, now that the hour of exposure was upon her, Milly, terrified penitent, was only too ready to agree, to admit, to abase herself, and declare that everything that had happened had been her fault alone.

§

To add to her bewilderment, she found she couldn't pray. At intervals during the night she knelt down by the bed and tried to, passionately seeking help, seeking some gleam of light through her confusion; but no words came. Long since, under Arthur's influence, who was not a praying man, she had parted company with prayer, and now when she so urgently needed guidance, and the kind of calm which comes from lifting up one's heart, her heart wouldn't lift up. Not a word came. Dumbly she knelt, gripping the sheets, and her heart stayed where it was. Also, every time she went on her knees she had a dreadful feeling that Ernest was somewhere quite close, looking on sardonically.

Was she going to be haunted? Had she not done with Ernest after all? Crouched by the bed, a heap of crape, for she was still dressed as she had been all day in the expensive widow's outfit ordered for her by the family with the lavishness befitting a widow considered at the time of ordering to be rich, she tried to shut out this feeling of his immanence by burying her face in the quilt, and making renewed attempts to send some sort of petition for help up out of her frightened heart.

Not the least use. Nothing moved upwards within her; nothing even stirred. Her heart, her mind, her soul, stayed flat inside her body on the ground, all jammed together, it seemed to her, in a hopeless, immovable mass.

Part of her punishment she supposed, slipping down in a sitting position, her cheek against the bed, that she shouldn't be able to pray; part of her punishment that she should be made to feel utterly abandoned. She was abandoned in every sense of the word. The Botts, in a few hours, would be using the word when they talked of her—of her they had always, she knew, thought so much of. How artful she must have been to have produced such an impression of guiltlessness on them, how she must have lied, how she *had* lied. She was sodden with lies. In the very first year of her marriage she had become an active liar, and had so continued fluently ever since. That was when Ernest forbade her, after Agatha's disgrace, either to write or to receive letters from her sister so long as they lived; and she, having briefly struggled to obey him, found she couldn't, because she loved Aggie too much, and, like the young coward she was, didn't dare tell him, but had begun to write and receive the forbidden letters almost at once, and had gone on doing so till as lately as a week ago, artfully smuggling them in and out, growing very skilful in deceit, sometimes even meeting Ernest, if he came into the room unexpectedly, with a serene face while there was a letter at that very moment in her pocket.

Clear to Milly was it that those letters had been the first stones in the great fabric of deceit which had reached its climax in Arthur, and now had fallen on her and crushed her. *Be sure your sin will find you out,* floated through her mind. Was that in the Bible? It was certainly true. Here she was, found out at forty-five— so infinitely more terrible than being found out at twenty—toppled right down from the pinnacle of universal affection and respect one somehow gets put on by the time one is that sort of age, into the mud; and during the next few hours she was going to be exposed as that most distressing and ridiculous, surely, of all sinners, an elderly Magdalen.

Flight, flight, cried Milly at the intolerable thought, clutching the bed-clothes and pulling herself to her feet —never to see any of them again, to get away, away from this place, this house, this room with Ernest looking on sardonically at the success of his punishment. . . . The room was full of Ernest. He had not been, alive, a laugher, but she had an awful feeling that now at last he was amused. Ernest brought to this by her, brought to this evil gloating by her wickedness. . . .

"I'm going to make up—oh, I'm going to make *up !*" she gasped—somehow, someday. . . .

But even this aspiration, like her efforts to pray, fell back upon her, and the words, as they came out on a sob, struck her as suspect, as having a double meaning, as being, perhaps, considered appropriate, by whatever Power sends thoughts into minds, to her condition of Magdalen. Or was it Ernest, close beside her, mocking her by putting them into her head?

Ah, but this was awful—she was being haunted.

Panic-stricken she ran and turned on more lights, all the lights, and then, hurrying about the room, began pulling out drawers and snatching together the few things she couldn't do without. Flight before it was too late. . . . Flight before the servants were up and saw what she was doing. . . . Flight before the Botts came round and caught her, and forced her to stand up before them, naked in her sins. . . .

§

On the dim landing where there was a smell of shut-up varnished wood, and linoleum and cigars, the grandfather clock was ticking enormous ticks in the silence, and the faint light of the new day struggled faintly through the stained-glass window, when, just after five, she crept out of her room, clutching her suit-case and her bag. In the bag was all the money she had till she should have got her thousand pounds. There was not much—less than five pounds; but enough, Milly thought, to hide her in London for a day and a night until she had been to Ernest's solicitor. That was the first thing to be done, she saw, and quickly, so as to finish with the past and get away to Agatha. For it wasn't so much a conscious decision as a homing instinct that was sending her straight to Agatha. To her sister would she go, who loved her; to her own flesh and blood. Aggie was the one person in the world who wouldn't judge, who wouldn't condemn even if she wanted to—which she never would—because of what she had done herself. With her she would be safe.

She gave a little sob of longing, as she crept down the stairs, to be safe, to be out of all this, to be far away from everybody connected with the past, among people who, except Aggie—she would have no secrets from Aggie, she would tell her everything as freely as she would tell God—would never know anything about it. Aggie would understand; Aggie would love her—just love her, and not mind anything. . . .

The stairs creaked, and each time they did that she stopped, her heart in her mouth, and listened. How strange and different the house looked. Things that were as familiar to her as her own face—the oak staircase, the suits of armour at the turnings, the sea-scapes in their handsome gilt frames, the hanging terra-cotta baskets with ferns in them—these treasures of Ernest's, that she had lived with so long and knew so well, already looking like ghosts, done with, dead. She crept along among them for the last time, the only living thing in what had suddenly become a mausoleum, tak-ing infinite care to make no sound, patiently undoing her long crape veil—part of the outfit ordered for her—from the knobs it got caught in on the suits of armour, and each time the stairs creaked stopping, and holding her breath to listen for movements in the servants' rooms, her heart seeming to beat as loud as the grandfather clock.

But it was the hour when servants sleep most heavily, and no one heard her go except Ernest's Pomeranian, who slept in the study and began to yap when she got down into the hall—perhaps, by some strange dog in-stinct, knowing she was doing something she oughtn't to. How often, then, if that were so, thought Milly, tremblingly unfastening the bolts of the front door, should he in the past have yapped at her. But he hadn't. He had been cool to her and silent, sniffing at her shoes distrustfully, saving up his noises for now; so that the last sound she heard from her old home as she left it for ever was a shrill, violent yapping.

Was it derision? Was it vindictiveness on behalf of his master? She hurried away pursued by the sound;

and it seemed to Milly, in her collapsed condition, that it was the voice of Ernest, using the dog as his mouth-piece, and in this manner saying good-bye.

"*You can't escape—you'll never escape,*" the yapping seemed to call after her.

"Oh, but I *can*—I'm *going* to!" Milly's heart cried back, as she fled down the drive and out into the road.

§

Not till she had turned the corner did the shrill per-sistent yapping fade away, and leave the dawn in peace. Titford slept. Its blinds were carefully drawn, and its aspect was one of deep repose. No one saw the surprising spectacle of Mrs. Ernest Bott, so well known and so much appreciated as a kind, little well-off woman who gave no trouble, swathed in her new mourn-ing, hurrying along at a pace most unusual, and carry-ing things a person of her age and standing didn't carry. Yet the very emptiness of the streets made Milly stand out immensely conspicuous, a round black splodge on the pale clearness of the morning, had anyone been peeping from behind those closed blinds; and as she approached the vicarage of St. Timothy and All Spirits, whose inhabitants, she knew, were addicted to pious practices at strange hours, she pulled the crape veil which hung from her bonnet forward over her face, taking cover behind it from the possible eye of some early Christian, who should be preparing, by opening a window, to let in God's air on his orisons.

This made her hot. She was hot already, from the run to the gate and the scared hurrying along Mandeville Park Road, and the crape veil made her hotter. By the time she was out of the residential part of Titford, where in nearly every house people whose names were on her visiting list lay sleeping, and had reached a path that led

northwards through some small holdings in the direction
of London, she was in a state of extreme melting
warmth. Her crape stuck to her. Beneath her widow's
bonnet—the Bott tradition dressed its widows for their
first six months rather like Queen Victoria—little drops
of perspiration slid down her temples into her muslin
collar; under her heavy cloak all seemed liquefaction.

But she hardly noticed. Her heart was thumping
with relief, as well as exertion. Every yard put between
herself and Titford increased her relief, as well as her
breathlessness. That haunted bedroom in Mandeville
Park Road was behind her. Ernest hadn't come with
her, she felt, beyond the hall door. She had escaped.
And she had escaped from the really intolerable shame
of meeting the Botts. Presently, long before they were
waking up, she would be in a workmen's train, disappearing into the all-engulfing privacy of London. No
one would find her during her few hours there. She
would call on the solicitor, and get her thousand pounds
—unversed in the law's delays, Milly supposed she had
but to apply in order to receive—and immediately
vanish into obscurity; and then, while the family was
perhaps trying to look for her, though surely it wouldn't,
surely it would be only too thankful to let her go and
forget her, she would be far away beyond its reach, on
her way to Switzerland and Agatha.

Agatha. Hurrying across the allotments, her back to
the past, her face to the future, Milly kept her thoughts
passionately concentrated on Agatha. If she didn't,
Arthur obtruded; and from the thought of Arthur she
turned with a shudder. She wouldn't, she couldn't, think
of him. This was no moment for Arthur. Directly Ernest
had his accident she began to shudder away from Arthur
almost as if it were somehow his fault that the awful
thing should have happened—from Arthur, away on

his Easter holiday in Rome, whole and alive anyhow, if not actually robust, enjoying himself poking about among excavations, while Ernest, the wronged, lay helpless and broken on the bed he was to die on; and then, after his death, when the sympathizing Botts were comforting her in that bedroom and imagining her good, the thought of Arthur, when it did manage to creep into her mind, made her quite sick. Her fellow-sinner; who would now suppose he had got to marry her. Suppose he had got to marry her! Her head drooped lower in shame. ("There, there,—poor little Milly," said the Botts, patting.) She had brushed the humiliating thought aside. That was what love came to in the end, however splendidly it flamed in the beginning: to supposing one had got to marry her. *Got* to. As though two blacks could ever make a white; as though, if she and Arthur did marry, there could ever be any happiness, with Ernest between them, and his dead, accusing eyes.

No, no—only legitimacy for Milly now; perfect open-and-above-boardness, complete absence, for the rest of her life, of holes and corners, of plots and lies. Legitimacy, legitimacy . . . her spirit, raw with the sudden descent of the punishment that sooner or later, she now saw, overtakes the other thing, craved for its pure clear safety. Even if it were dull, legitimacy was better, she now abundantly realized, than any flashes of apparent delight its opposite might produce; while as for when it also meant love, and the knowledge that one wouldn't be judged, what could the love and necessary absence of judging that Arthur would provide, offer? Besides, she desperately wanted to tell someone she trusted all she had done, and, in telling, free herself of part, at least, of the burden. She couldn't tell Arthur; he knew already. He would say, on hearing of Ernest's death and the Will, "Well, now we must be married——" and then explain that he was afraid he had caught another cold.

For Milly, Agatha had become salvation. She longed for her, as the thirsty long for water; she panted after her, as the soul of the Psalmist panted after God. Always Agatha had been affection, and close blood-loyalty and shared memories of childhood, but now she was also salvation. Only Agatha could take her by the hand, and pull her up out of the swamp of shame she was floundering in, only she could help her to a new, cleared-out life. Since that hasty secret departure from Mandeville Park Road a quarter of a century ago—what nonsense, Milly had long thought, who had done such much worse things later herself, for Ernest and the Botts to make such a fuss about it; yet she too, at the beginning, had been appalled—they had never set eyes on each other. But their letters, after a slight preliminary coolness on Agatha's part, who had resented the way Milly, still trying to obey Ernest, hadn't at first written back, became gradually warmer and warmer, as letters easily will when the writers do not meet, developing at last, each more and more needing an outlet, into real outpourings. Every thought of their hearts had presently been poured into these letters, except, in Milly's case, those thoughts of her heart which had to do with Arthur. Of these she had not written; Agatha was unaware of Arthur. And since, after the first few years, they began to be dissatisfied with such photographs and snapshots of themselves as were taken, and felt they would be misleading, they left off sending any; and then, having nothing to go on when they thought of each other except what they wrote and the recollection of what they used to look like, they began unconsciously to build up images in their minds, increasingly bright and beautiful, and to these in their letters they more and more addressed themselves.

This bright image of Agatha was what Milly now kept
her eyes fixed on, as she hurried along clutching her suit-
case, which seemed to grow heavier with each step.
Towards it she was at last actually going; in a few hours
it would be reality, and at its feet she would have
dropped her sins. Aggie would fold her to her heart,
and understand and love her as much as ever, Milly
knew, for Aggie too had sinned, though only, it was
true, for three weeks, and then only because she couldn't
help it. Compared to Milly's ten years, Aggie's three
weeks were, of course, a mere flea-bite, but even so they
were going to make it easy to tell her about Arthur.
At least she wouldn't be surprised, and couldn't be
shocked. Milly might have worked on a larger canvas,
but on a smaller scale Agatha had done the same thing.
She would utterly understand. And she was the one person in the whole world—except Arthur, who didn't in
the nature of things in this matter count—with whom
Milly would be safe from condemnation.

Safe from condemnation, whispered Milly; hidden in
love; beyond the reach of pointing fingers, or averted
eyes. She sighed. Perhaps it was cowardly to want to
dodge her punishment, to hide from it in Agatha's arms,
perhaps a finer character would have stayed and faced
the Botts. But that was just what was the matter with
her, she thought—she was a coward. She hadn't the
courage either of her repentance or her sins. She hadn't
the courage of anything. In the littlest matters, on the
smallest occasions, hadn't she always searched for the
easiest way out, anxious only to avoid unpleasantness?
What had her acquiescences and smiles been, except,
in miniature, what she was doing now—flight from
black looks, flight from mere disapproval? Beyond
everything she dreaded scenes, and somebody with a
loud voice being angry. She would take, she knew, and

had taken, endless pains to please, to keep everybody
happy. Her differences of opinions—and she had many
—were all secret. Yes; she was a coward. And such a
tactful coward that nobody ever guessed the real reason
of the amiability that had made her so popular in Titford, and so much liked by the Botts.

She stopped, and putting down her suit-case wiped
the perspiration from her face. No one, she thought,
could possibly be more vile. She was in the middle of the
allotments, which were quite empty at that hour, and
she put up her veil to get her breath. She was very hot.
She held her arms away from her warm, damp body, and
lifted her uncovered face to the cool morning air, and it
seemed to run to meet her with a kiss. Exquisite fresh-
ness and newness—the whole world washed clean,
thought Milly, her upturned face and swollen eyes
caressed by the soft pattings of an uncondemning little
breeze. "Oh, how delicious—how sweet—how kind"—she
whispered, standing quite still, her eyes shut. Really the
morning seemed to be gently kissing her—"Just as if,"
she thought, "I were somebody good."

§

It was too early for the earliest train, and her idea
was to walk towards London, and pick up the first one
she could at some station that wasn't Titford. If by
chance she were to come across a taxi she would take it,
and she would go to Bloomsbury, where her father used
to live, and where she had spent her childhood; for she
remembered there were many lodgings to let in Bloomsbury, and in one of these, as close as possible to the
house where she had been young, she would stay that
day and night, see the solicitor, and continue to Agatha
next morning. "And when I have slept," thought Milly,
picking up the suit-case and going on again, "and when

I have had something to eat, perhaps I shall feel different."

But in spite of her having had no food since the lunch
brought up to her bedroom on a tray the day before, and
in spite of her not having slept at all, her mind already
seemed a little clearer. It was her body at that moment
which was chiefly troublesome—so hot, so much out of
breath, and with hands and arms aching because they
had to carry a suit-case and a bag. Her feet hurt her,
too, and she was altogether deplorably out of condition,
and a very fit subject, she told herself, angry with her
abundant, overfed flesh, for the rigours of expiation.
But these very discomforts and difficulties released her
mind, detached it awhile from its distress, and by the
time she had got as far as Tulse Hill she was in that
condition of fatigue which prevents all thought, and
only seeks for something to sit down on.

This she found at the station.

A woman, surrounded by bundles and carrying a
baby, moved up along the wooden bench with alacrity,
solicitously making room for her.

"Don't I know what it is, mum," she said. "Ah dear,
ah dear——" and shaking her head at nothing, she
jogged the baby, which cried, up and down on her arm.

She was unable to take her eyes off Milly, who, sitting
on the edge of the seat because else her feet wouldn't
reach the floor, her hands in her new black gloves and
neat white wrist-bands tightly holding her bag, kept her
gaze carefully fixed on the bit of sky she could see
through the top of the window, so as to avoid looking at
the woman: for who knew if she mightn't be somebody from Titford?

"'Eaven," thought the woman, respectfully watching
this absorption in the sky. "That's what she's thinkin'

of, poor dear. Awful the way them real bad bereavements rejuices one."

Some workmen coming in, when they saw the figure of grief so manifestly recent and deep, removed their pipes and left off talking; and the clerk in the booking office, short in his manners as a rule at that hour, on finding his pigeon-hole presently blocked by blackness instead of the usual workman, paused in the act of slapping down the ticket, and handed it to her politely instead, with the air, almost, of offering a condolence.

Everybody seemed sorry for her, and anxious to help. When, having got to Victoria, she wished to cross the street, a policeman briskly stepped forward and held up a fruit barrow, there being nothing else to hold up at the moment; when, having walked as far as the Abbey, she tried to get into it, for she thought that in that great calm place, hallowed by centuries of prayer, gracious with centuries of blessing, she might perhaps be able to find the words which hadn't come in her dreadful bedroom with Ernest at her elbow, and at last send up an appeal for forgiveness, the policeman on duty was quite apologetic, and ashamed of it, whose function was surely to offer consolation to the bereaved, for not being open; and when she approached a taxi, which was lazily taking up its position on an empty rank as though it were only just awake and still yawning, and said to the driver in the gentle, deprecating voice marriage to Ernest had taught her, a voice which long had become second nature to her, turning up a little at the end of its sentences, providing, in its slight final lift, a query to serve as a loop-hole through which she might quickly withdraw whatever it was she had said if anyone showed signs of not liking it, "Taxi?" and the driver looked round languidly, not repudiating, for he knew he was a taxi, but indifferent, the minute he saw her shrouded figure he leapt into instant life, jumping down and opening the door for her, and hoisting her in as if she were not only heavy but precious, and driving her to Bloomsbury with the precautions of one in charge of an ambulance.

"If they only knew," thought Milly, taken aback by all this.

She hadn't been prepared for attention and kindness; they were the last things she wanted. She had hardly glanced at herself in the glass before leaving, intent only on getting away, and was not conscious of what she looked like. Just something black, tying on a bonnet with trembling fingers, and a chalky white face peering out of swathings of crape—this she had seen but not noticed, her whole attention fixed on flight. She now perceived she had been foolish. Only in her oldest, plainest clothes should she have come away. True they would have been an admission to the solicitor that she had no moral right to dress as Ernest's widow, but why not admit what he already for certain knew? As usual, she was getting kindness from everybody by false pretences. Just as in Titford she had skulked behind smiles, now she was skulking behind the solemn appearance of legitimate grief, taking in policemen and honest married women, a Magdalen in widow's clothing.

Odious, thought Milly, shrinking into the corner of the taxi, instinctively trying to shrink away from herself. She would strip off the mourning as soon as she got her money, and buy herself ordinary things in which nobody would look at her twice. Not as a widow would she travel to Agatha. Her weeds, along with the rest of her hypocrisies, should stay behind in England. Perhaps they ought to be returned to the Botts. They were, after all, quite new, and belonged to the family, which would, she supposed, presently get the bill for them. But there were difficulties about sending them back. It might strike the Botts as cynical, as the conclusive proof of loss of shame, if, on opening the enormous parcel, they found it to contain an empty set of widow's weeds.

Well, she would think that out presently, when she had had some sleep. All these thoughts whirling round in her head would settle down then, and sort themselves out, wouldn't they? Oh, yes, they would—she was going to have peace, peace, she whispered, as she watched, heavy-eyed, the increasingly familiar landmarks. A longing to crawl back into the past, into innocence, into a pre-Bott condition, filled her heart. Incredibly beautiful, or so now it seemed, had life been in Bloomsbury; golden, glorious. Along its shining streets—surely they used to shine?—she and Aggie had played with hoops that must have been made of stars. Through its lit, mysterious windows had floated, in the summer evenings, music that drew them out of bed, and held them spell-bound. In the garden of their square marvellous things had happened, and the trees in it had been bright with magic fruits, and the air had quivered with the flash of strange wings. And later when she was older, but still so close, so close to beauty, Milly remembered, in the drawing-room of their house, with its long windows opening on to a little iron balcony, Ernest had courted her—Ernest, the prosperous suitor who could open the gates of ease for her hard-working father and young sister; and she, never courted before, had listened bewitched to his words of love, and had believed every one of them.

What she hadn't known then, thought Milly, as the British Museum with all its memories of her father, who had been a librarian there, and later of Arthur, came in sight, was that people get over love. It was like an illness, she thought, staring at the familiar building, at the familiar porter at the gate—he seemed to be the same porter—and at the pgieons, who also were apparently the same ones,—an illness that ran its course. But, unlike an illness, when it was over, instead of feeling better one felt worse.

She hadn't known that then. How should she? She was only twenty, and had never had a real lover before, and for all she knew Ernest was the perfect lover. Strange to remember his husky, moved voice when he said good-bye to her the evening before their wedding and took her in his arms and told her he was going to make her happy for ever and ever and ever; strange to remember that he absolutely meant it, Ernest meant it, who never afterwards said anything the least like it; and strange to remember how sure-footed she had been among words right up to her honeymoon, and then the twenty-five years of learning the right answers. And within those twenty-five years, because she had not been able to bear the little that was demanded of her—it seemed so little now that it was over, such a little time to have stayed good in—because she was weak, lonely, and a fool, within those twenty-five years, curled up like a scarlet snake, lay her ten years of sin.

Milly pulled herself together. Even though she had had no sleep or food for ages, she mustn't let herself exaggerate too much, she thought. That word scarlet. She might have some justification for calling her long, placid connection with Arthur a snake, for it had been full of deceit and treachery, but it hadn't been a scarlet one. Ernest had probably used the word, thinking inflamed thoughts, as the wronged and imperfectly informed must; and the Botts, acquainted with the Apocalypse, in their just anger would presently no doubt talk of the Scarlet Woman. But she herself, who knew the details of those afternoons, couldn't. Years ago, perhaps, she might have; just at the beginning; the vivid beginning; like a flame. . . .

She stared out of the window, her lips pressed together to prevent their quivering, as she remembered the beginning, and the terror and wonder and warmth of it. Were all beginnings warm? Were all endings bleak and sorrowful? See how even Ernest at the beginning had been warm, vowing to make her happy for ever and ever. And he was dead, and he hadn't made her happy, and she hadn't made him happy, and it was all over, and here she was come back to the place of her youth alone, middle-aged, disgraced, poor, with nothing left at all, except what yet might be saved of her perishing soul.

Yes—and Aggie. Aggie was still there, still living. So long as there was Aggie, how could she say she had lost everything? Ah, dear, dear sister, whispered Milly, her mouth relaxing, dearest little sister—little only because she was younger, and one felt so motherly towards her, being married and taking her into one's home and all that, but really a head taller, a long slender thing, bright-eyed and bright-cheeked that day when Milly got back from her honeymoon, and found her on the steps in Mandeville Park Road to welcome her. She had looked like a vivid flower, in spite of the mourning she was dressed in for their father. Milly had put her arms round the electric young body and hugged it to her heart, whispering, with kisses, that she was going to take such care of her. And so she had taken care of her, till the day three months later when, without a word of warning, Agatha eloped in the middle of the night,

appalling Milly, who hadn't then realized that people
sometimes do do things like that, even when they are
one's own sister.

If she had had ten pounds in her purse, instead of not
much over four, she would have gone straight to Agatha,
without waiting to see the solicitor about her money,
which could be sent on afterwards; but Agatha lived in
an almost inaccessible region, and Milly was sure that
it took more than she had to get to her. Perhaps, though,
it was just as well she couldn't go that day, she said to
herself, as she sat drooping in the corner of the taxi, for
she was very tired now, and much exhausted by her
long hurried walk to Tulse Hill. She would have liked to
have slept properly before she saw Aggie and told her
about everything; she felt she could bear no more emotions or exertions till she had slept. If she could get into
some quiet room and go to sleep, begin with sleep, and
then, when she had slept and slept, have some food, she
might be able to see more clearly and think better.
While as it was, thought Milly, staring out of the window with dim eyes, she wasn't able to think properly at
all. Just confusion in her head, and confusion in her
heart, and both so heavy, and aching, and afraid. . . .

§

She stopped the taxi at the corner of Russell Square.
From there she would walk, and into the first house that
had rooms to let she would go and take one, if it was
cheap enough, and lock herself into it, and sleep.

Russell Square didn't appear to desire lodgers; at
least, she saw no signs of such a wish, and she went on
into Woburn Place, and stood a minute staring at the
church she had been married in. From there she drifted
into the square where her father had lived—one of the
humbler ones, for, though intelligent, he was poor, and

the thought came into her mind that if she could find a
room in that square she would sleep more profoundly
and healingly than in another.

Her old home was right away in the farthermost
corner, and before beginning to make inquiries, in spite
of being tired and foot-sore, she felt she must go and
look up at its windows; and as she got nearer she saw
there was a notice board on its railings.

Her heart gave a thump. She hurried her steps.
Probably it was only the announcement of a school or
some institution. Catching hold of her bag and suit-case
with one hand, she impatiently lifted her veil with the
other so as to see better, and as the letters of the first
line on the board were big and gilt and shone in the sun,
in another yard or two she was able to read:

THE HOME FROM HOME

APARTMENTS TO LET

and in yet another yard or two the smaller letters of the
succeeding lines, which were arranged like this:

EVERY COMFORT

LADIES ONLY

NO GENTLEMEN OR DOGS

INDIVIDUAL STUDY

Milly stood gazing. How wonderful. How providential. Wouldn't this bring her peace, to go back into
the very house of her happy youth? Wouldn't this be
the place of all others to hide in, to rest in, to grow calm
in, and perhaps to pray in? For it was really remarkable,
she thought, considering her long neglect of her prayers,
how much not being able to say any worried her.

The door stood open, it being the moment of the day

when air was admitted, and she went up the familiar
steps. Positively the last time she had been on those
steps was going down them on her wedding day as
Ernest's bride. Her father died suddenly while she was
on her honeymoon, and Agatha, telegraphed to, had
moved herself and her belongings to Titford by the time
Milly got home, so that she had never entered the house
since—no, nor even been to look at it since Arthur came
into her life, and quieted her. Before that she had made
occasional wistful pilgrimages to the scene of her youth,
but for more than ten years now she hadn't been that
way, and the last time she saw it the house was still a
private house.

Now, just in time for her, it had thrown open its
doors. Was she, after all, being guided? And there was
that other strange coincidence—the widowing of Agatha
three months before her own, both their husbands, who
had seemed so permanent, disappearing almost simul-
taneously, and so making room for her reunion with her
sister, for their taking up life together again at the point
where it had so cruelly been broken off. Did there not,
in these things, appear to be a hand?

She put out her own right one to ring the bell; but
the manageress—the owner of the boarding-house called
herself the manageress, suggesting behind her a grave
company of elderly men, to whom she could refer when
she needed support—who had been observing Milly
from the dark background where she was superintending
a servant whose habit it was to sit down directly she
wasn't superintended, darted forward, and in accordance with her practice of making every lodger or
possible lodger feel she was her special friend, clasped
her hands and exclaimed sympathetically, as her eyes
flicked over mourning figure, "You poor, poor *dear!*"

"Can I—have a room?" asked Milly timidly, for she

had again forgotten for a moment what she looked like,
and was again taken aback.

"A room? I should *think* so. *Fifty* if you like," said
the manageress enthusiastically. "Why, I wouldn't
turn a *dog* away if it had lately lost its——"

She broke off, and taking Milly's suit-case from her
drew her quickly into the dining-room, for her new
guest struck the manageress, who prided herself on the
rapidity with which she sized up lodgers, as the sort of
person who had to have her mind made up for her, and
until she was safely in the dining-room, and the door
shut, she might go away again; and competition was
severe, and opulent widows scarce, and one had to be
quick and snatch, if only to save ladies from all one's
rapacious neighbours.

"It would be for quite a short time," faltered Milly,
shrinking under the effect the well-known old dining-
room, combined with the hungry-eyed new authority in
it, produced.

"*Any* time, short *or* long," said the manageress, pushing up an easy chair and somehow getting Milly into it,
and then, with swift sweeping movements, clearing up
a litter on the table which looked like the remains of
someone's supper. "But I wouldn't mind making a bet,
if I ever did such a thing, which of course I don't, that
it'll be *long*, Mrs.——"

"Bott," said Milly.

"Bott," said the manageress. "My friends—I always
look upon the ladies here as my friends, and no gentlemen or dogs admitted as you saw on the board outside,
for they only lead to trouble—ah, yes, and *don't* they,"
she added, stopping to gaze with warm compassion at
Milly. "I mean the gentlemen of course, though dogs are
a great nuisance too. Well, we won't speak of that now,"
she went on, carrying what she had cleared up off the

table to the sideboard, "will we? Later on you'll tell me
all about it, won't you, Mrs. Bott. And meanwhile we
won't be morbid, we mustn't give way, *must* we? We owe
it to our dear ones, *don't* we, not to do that. What *you*
want now, I can plainly see, is breakfast. Isn't it? For
you can't have had any yet, and it does make such a
difference whether one has had something to eat or not.
Yes—as I was saying, my friends, my ladies here, never
want to leave. It's *home* you see, Mrs. Bott. Real *home*.
Comforts. Individual study——"

Ah no, thought Milly, not this place; she couldn't
bear this place. "I expect your charges——" she began
timidly. "I can't afford——"

Charges? Afford? The spirit implied by these words
seemed to the manageress unworthy of the scale of
expenditure which had obviously been applied to her
new client's clothes.

She ignored them.

"You're not to think of *anything*, you poor dear," she
said, smiling down at her with such determined encouragement that Milly's heart sank, "except that you've
come home. We'll talk business, if you want to, when
you've had some breakfast. I was a V. A. D. in the War,
and know that breakfast comes quite *first*."

And she hurried out of the room calling to the servant,
and, getting no answer, because she had withdrawn into
the basement, where she was sitting down, went along
the passage to the head of the back stairs.

How well Milly knew that passage, and the back
stairs hidden round a bend at the end of it. She got up
quickly, very red and ashamed, and stole to the door,
picking up her suit-case on the way. She must get
away from this. She couldn't stay here. What silly
sentimental idea of finding comfort in the past had made
her come in? As though past happiness could ever com-

fort, as though it could ever do anything but stab one!
Escape, escape, she thought, as she had thought during
the night in her bedroom; escape while there was still
time. . . .

And she stole out on tiptoe—it struck her, humiliat-
ingly, that she was becoming practised in stealing out of
places on tiptoe—and finding the front door still open, for
the house's habit was to air itself for half an hour, was
about to go through it and make with what dignity she
could for the nearest corner, when the manageress in the
basement, warned by some instinct that all was not
well above her in the hall, suddenly reappeared.

"Why—Mrs. *Bott!*" she exclaimed.

Absurd situation. Ridiculous to mind what this
strange woman thought. Yet Milly felt as much
ashamed as if she had been a naughty child caught doing
wrong. Why couldn't she say, why hadn't she been able
to say at once in the dining-room, that she didn't think
the house would suit her, and simply go? Why should
she always be silent, faced by determined people, and
give the quite wrong impression that they could do what
they liked with her, and then have to get out of her
difficulties by deceit?

Very red and foolish, she came back a little way into
the hall. "I'm afraid——" she began.

The manageress was full of suspicions. Was this
merely the latest form of thief, and were spoons at that
moment in those crape pockets? Or was she another of
the shilly-shallying vulgarians who didn't know either
when they were well off or what was due to a lady running a house, and walked out without so much as a good-
morning? Vast had been the manageress's experience
of the seamy sides of lodgers, and she had learned much
firmness in dealing with them; indeed, one either had to
be firm in her profession or go under and starve. What-

ever this one was, thief or vulgarian, she couldn't be allowed to leave in such a manner, but nothing ever being lost by diplomacy, the manageress knew, she said, very nearly as warmly and sympathetically as before in spite of her black suspicions, "Afraid? Poor Mrs. Bott. Poor, *dear* Mrs. Bott. Nothing to be afraid of here, you know. And I've just been ordering you some nice hot coffee, and a poached egg on toast."

"I was thinking——" began Milly again.

"I know, I *know*," interrupted the manageress, taking the suit-case firmly out of her hand. "But you mustn't, you really must *not*. No good thinking and brooding—it only makes it all so much worse."

"I was thinking," said Milly, making an effort, "of leaving."

"Leaving!" echoed the manageress, in a voice of astonishment. "Leaving what?"

"Here," said Milly.

"But you've only just come."

"Yes, but——"

"You poor dear," said the manageress soothingly, "you're in such a state of mind that you don't really know what you want. But I know—it's breakfast. Gladys!" she called down the passage, "be quick, now. We want that breakfast up *at* once. And when you've had it," she said, turning to Milly and taking her arm, "you shall go on your way rejoicing. Only I wouldn't mind betting, if I were the sort of person who does bet, which of course I'm not, that you don't. Not rejoicing. Nobody has ever left me yet rejoicing. They want to stay here. They hate having to go. It's *home*, you see, Mrs. Bott. Suppose," she suggested brightly, "while we're waiting for that breakfast, we go upstairs and take our bonnet off, and bathe our eyes in some nice cool water? Yes, I know what—I'll have the breakfast sent up to your room, and then you can rest quietly, and perhaps get right into bed and have a good sleep."

A remarkable woman, thought Milly; and really seeming to understand what one needed most at the moment. If only she herself had a tenth part of such single-minded determination.

She gave up. Breakfast and sleep. After that, after having had those, and been restored by them to clearness and courage, she could still go away. Nobody could force her to stay there, and meanwhile it wasn't worth while arguing.

She found herself being led up the familiar stairs, covered now with neat linoleum instead of the shabby old carpet of her youth, up past the drawing-room on the first floor, up to the next landing, where her bedroom used to be, and Agatha's.

"No, not in there," whispered the manageress drawing her away, for she had paused instinctively before the shut door that had once been hers. "It's engaged. A lady arrived late last night—in fact in the small hours, but I never turn trouble away. A widow too, I'm afraid. Ah, dear. Sad world, isn't it. I hope she's still asleep, poor dear. Out of breath? They *are* rather steep. Just one more teeny, weeny little flight—the rooms on this floor are gone, but upstairs—it's lucky, for I'm usually full right up. Well, sit down a moment, then. Yes, yes—I can see you're out of condition, poor Mrs. Bott. Sh-sh we mustn't *talk*—my poor new friend in there——"

Milly, sympathetically assisted by the manageress, did sink down on a chair that stood on the little landing, out of breath after climbing stairs she used to fly up two steps at a time, generally chased by Agatha, whose aim was to pinch her legs. Outside what used to be her bedroom door stood a pair of black boots, trodden down at heel and so much wrinkled that they seemed to be frowning, and on the mat, awaiting the pleasure of the lodger within, was a small and battered brown tin can of hot water.

The manageress, her finger on her lip in case Milly, who up to then had hardly spoken a whole sentence and was evidently without breath to spare, should begin to talk, and perhaps be so much unlike her clothes as to ask what her room was to cost before she had been got safely into it and used it, placed herself in front of the boots and hot-water can, neither of which, she felt, did her establishment credit; and while she was standing like that, and Milly on the chair was panting, and both were silent, the bedroom door opened, and the lodger, in search of her hot water, appeared.

The manageress sprang aside, and the lodger, surprised to find two people where she had expected emptiness, because of the silence which had succeeded the talking that had been annoying her for the last ten minutes, stood a moment, staring.

Milly stared back, her lips apart. They stared at each other.

She was a tall, bony woman, with thin grizzling hair scraped together on the top of her head preparatory to washing her face, which was much lined and strong featured—a discoloured face, battered by exposure, apparently, to hard winds and hard water. And round her shoulders she held together a petticoat thrown over her nightgown, and her nightgown was of flannel.

"Oh, dear——" exclaimed the manageress, but not with nearly so much emphasis as she used to Milly, because of the boots. Really those boots. In the dim light of the late arrival the night before she hadn't noticed them. "I'm sorry. We've wakened you, and I meant you to have a good rest."

The lodger said nothing, because she was staring at Milly, who was staring at her. Then she stooped, and without a word picked up the can and shut her door.

Milly shifted uneasily on the hard chair. Her eyes were fixed on the shut door. What a grim woman. And staring as if one were a ghost. . . .

"Rested?" inquired the manageress, brightly smiling, because even if this lodger were an impostor, and were trying to get away with the spoons—she would go and count them the minute she was free—she did look exactly like the kind one is proud of, in her beautiful expensive mourning, and brand-new patent leather shoes. "Feel like going on up?" she asked cheerily.

Milly looked at her a little bewildered, collecting her thoughts. She had forgotten the manageress. Yes— she supposed she did feel like going on up, she said in rather a dazed way—"If you ask *me*," the manageress said to herself, "I should say she wasn't quite all there."

And, helped by the firm hand on her elbow, she did so; and neither she nor Agatha knew that, after twenty-five years, they had just met again.

⁜(*IV*)*⁜*

The reason Agatha lived in Switzerland was because she had married a Swiss.

The Botts' view of her, for many years past not discussed any more, but none the less perfectly clear in their minds, was that she had brought scandal on the family, shame on Milly, and ruin on herself by eloping under particularly shocking circumstances. It is true that by the time Ernest died she had done it a very long while ago, but that made no difference to the Botts, who absolutely drew the line at any public scandal; for this scandal, which had been very public—even the local papers were full of it—had neither been forgotten nor forgiven. Gross immorality combined with gross ingratitude, and getting into the local papers—who is going to forgive that? Even if one manages to forgive it one can't forget it, the Botts felt. And they didn't; and they hadn't.

Received into Ernest's house on her father's death as an orphaned and penniless sister-in-law, received with kindness and hospitality, and not a word of reproach, in spite of it being no joke for a man to wake up from his honeymoon and find he has got to keep two women instead of one, after only three months of it Milly's sister revealed the sort of deplorable stuff she was made of by getting out of a window in the middle of the night, and running away with a Swiss. A *Swiss*, mind you, said the outraged Botts to each other, who, if ever they had thought of Swiss persons at all, which was practi-

66

cally never, had thought of them solely in connection with clocks, alps, and waiters.

This was bad enough, surely, by itself; quite bad enough, without having anything more added to it. There was, however, more added to it, for it presently transpired—and this, though it didn't get into the local papers, was whispered in the local drawing-rooms —that the pair had lived together at first without being married. Milly, they understood, tried to explain to Ernest, who very properly declined to discuss it and desired her to rule her sister out of her life once and for all, that it wasn't Agatha's fault, but was owing to some unexpected delay because of the different nationalities. As if that could excuse immorality! And what was delay for, except to wait in? It was only after three weeks of shame, so the Botts learned, and also the whole of Titford, that the position had been legalized, and the girl proceeded with him who had been her paramour—the Botts shrank from the word, but pronounced it—and was now indeed, it seemed, her husband, to Switzerland, where he kept, the Botts receiving their last straw in shocked silence were given to understand, an hotel.

They couldn't get over it. They never had got over it. Kind and affectionate as they were to Milly, devoted to her as most of the brothers afterwards became, they yet deep down in their hearts remembered what her sister had done. Useless for them to try to wipe Agatha out of their minds; they only succeeded in wiping her out of their conversation. An hotel-keeper as Ernest's brother-in-law. A person who bowed to one on a doorstep, and rubbed his hands. A person who presented bills on departure, which one paid. What a nice thing to have become mixed up with! No such connection, nothing approaching such a connection, had ever yet got into their

family. Alps became sore points with them. The word
hotel made them start. When they went to Italy they
went by the Mont Cenis and Modane. When Le Bon—
his name, they considered, should certainly have been
Le Mauvais—a cordial man, who wanted to be friends
and wore a glossy black coat and a white tie even at
breakfast, invited them, as he did to begin with, to come
and stay at his hotel as long as they liked free of charge,
it was regarded as the deadliest insult and ignored.
When his wife wrote, as she did to begin with, letters of
apology, and even of affection, to Ernest, for Agatha at
the time of her disgrace was only nineteen and an
optimist, not only did he take no notice of them but
forbade Milly to do so, either then or at any time during
the rest of her life. And when at last Le Bon died, which
he did in his wife's arms, a place he had rarely been out
of and was not displeased, after twenty-five years of it,
to have an opportunity of leaving, for *la bonne Agathe*, as
he called her, was so energetic—*d'une énergie formidable*,
he thought sometimes with a sigh, he having latterly
become very tired of the hardness of life, and realizing,
on the verge of leaving it, how little real pleasure it had
given him—when at last he died, the Botts were unaware that the creature, as they referred to him in their
thoughts, had ceased to exist.

Milly didn't tell them. To tell them would have exposed her own steady disobedience and deceit. Besides,
he was unmentionable. Milly didn't care to imagine
what Ernest's face would look like if she suddenly began
mentioning Le Bon. She did tell Arthur of his death;
and he said, very kindly, and completely uninterested,
"Poor fellow," and after that, except in Agatha's letters,
Le Bon seemed to drop finally out of life.

But in Agatha's letters, with how strange a splendour
did he now begin to glow. From the first they had been

written in a strain of almost exaggerated satisfaction
with her marriage, so that Milly well knew Aggie had
loved her Swiss and been happy with him, but she
hadn't realized how great that love and happiness had
been till she read the letters written after his death.
What pale things her condolences and sympathies
seemed, offered to that flaming sorrow. Agatha's letters,
during the whole twenty-five years, had been on the
romantic side, and apt to be rather taken up with Swiss
meadows and mountains and moons, and the sorts of
things one felt in their presence when love walked beside
one; but they now became drenched in poetry. She
seemed to have read a great deal of it, and had it apparently at her ready disposal in her mind. Arthur and
Milly had read a great deal of it too together, during
those quiet afternoons of sin, but it had never got into
Milly's letters,—not to quote, that is, not to put in verse
after verse. Agatha's letters, after her husband's death,
were so full of it that it was difficult to find the places
where it left off and she began. She hardly said anything
about herself any more. The things became passionate
applications of the great thoughts of poets to Le Bon.
Shelley, Tennyson, Matthew Arnold—all were grist to
Agatha's elegiac mill, and all of them, according to her,
must have had Le Bon prophetically in their minds.
They *described* him, she wrote.

Milly marvelled. She was stirred by the *post-mortem*
letters to her depths. This was love. This was the real,
blazing thing. The very envelopes, mourning-edged,
seemed to scorch her fingers with black fire. Fancy all
that having been inspired by a Swiss! Milly couldn't get
over it. Except at the beginning with Arthur, she had
never felt what Agatha appeared to feel every day as a
matter of course; compared to the rich, warm blood
Agatha was full of, Milly realized that she herself was

mere milk. "It's wonderful how fond Aggie was of her husband," she said to Arthur one afternoon, coming to their meeting fresh from another letter. And Arthur again said, very kindly, and completely uninterested, "Poor fellow."

At no time had there been nearly as many letters from Agatha to Milly as from Milly to Agatha, but they made up for their infrequency by being extremely long—as long as they possibly could be, without having to have another stamp. After Le Bon's death they became even more infrequent, and once or twice hadn't a stamp on them at all, so that Milly knew how deeply distracted poor Aggie must be. Yet how splendid she was through all her distraction, going on with the hotel in spite of the weight of her sorrow, carrying on as Gaston, she wrote, would have wished, even launching out into new developments and opening it, for what remained of the winter, as a ski-ing resort. Such grit deserved success; and success and happiness, Milly reflected proudly, but also wistfully, had attended Aggie's footsteps from the moment she had taken her own life into her hands and fled from Ernest's house—the success and happiness which await those who dare, who defy, who go straight for what they want, and don't sit at home smiling anxiously at husbands.

Still, at this time, some weeks before Ernest's death, and entirely unconscious that he had found her out, Milly wasn't really wistful; she was quite content, really, with things as they were, enjoying her popularity in Titford, and the affection of the Botts, and, unknown to a soul, as she supposed, the devotion of Arthur.

Or was it, she sometimes wondered, her devotion to him that she enjoyed?

Well, perhaps. It didn't matter. So long as there was devotion, thought Milly, her good and sweet eyes—they had remained good and sweet, in spite of her life of sin—maternally watching Arthur, as he sipped his tea and warmed his lean hands round the cup—so long as there was devotion, after ten years of intimacy what did it matter whose it was?

And indeed she was right about Agatha's grit. Agatha was all grit. Such was the amount of it in her character that, for a whole quarter of a century, she was able to suppress any word in her letters which didn't breathe pure contentment and happiness. Because, from the first, she had set her teeth and had made up her mind that neither Milly, her well-off, comfortable sister, nor the hostile and unjust Botts to whom she belonged, should ever know she was being punished.

§

Yes; she was being punished all right, the Botts, who believed in justice, would have been glad to hear, though it was also true her marriage was a success. It was a success, that is, in every way except one; but that one way was so important that its absence sent Le Bon at last from sheer underfeeding and anxiety to his grave, and ground Agatha to the bone. For there has to be money; there has to be some money somewhere if a man is to be placid, and his wife not become just bone. Le Bon, kind and incompetent, whose nature it was to be happiest in tranquillity—*la tranquillité avant tout*, he used to say to himself in the early days of his marriage, before he was so hungry, when Agatha had reproachfully been reaffirming her belief in *l'amour avant tout*, a belief which really surprised Le Bon, who never would have eloped with Agatha if she hadn't eloped with him, not being by nature an eloper, and who felt that much *amour*, indeed any, once the honeymoon was over, was incompatible with marriage and the increasingly sordid absorptions of their life, and Agatha herself was later to replace the word *amour* by *le manger*—Le Bon had less and less money with every year that passed.

Every year his hotel was a little emptier than the year before, and accordingly also his pockets, and also, disastrously, his stomach; every year new and bigger hotels in more convenient and quite as beautiful spots sprang up, and they had central heating and modern sanitation, and his hadn't. His was a small wooden house by itself, far from railways and three miles from the nearest hamlet, tucked away in a dimple on the face of the mountains,—a very lovely dimple once one was in it, but difficult to reach except for hardy persons who didn't mind mules. In the early days, the relatively prosperous days, when Agatha was young and full of determination to make the thing an enormous success, and show Milly and Ernest and all those other base Botts that they had been wrong about her marriage and she gloriously right, active English clergymen, including several of the wirier bishops, used with their wives, who also were wiry, to spend their Augusts there. Madame Le Bon being English made it, they declared, so comfortable and home-like—who was she by the by? Oh, nobody particular; suburbs. She knew about thin bread and butter, and real English tea. She knew that water, unless it is cold, must be hot. And if she couldn't let one have proper baths in a bathroom because of there not being a bath-room, she at least understood about sending up tubs. The wives talked friendlily to Madame Le Bon—a nice young creature, quite a lady, they said; the bishops were most kind, never failing to give her a cheery word as they passed in and out, even courteously asking her to sit down when they called her to the *salon* to consult her about a mountain excursion; and everybody punc-tiliously paid their bills.

Great days; compared, that is, to what came after them. But even in them there were money troubles. The season was so short; the English—scarcely anyone who wasn't English was fond enough of exercise combined with frugal living to come up that steep bridle-path to the simple little hotel at the top—only had holidays in August and September, and by the middle of September the sun went off the dimple early, and it became so excessively cold that however hardy the visitors might be they needs must go down to warmer places; and then the shutters were shut, and the desolation that was to last ten months began, and no more money for another year was to be expected.

Winged by pride and youth, and determination that those Botts should never be able to say, "I told you so," Agatha did all, and more than all, mortal woman can do to help her Gaston through the empty months. She scoured, and cooked, and baked; she diligently collected fir cones and wood for the fire he liked to dream by; she dragged the bedding out of doors with her strong young arms, to air it on the frozen snow in the hot mid-day sun of winter; she industriously mended and patched the thin, torn sheets—clergymen seemed to kick a good deal in bed, she thought; she anxiously cherished the important goats, and hung maternally over the important chickens; and, having settled Gaston comfortably in his chair by the fire after tea, and given him the pipe that was to persuade him he had eaten his fill, each day she walked forth alone in the tremendous twilights, when evening filled the distant valley as if it were a bowl, creeping slowly higher and higher, putting out the red reflection of the sunset as it crept, till at last only the solemn circle of the highest mountain-tops stood above it in a ring of light, and with her face turned upwards to the freezing purity of those lonely slopes of snow, solitary in the utter silence, she replenished her courage and renewed her faith; for, at the end of a long day's work, both of these things, Agatha found, were apt to flicker.

They shouldn't flicker, she vowed. She wouldn't let them. It was so beautiful there, she thought while she was still young. She lived in the very heart of beauty. She lived too in the very heart of affection. Outside, that marvellous winter purity, that honeyed loveliness of June, inside, waiting for her, her kind Gaston. She had only to go out for a minute at the end of the day to be calmed and rested. Why should she let herself be cast down because they had no money? Things were going to be better. She would *make* them be better. Those Botts should never——

At this time Agatha was in her early twenties, and very strong. Ten years later she was still doing these same things, and still going out every evening to the stars; but only now so as to get a breath of fresh air, and not thinking very much about anything in particular as she blinked at them with tired eyes. She was tired. She had had, by then, fifteen years of it. Each of these years had been harder than the one before, and her body, with no such thing as a roundness or a softness left anywhere about it, had become very bony.

Still—those Botts. They shouldn't know, thought Agatha, laying back her ears; not one of them should know. If she wrote to Milly of her distresses she would help her, no doubt, but sooner or later, being a Bott, and to judge from her recent letters a settled-down and contented Bott, she would leak, and that vindictive Ernest get to know of her plight, and rejoice. Besides, how rich she was really in her Gaston. As far as *he* went, his disposition, his unfailing gentleness and courtesy, how happy she was. He was exactly like his surname.

She often wrote this to Milly, how exactly like his sur-name Gaston was. And he couldn't manage for a single minute without her, he entirely relied on her. Agatha loved to be relied on. She had no children, but she didn't miss them, with Gaston relying on her. He was her child; more to her, indeed, than any child could have been, and needing her every bit as much. It was always she who, in the constant crises of their economi-cal life, comforted him and held him up. She was the stronger. She loved being the stronger, loved having her energetic finger in even the smallest of Gaston's little pies. For instance, without her he couldn't so much as decide which tie he was to wear. She loved that.

And she dared say those Botts were imagining her regretting what she had done. Regretting? Never, said Agatha, still said Agatha even fifteen years after she had done it, such was her pride and such her indomitable determination. And she blinked with tired but defiant eyes at the icy bright stars above the glittering, empty, silent slopes of snow. Such a lot of snow. Pity one couldn't eat it, she thought.

Ten years later nobody would have known Agatha. By that time she was forty-four, but she looked, as the other working-women in those high parts looked at the same age, the infrequent mud-coloured peasants, not to be distinguished at a distance from the soil they worked on, well over sixty. Her skin, stretched tight over the bones of her face, had a curious varnished appearance,—that was because of the fierce sun, and the fierce snow-light, and the great biting winds that brought the win-ters, and the water that cut one, when one washed, like a knife; and her body was a dry, taut rope. These years had included the war years. The war finished the hotel. Nobody came. It stood quite empty, with its shutters shut. She and Le Bon lived entirely on the milk and cheese they got from the goats, and the bread they made from a patch of rye they cultivated in the summer. Le Bon relied on her more than ever, but he no longer asked her which tie he was to wear, because there were no ties left. This, however, didn't matter, for as he didn't shave any more his beard grew, and it presently hid the place where there wasn't now a tie, and he looked as neat as ever. His beard, though, was very white, and Agatha finally saw what she hadn't so much noticed before, because he had been a tidy, bald man for a long while, with hardly any hair to show what time was doing to him, that her husband was old. Very old. A small patriarch he looked, once his snowy beard really began to flow, and she sometimes caught herself staring at him in surprise, so unlike the man she had eloped with was he. He too, for his part, sometimes let his pale glance rest on Agatha in anemic wonder. This knotted, battered, gaunt woman—was it possible? Le Bon sighed, and closed his eyes.

In the twenty-fifth year of their marriage he began to die; not from any specific disease the doctor, reluctantly ascending the mule-track, could discover, but from inability, apparently, to go on living. Also he didn't want to go on living. He had had enough. It was so cold alive, and his stomach was so empty, and his bed so thin and hard. His poor Agathe also was thin and hard. Enough, enough. "*C'est assez*," were his last articulate words, caught by Agatha as she bent over him in despair; and even in his choice of last words Le Bon continued kind, for what he really wanted to murmur was, "*C'est trop*." But that would have hurt his poor faithful *amie*. Gentle and polite to the last, Le Bon died; and the hotel was sold at once for almost nothing to the proprietor of the big hotel down in the valley, who had had his eye

on it for a long time past, for he wished to acquire a
small *dépendance* high up, as an object for the excursions
of his more active clients.

Agatha was kept on as book-keeper. The post was
offered her partly out of kindness, partly because she
knew the conditions so thoroughly, and partly because
she would be cheap. She took it in spite of the tiny
salary, for where was she to go? She had to live somehow; and less than ever, now that Gaston was dead,
was she going to say a word to Milly about being poor,
and so confess his incompetence, less than ever, after so
long holding up her head as the wife of the successful
and flourishing, was she going to throw herself, penniless
and beaten, on the Bott compassion. Besides, what
was the use? The inexorable Ernest still cut her off
from Milly, who still, she wrote, had to hide their letters.
So that even if she humbled herself enough to go as a
suppliant, she would probably be spurned. A suppliant?
Gaston's widow a suppliant? She would *starve* first,
muttered Agatha, laying back her ears.

So she stayed on as book-keeper, and grimly watched
what just a little capital and just a little competence
could do in turning Gaston's failure into quite a promising concern.

It was at this point that she took to the poets. Compared to the huge labours of her former days she had
hardly anything to do, and was also being fed properly
for the first time for years. So she began reading poetry
—little volumes grateful clergymen, not quite liking to
tip her, presented to her on leaving the hotel. They were
Golden Treasuries, and Oxford Books of Verse; and as
she studied *Thyrsis*, and *Adonais*, and *In Memoriam* it
seemed to her uncanny how they all might have been
written of and for Gaston. She couldn't send many
letters to Milly because she couldn't afford the stamps,

her salary going in paying off the bills for her mourning, which she had been forced to buy on the instalment system, but, when she did, her reading filled them with the strange threnodial passion which made Milly marvel. Up in her room under the roof she copied the splendid stuff into her letters with clumsy, determined fingers, for her hard work out of doors and in had stiffened and coarsened them; but no difficulty ever stopped Agatha from doing what she felt was right, and surely it was right, it was her sacred duty, to let Milly, and perhaps through some dropped word of hers also those vindictive Botts, know the kind of man Gaston had really been. Noble and misjudged; gone to his grave noble, and patient, and misjudged. Agatha wept to think of it, tears of scalding pity for Gaston, tears of scalding indignation at the long-drawn-out implacability of the Botts. Milly, her little sister, who alone in the world, now that Gaston was dead, represented love for Agatha—there she was, surrounded and hedged in by the inimical family, and out of reach of anything except letters. On Milly's behalf, Agatha said to herself, wandering alone, as she had so often wandered in the icy dusk along the snowy track that led up the mountain, she would unhesitatingly and gladly have laid down her life. But Milly didn't need her life. Nobody needed anything that she could give, who could give so much, so lavishly, of devotion.

Agatha wept. Then one day at the end of March, when the snow was beginning to be patchy, and gentians seemed suddenly to have been poured out over the grass as from the gigantic bucket of a god, and the last of the ski-guests were preparing to leave, Agatha saw in the *Continental Daily Mail*, which was the English newspaper provided for his *clientèle* by the proprietor because it was cheap, that Ernest was dead.

She was much shocked. She walked over to the window, and stared out without seeing anything. Ernest dead, with all his unkindness still upon him. And little Milly a widow now, going through what she herself was suffering—the loneliness, the gnawing loneliness.

She knew no details. Ernest's death came under the heading *London Traffic Alarming Increase in Accidents*, and was lumped together with several others. But the name and address caught her eye at once; and at once, before she turned away from the window, she had made up her mind.

No obstacles separated her from Milly now. They were both, alas, free. She knew where her place was: it was at Milly's side. And however painful it would be to meet the rest of the Bott family again, she would bear more than that, oh, far, far more than that, she who by this time was so much used to bearing, so as to be with Milly in her sorrow. Ernest had been a stern man, and —she must say it, in spite of his being dead—a cruel man as far as she was concerned, but not, she understood from Milly's letters, otherwise. Milly had seemed content and happy, especially during all these later years, and certainly had had everything that money could buy. And Agatha was so tired of being poor, so much afraid of the dreadful future, when she wouldn't be wanted even as a book-keeper. With Milly, she would get into harbour at last, into a safe, quiet harbour, even if a sad one; though indeed Milly's wealth was not why she so instantly decided to go to her—it merely made it possible.

Determined as ever where someone she loved was concerned, she at once threw up her post, scraped together all her worldly goods, which were so few that the same small bag she had run away from Titford with was emptier than it had been twenty-five years before, and going down the bridle-path she would never probably tread again, she went to the mother-hotel in the valley, and told the proprietor so firmly that he must lend her money for her fare to London that, hypnotized, he did it at once. Her sister would pay back, said Agatha, her gaunt head held high with pride. Her sister was rich. . . .

The proprietor, who had been about to give this poor Madame Le Bon, this excellent woman who had so much suffered and whose hotel he really had picked up very cheap, the fare as a parting gift, hereupon gave it to her as a loan. Foolish, he thought, if the sister were rich not to allow her to pay; and the poor creature, even for the loan, was all gratitude.

And when she arrived in London close on midnight, and tried to go to Titford so as to fold Milly to her heart at once, fold her even as she herself had been folded by Milly that long-gone day of homecoming, and promise to take care of her and tenderly love her, even as Milly had promised—Agatha remembered each word; she never forgot words—to love and take care of her, when she tried to go to Titford she found she couldn't, for the last train had left. So, taking her bag in her firm grip, for these exertions were child's play to Agatha, taut and sinewy with labour, she set out in the London night to find a cheap lodging, walking—it was nothing to her, a walk like that—all the way to Bloomsbury; for she too recollected, as Milly next morning was going to recollect, that in Bloomsbury there used to be many lodgings, and she too thought it would be consoling to spend the night in the place where she used to be young. And though she lost her way, and found herself in Piccadilly Circus when she was aiming at where she remembered Trafalgar Square used to be, she was treated with respect, and in no way interfered with; and when she did finally reach the squares that had clustered round her childhood, she was unable to resist, in spite of its being so late, going first, before she searched for a room, into the very one she and Milly had lived in—just for a moment, just to look at the house a moment after all these years, and all that had happened in them, and because her heart was brimming. And she too then saw what Milly was going to see next morning, that there was a notice board up.

The light from the nearest lamp enabled her to read its legend.

She stood gazing at it.

How strange. How providential.

And going up the steps, although it was by now past one and the house was shrouded in sleep and silence, she rang the bell.

The board said *Apartments to Let*. It said nothing about their not being to let at night, Agatha remarked to herself on getting no answer; therefore she would go on ringing till somebody came.

She did; and the first person who came was a policeman. He walked slowly along the square, looked at her, and then walked away.

The next person who came was the lady next door, who put her head out of an upstair window, and said it was no good ringing because they were deaf in there, but, if it was rooms she wanted, she herself——

Then came the manageress; hurriedly, in a dressing-gown; instinctively, through her slumbers, feeling all was not well down on her door-step. And quickly unbolting the door, she was just in the nick of time to prevent that harpy in the next house, that vulture, that low-down non-player of the game, that snatcher-away of other people's ladies, from carrying off her lodger.

"You poor, poor *dear!*" she cried when she saw the tall mourning figure, remembering even at that hour to welcome sympathetically.

"I want a room, please," said Agatha briefly, coming in and firmly putting down her bag on the hall table.

"Why, that's just what I *want* you to have," the manageress assured her, who hadn't yet seen her boots.

This was how Agatha came to be in their old home next morning when Milly arrived, and they didn't recognize each other.

(V)

THERE is no forgetting a voice, however.

That evening, after having slept the whole day the sleep of complete exhaustion, hardly stirring from the position she had dropped down in on the bed directly after her breakfast, Milly woke up to find the room dark, and the day manifestly over.

She sat up, instinctively tidying her hair, and by the light of a lit window in the house opposite saw that the breakfast-tray was gone, so that someone must have been in the room since she fell asleep. And she hadn't heard a sound; not all day had she heard a sound.

O blessed sleep ! O comfortable bird ! quoted Milly—for by now, having had so much poetry read aloud to her by Arthur, she knew quite a lot of it inaccurately; and she apostrophized sleep in this manner because she felt quite different, restored, by those few hours of withdrawal into unconsciousness from the pressure of life, to clearness of mind, her head no longer aching, and not even remembering for several minutes that she was a fugitive and a penitent.

When she did, it came as a shock, for she felt so good and peaceful. Was she really wicked? Of course she was. The Botts knew all about it by this time. It was their knowing that made her wicked; it was Ernest's having found out. If nobody had ever known. . . .

She turned her mind resolutely away from a line of thought manifestly discreditable in one who repents.

Here she was hankering after the comforts of secrecy again, the shelter of deception. She would get up, and go out into the square for a little, if it weren't too late, while her room was being tidied for the night, and try to think more rightly. Just having had a good sleep mustn't be allowed to blind her to the facts of her situation; conscience couldn't be a thing at the beck and call of one's physical condition.

And as she was feeling her way across the room to where her bonnet was, for there seemed to be no matches or candle or electric light, and the blind of the window on the other side of the square had been pulled down, something suddenly smote her motionless.

A voice.

She stood listening, stiffened into an intense attention. Whose?

She held her breath, pushing the hair back from her ears. Was this house really haunted?

Downstairs it was. But whose? Whose voice? Oh —but *whose?*

Trembling, she felt her way to the door, and opened it a crack.

The voice went on. Down in the hall, it seemed to be. And another voice mixed up with it—that manageress woman's, apparently.

Years seemed to roll back from Milly as she listened, staring into the dark, spell-bound.

"No, no—it is much too late, thank you," she heard the voice say distinctly, "much too late for dinner, thank you. Yes, I was aware it was at half-past seven, but I have been delayed. Is there no letter for me? I was expecting one. No doubt I shall be receiving it by the first post to-morrow, then. And after that I shall be leaving——"

"Leaving?" It was the manageress's voice which here became distinct. "You can't."

"How—I cannot?" inquired the other voice.

"Not without a week's notice. This isn't a hotel."

"And after that," repeated the voice with a kind of melancholy firmness, "I shall be leaving. I am only waiting to hear from my sister. She lives at Titford. I wrote to her this morning, and her reply should certainly be here by——"

Milly waited to hear no more. She pulled open the door, flung herself through it, groped wildly till she found the banisters, for no light was on up there and only a very dim one was burning far below in the hall, and hanging on to them, obliged to feel for every step because it was so dark, she got down the stairs somehow, catching her feet in her long skirt, kicking them free again, stumbling, clutching, and making queer little noises as she went.

"Aggie! It's me—it's Milly—I'm here too—Aggie, Aggie!" she called out, frantic lest the voice should go away before she got to it, lest something should happen and they miss each other, lose each other again, disappear again into more endless, heart-breaking years. "Wait! I'm coming! Aggie! Oh—*Aggie !*"

And there was a tall enveloped figure, bonneted and cloaked, dark even in the darkness, running up towards her, reaching up the stairs towards her, exclaiming, calling out too, and Milly's last words were sobs in Agatha's arms.

§

"*Well*," thought the manageress.

She stood unnoticed at the foot of the stairs, an astonished witness, in the dimness, of the rush together of her two latest lodgers. Fancy the quiet-spoken Mrs. Bott making such a noise. And the other one, the hatchet-faced one, as soft and sobby now as you please. Such a hullabaloo she hadn't heard since that Miss Scrymgeour left, and wanted not to pay most of her bill.

She stood hesitating a moment, wondering whether this perhaps was one of the rare occasions on which the bright front-door light oughtn't to be turned on, the light reserved for arrivals, but decided that it wasn't. No good wasting. She would be, however, tactful. Evidently an unexpected reunion. She would show that she knew when not to intrude. So she withdrew into the dining-room; but in order to avoid possible unpleasantness, for emotional ladies were apt to wander out of the house when they were having their attacks, and forget all about things like bills, as a precaution she softly locked the hall-door, and put the key in her pocket.

§

At that time of evening the ladies of the *Home from Home* were supposed to be either in the drawing-room, which had what was needful though not excessive in the way of lights, or in their bedrooms, which were furnished each with a candle. No provision was made for conversations on staircases. The staircases and the passages were left in darkness. Ladies, the manageress had discovered, were patient about lights, content to grope their way to bed; therefore, naturally, she didn't give them any. One had to save where one could. Life was hard, and bankruptcy at all times just round the corner.

So that it was in the dark that Milly and Agatha met again, and knew each other only by their voices. Mere shadowy blotches locked together on the stairs, they swayed to and fro in the closeness of their embrace, while the manageress, withdrawn into the dining-room because she was tactful, kept the door ajar because she was interested.

They could see nothing, they could only hear and feel; and what they heard, for a long time, was just sobs, and what they felt for a space they didn't notice, because their minds were empty of everything except the blessed, blessed comfort of there being two of them. Two. In a desolate, frightening world, what magic in just that!

"Oh, nobody should *ever* be only one!" sobbed Milly clinging, her face buried in Agatha's crape, overwhelmed by the pure joy, the exquisite relief, of having as by a miracle reached protection and love already. Bliss flooded her heart. It was like coming home after long, distressed wandering; it was like being safe after deadly fear.

"Why, my Milly? What, my bereaved one?" wept Agatha, clasping her tight, and washed by such deep emotion that the feel of Milly's figure, definitely substantial and different, in fact not the least like Milly, caused her no surprise, didn't even get through into her consciousness.

"My Aggie—oh, my *Aggie!*" sobbed Milly in reply.

"My Milly—oh, my *Milly!*" wept Agatha, clasping her even closer.

And the manageress, just inside the dining-room door, thought, "*Well.*"

It was one of those rare moments of love surprised, of complete surrender to emotion. No questions came into their heads, because for those few seconds they had no heads, only hearts. They didn't think; they felt. Sweet, and warm, and incredibly comforting was it to be close to one's sister again, touching her, holding her to one's heart for the first time for such long years. Milly forgot everything that had happened since she last saw

Agatha; she forgot there had ever been any Botts, and a man called Le Bon; Ernest was wiped out as completely as if he had been the merest temporary mess; Arthur wasn't given a thought. Blood was all that mattered,—blood, and the binding memories of childhood. Only one's sister had the same memories, only one's sister could love one without wanting anything back, with no after-thought, with just sheer, single-minded love.

"Do you remember how we used to laugh?" sobbed Milly into Agatha's crape.

"Alas," was Agatha's reply, also a sob.

Twenty-five years—"Oh, think of it, *think* of it, Aggie,—it's twenty-five years!"—since last they had heard each other's voices, twenty-five years since that casual good-night on the final evening in Mandeville Park Road, the usual casual good-night, Milly really casual, nodding at the door of her bedroom, Agatha feverishly determined to be casual, as she went into hers only to get out of it again almost immediately through the window. How vividly Milly remembered Agatha as she had seen her last, standing with her hand on the knob of her bedroom door, reed-like in her tall grace, a mass of dark hair bundled together low on her little white neck, her head turned towards her, and the light from the gas-burner shining down on her flushed, bright young face. And Agatha, holding Milly tight and subconsciously feeling her so substantial, had an equally vivid vision of the small, slim thing calling out carelessly, "Good-night, old Agg," across the passage—her bird-like little sister, a year older than herself and already married, but so untouched, so free from the tremors and complications which collect the minute one has told a man to wait for one beneath one's window.

"Milly—my little Milly——"

"Aggie—darling sister——"

And the manageress, just inside the dining-room door, her ears stretched, thought, "Sisters. *Well*."

§

It was a great moment. It couldn't possibly go on. It ended when Agatha loosened her hold to take out her handkerchief, and wipe her streaming eyes. Then Milly, whose face had been buried in Agatha's crape, which had an odd smell, she was subconsciously aware, neither quite like ink nor quite like glue, but very like what both would be like if they got together, drew her head back a little so as to breathe; and the minute she could breathe she began to talk, and the minute she began to talk Agatha began to talk too, and the minute they both began to talk, instead of just sobbing and exclaiming, the spell was broken, they left off being only hearts with no heads, and the pure unquestioning joy, the pure unquestioning thankfulness, was over.

"But how—but why?" asked Milly, having hastily wiped her eyes, peering up into the shadowy face surrounded by the folds of thrown-back veil.

"Is it not strange," said Agatha, her voice vibrating and her *r*'s much more in evidence than they used to be making her sound almost as if she were a foreigner, which of course she wasn't, Milly said to herself, except perhaps technically, "that we should meet again like this, and here."

"Oh, Aggie—*isn't* it," said Milly, awe-struck by these coincidences, and oblivious to the fact that she and Agatha were on a staircase, and that probably everybody in the house could hear. "Both widows."

"Both widows," repeated Agatha vibrantly. "Old widows, my Milly."

"Not very old," said Milly. "It's only three months

since you—— And poor Ernest—it only happened last week."

"Alas, in that sense we are both tragically young," said Agatha. "I was thinking of our ages."

"Our ages?" echoed Milly, who hadn't been used to thinking of her age, what with Arthur, and her admiring brothers-in-law, and she always having been so much younger than Ernest, and one thing and another. "Why, I'm not so very old, and you're a year less, Aggie darling."

"I am old," insisted Agatha in her deep voice, "old, and broken."

"I never heard of such a thing," cried Milly—almost laughed Milly, still lit up with the joyful confidence the miraculous reunion with Agatha gave her. That wasn't how they were going to begin life together again, by being old and broken. However old they might be, and of course they weren't young, they were *new*, Milly said to herself—from that day on she, anyhow, was going to be brand-new. It was the only way to make up, to wipe out, to start fresh.

"How can you be old and broken, Aggie darling, if I'm not?" she inquired.

Whereupon Agatha put her away from her, holding her at arm's length as though to search her face, which she couldn't do because of the dark and said, "Do not tell me, my Milly, that you are one of those women who refuse to accept age?"—and a faint surprise, very faint, hardly surprise at all, fell like a tiny shadow across Milly's brightness.

"Let's go to your room or mine," she suggested, suddenly realizing from a little sound in the hall below that they weren't perhaps quite as much alone as being in the dark made them feel they were. "There's so much to say. We can't talk here——"

"Indeed and indeed there is much to say," agreed Agatha; and as they began slowly ascending the narrow stairs, their progress made difficult by their clothes, and also because Agatha encircled Milly with her arm, which felt like a hoop of iron round the soft, abundant flesh, Milly went on, "We shall have to sit up all night talking. How did you know, Aggie? How is it you are here—in this house, of all houses?"

"How is it *you* are here, my little one, away from your home so soon after——"

"But how did you know about Ernest? I hadn't time to write. It was all so sudden, so dreadful——"

"Hush, hush," Agatha interrupted, tightening her hold as if to protect from sad thoughts; and the stairs being steep, and their skirts long, and their bodies of different sizes, it was very difficult to get up like that at all. "Do not dwell on that side of it—not on the shocking outward circumstances. You must only think of him as happy now, my Milly, and at rest."

"But how did you *know?*" persisted Milly, unable after her experiences in that haunted bedroom to believe Ernest was at rest, but unwilling to say so to Agatha,— not yet, not at that moment, not on the stairs. Presently she was going to tell her everything, from the beginning. Her confession was to be complete. There shouldn't be the shadow of a secret between them, there shouldn't be the shred of a veil of pretence. What one had done, thought Milly, aware of many things she hadn't realized before she was found out, could never be as bad as pretending to someone one loves that one hadn't done it; it was that which rotted one's soul. Besides, why pretend? Aggie was her sister, who loved her. Love always understood and forgave. It didn't judge. It never condemned. There had only to be enough of it for it not to be able to help understanding, and therefore forgiving. Aggie's

love and hers for each other was great enough to get
over fifty Arthurs. And in that high moment of reunion
Milly felt that she would with perfect confidence have
told her much worse things than Arthur, if she had had
any to tell.

"How did I know?" repeated Agatha, her voice
vibrating. It seemed to have grown much deeper and
bigger. It pulsed. It reverberated through one, and
made one feel as if one were full of bees. Perhaps it was
like that because she lived among great mountains, and
her voice grew to match them—her voice, her heart, her
whole outlook. Witness her letters. So wonderful, so
full of—well, outlook, finished Milly, unable to express
it any better.

"There seems," Agatha went on, as they slowly continued to ascend, "to be a fate which decrees we shall
always know quickly enough of sad things. I chanced to
take up a paper at which I usually do not look—the
Continental Daily Mail—and there it was. Such a shock,
my Milly—take care, don't stumble—such a shock to
read of it suddenly in cold print. His name caught my
eye immediately. He was with other accidents. Poor,
poor man. Harsh in his judgments, perhaps. Perhaps,
too, narrow in his views. And I have sometimes
thought obstinate in the persistence with which he held
them——"

"Ernest," thought the manageress, straining her ears
now in the hall, into which she had crept from the dining-room because the voices, receding, were becoming
indistinct, "must be the late Mr. Bott."

"Aggie," thought Milly, "talks differently from the
way she used to. Or is it my imagination?"

"But that," continued Agatha, "is all over now. His
death filled me with nothing but pity—I assure you,
Milly, with nothing whatever but purest pity and for-

giveness. I owe him no grudge now, gone like that, in a moment. Poor Ernest." She sighed. "I came at once."

"But suppose we had missed each other?" said Milly, stopping a moment to get her breath, for not only did the stairs make her pant but she was struck by the extreme unpleasantness for everybody if she had arrived on Aggie's mountain to find her gone, and Aggie had journeyed to Titford to fall into a nest of violently hostile Botts. "Wouldn't that have been too awful———"

"How could we have?" vibrated Agatha, stopping too but still keeping hold of Milly. "I would have waited for you in Titford till you returned. I wrote you there by the first post this morning."

"But I wasn't going to return. I was on my way to Switzerland."

"To Switzerland?"

"To you. My one thought since yester—ever since it happened, has been to get to you."

"But———" began Agatha, struck in her turn.

She was silent, staring at the dim face before her. Really the way Providence was intervening was little short of miraculous. She too had made up her mind there should be no more pretences between herself and Milly; she was going to tell her everything at last— lay aside the pride she had wrapped herself in since the day of her elopement, and explain at last the whole distress and struggle of her life. Painful, most painful, after the things she had written; but infinitely more painful if Milly had gone to the hotel and heard the story from other lips, heard just the sordid facts without the excuse, indeed, the justification, of the motive— a motive which surely, Agatha said to herself, was not ignoble? To love the husband of one's choice, and protect that choice from the attacks of vindictive relatives, all waiting for a chance to let loose their intolerable

"I told you so's"—was that ignoble? But she would rather tell Milly about it herself; much rather. After all, she had consistently and for years given wrong impressions—her enemies might even say that she had been untruthful,—and to confess this was going to be difficult indeed, with Milly no doubt remembering the tone of her letters, the constant praises she had sung, and meant, of the good, the beautiful, and the true. Best of all would be, of course, if it were only possible, to continue to conceal, thought Agatha, shrinking from what she had to do; but being with a person constantly, as she was now going to be with Milly, was very different from merely writing to that person. It would be impossible, she was afraid, in daily conversation to keep up that which had been easy in letters.

"Had you done that," she said, her voice deeper than ever with the profound dislike for the necessity of so soon having to lay herself bare, "you would not have found what you expected."

"No," said Milly, reaching up and kissing her. "I wouldn't have found *you*, darling."

"That is not quite what I meant," said Agatha; and added, after a pause of struggle, "I have a confession to make, Milly."

"A confession?" repeated Milly. "You, Aggie?"

"A confession?" repeated the manageress under her breath, creeping up a few stairs, anxious to hear to the last.

"Perhaps I should say an explanation," said Agatha, her pride kicking even on the way to its death-bed.

"I'd rather it were a confession," said Milly with a nervous, small laugh. If Aggie too had something to confess, how much easier it would make everything. The idea, however, was ludicrous—what could Aggie, alone up on her mountain, possibly have done? One

their being connected with death in shocking circumstances, and having confessions to make, and wanting
to leave almost as soon as they arrived, and wearing
boots, one of them, that were a disgrace to a doormat
and bound to lower the house's credit, but that they also
weren't quite all there, pretending rooms were sub-let
without her knowledge—"If you ask *me*," she thought,
staring round and seeing nothing but the same instru-
ments of a meagre toilet which she had already examined
and appraised earlier in the day, and, under the bed, the
same pair of slippers which had been there before—
slippers worse even, if one were at all particular, than
the boots.

∗(VI)*∗*

IN THE room above, Milly was feeling about for matches, hampered in her movements by Agatha, who came too, holding her with loving solicitude by the arm.

"I want to see you, Aggie darling," said Milly, clumsily groping. "I *long* to see you."

"What I at this moment long for, my worn-out little sister," said Agatha, "is to see you resting. And then," she added with sudden sternness, "I will go down and ask that woman what she means by——"

"I've been resting all day," said Milly, proceeding, accompanied by Agatha, round the room and fumbling with her free hand. "Sound asleep for hours."

"Are you able to sleep?" asked Agatha, surprised, for she remembered how after Gaston's death she had not closed her eyes for many, many nights. But she added, after a brief pause, that she was glad indeed it should be so.

"They don't seem to go in much for light here, do they," interrupted Milly, fumbling.

"And yet," said Agatha, experienced in these practices but resenting them when applied to herself, "it will no doubt be charged us heavily in the bill. I suppose," she continued, moving about the room with Milly, holding her arm, "you now have electricity—it used to be gas, I recollect—installed in your home, even in the servants' quarters, and never need mind even if it should be left burning all night."

"Ernest minded," said Milly, absorbed in her search,

98

and knocking over what was evidently a candlestick; something anyhow fell on the boards with a tinny sound, and didn't break.

"Poor man," sighed Agatha. "He minds nothing now."

"I wonder," said Milly, stooping to grope on the floor, and upheld by Agatha's hold on her arm.

She found the candlestick, but it hadn't any candle in it. Once it had had one, for little beards of grease stuck about its rim, and broke off in her fingers.

"My little Milly," said Agatha, very lovingly, "you must have no doubts. You must think of Ernest as quite free now, with nothing more to worry him, poor man. "'Climbing,'" she quoted, though Milly didn't know it, "'other heights with other friends.'"

"I don't think he'd climb," said Milly, intent now on finding matches; perhaps there was a candle somewhere in the room if she could only see. "Ernest hated anything one has to go up. Last year he had a lift put in. Just to take him from downstairs to bed."

"*So* rich?" said Agatha, who knew what lifts cost to put in, because when, at the beginning, she and Gaston thought they were going to have a successful future, with more stories built on to their hotel and lifts added, they had spent their evenings consulting catalogues.

For the life of her she wasn't able to feel a twinge at this. A lift costing hundreds of pounds, thousands of francs, just to take a healthy man to bed—for accidents, she reasoned, are not like illnesses, and do not make one unhealthy beforehand,—while she in her mountain did not know where to turn for a daily dinner for her delicate husband.

"Yes, he was rich," said Milly, rubbing her hand along the top of the chest of drawers, and getting it very dusty.

Agatha struggled with and overcame her twinge; after all she too was now, however belatedly, going to benefit by Ernest's wealth. "How glad I am for you, my Milly," she said, "placed for the rest of your life beyond the reach of care and anxiety."

"Well," said Milly, her fumbling hand encountering a vase and catching it just in time as it was going to fall on the floor, "it isn't quite like that. Oh, Aggie," she broke off, "I've got so much to tell you!" And laying her cheek a moment against Agatha's shoulder, and finding it very bony, she added, "How *thin* you are."

"Naturally I am thin," said Agatha. "Sorrow whittles away."

"Does it?" said Milly a little uneasily, and continuing her groping—for what about herself? She, certainly, wasn't whittled. Still, nobody, she argued, could expect a figure that had been accumulating for years to disappear in a single week. Aggie's had had three months. Surely the most acute distress couldn't in a week——?

"Indeed it does," said Agatha. "It prepares us."

"What for?" asked Milly, moving along, followed by Agatha.

Milly, thought Agatha, under the shock of bereavement said strange things.

"What for, my bereaved one, except reunion?" she said gravely, "Is not that now our only hope, all that is left to us? That, and the comfort of knowing our dear ones are happy and at peace. You must think of poor Ernest now like that, Milly—as happy and at peace."

"Do you think he is?" said Milly. "I've been feeling—" she shivered a little—"that he was somewhere near—quite close to me—not really *gone* at all."

"Nor is he really gone, my Milly," Agatha assured her. "He is indeed close, watching over you."

"Not over, but just watching," said Milly, shivering again as she remembered the night in her bedroom at home.

"Watching *over* you, Milly," Agatha gravely insisted. "Watching over you in love. What did you say?" she added, as Milly, knocking against another ornament, made a noise which drowned her answer.

"I said I didn't think he was," said Milly.

Agatha stood still, and forced her to stand still too.

"My little sister," she said very gravely, "do not tell me that the shock you have had has destroyed your faith?"

"No," said Milly; and indeed it hadn't, for that sort of faith, the faith with which Agatha's letters lately had been filled, she had never had, so it couldn't have been destroyed. Gaston might or might not be doing and feeling the things that Agatha declared he was doing and feeling—he was a Swiss, and perhaps they were different; but that Ernest should be watching over her in love she simply didn't believe. Why should he? He hadn't loved her when he was alive; had hated her, indeed, so much that his one thought had been how best to prepare an elaborate punishment for her. She, by her wicked behaviour, had brought this hatred into his heart, this mean and cowardly—surely it was mean and cowardly?—plotting, and that he, in return for her having filled his heart with evil, should love her, was rather too much to expect. Hers was the double guilt. She was responsible for Ernest's meanness and coward-ice. And for Arthur's departure from virtue she was responsible as well. Her sins were thick upon her. She must tell Aggie—not let her go on a minute longer under false impressions—bother the candle—she would tell her at once——

And she was just going to give up the search for light and then and there pour out everything into Agatha's ears, when her hand brushed against a box of matches.

"Here they are," she exclaimed. "I've got them——" and freeing herself gently from Agatha's loving hold, she opened the box and struck a match.

Exactly in front of her, under her very nose, was another candlestick, this one with a candle in it, and sheltering the flame of the match in her hollowed hand from the draught coming through the open window, she turned away from Agatha to light the candle.

"I have so much—oh, so *much* to tell you, Aggie darling," she said, her voice trembling a little now that the moment of the confession had really come.

Holding the match in the loop of the bent-in wick to melt off the grease it was stuck in and get it free, she went on, "You'll have to be patient, patient"—her hand, and the match in it, shook—"and love me, love me. . . . Will you always love me, Aggie?" she asked. Whatever I have d—— whatever has happened?"

"My Milly," said Agatha, to whom this sounded once more like overstrain, but also oddly like what she herself was presently going to require of her sister, "have I not come all the way from Switzerland just for that—to love you always, and in turn be always loved by you?"

"I can't think," said Milly, with a sigh of comfort at this, and succeeding in freeing the wick and lighting the candle, "how I've managed to exist all this time without——"

She was going to say, "my own darling sister," but turning round at that moment, the lighted candle in her hand, her answer broke off. It froze and stopped dead. Silence engulfed it. Silence for ever swallowed it up.

They stared at each other.

And Agatha said, after what seemed to be a long while, in a voice of deep amazement, "Milly?"

And Milly said falteringly, as though her mind were groping for a way out, any way that shouldn't be this way, "It was *you*, then this morning . . ."

§

A great politeness overcame them. The room seemed to go stiff with it. And Milly's eyelids fluttered down, as the eyelids of those flutter who remember it is rude to stare at a stranger.

Turning away, she put the terrible candle carefully down on the chest of drawers—very carefully, because her hands were so unsteady.

Aggie. Where was she? Who was this she was shut up alone with? Her sister—what had become of her? This gaunt, stern woman, with the great eyes full of—yes, astonished hostility (why hostility?), this woman wasn't Aggie, couldn't be Aggie, she was only somebody who had stolen her voice. *My sister—oh, my sister!* rang like a frightened cry through Milly's heart, grown suddenly empty of what had filled and warmed it all her life.

She hid in politeness. So did Agatha, profoundly shocked and surprised by Milly's appearance. Indeed she wouldn't have known her again, thought Agatha, covered up in all that fat. Only her eyes and voice were left, and the rest of that which had once been Milly had disappeared into what seemed to Agatha, accustomed to the bones of life, to the highest thinking and the lowest living, to be the undoubted outward characteristics of long-continued, steady self-indulgence.

The word bloated came into her mind. She was deeply estranged. She stood in silence, staring at Milly's abundant and expensively clothed back. She had come to comfort her suffering sister, and where was her suffering sister? Real wretchedness, she said to herself, is never fat.

"I'm afraid," said Milly politely, still turned away, forcing herself to say something, and speaking in a voice so different from the one she had been talking in before that she noticed it herself, "you are very tired."

"Not at all tired, thank you," said Agatha, equally politely. "Merely older."

There was a silence. Milly, bent over the candle, busied herself adjusting the wick, which was inclined to smoke.

My sister—oh, my sister . . .

One could not, of course, Agatha knew, in a single week grow thin and grey-haired, though even that had been done by the great sufferers of history—indeed, some of them had only needed a single night, at least for the grey hairs,—but one could show traces of what one had been through. Milly showed none. Not a sign of any serious reaction to her recent experiences, or to any experiences. She looked like a doll; a plump doll. Pink and white, too; pink and white at forty-five. Could there be much real feeling, much real depth, in a woman who still, after a quarter of a century of further life, which, however prosperous, must have had at least ups and downs in it, looked like a pink and white doll? How, Agatha asked herself, was one seriously to comfort and help a doll?

The silence continued, and Milly, so as to do something to break it, for it was becoming unbearable, fetched the one chair, and brought it over to where Agatha was standing.

"Won't you sit down?" she said, not looking at her.

"Thank you," said Agatha, not looking at her either. But they saw each other; they saw everything.

The chair was rickety, and too low for Agatha, who sat on it cautiously, her long lean knees sideways. The last few days alone, she thought, her eyes fixed sternly on the chest of drawers, the awful last few days, each hour of which must have been packed with anguish for any woman who could feel well, were enough to drag furrows down the smoothest face. Not a furrow on Milly's face could Agatha see, not a wrinkle. There was a slight swelling and redness, certainly, about the eyes, but she hadn't come all the way from Switzerland to comfort a slight swelling and redness about the eyes. Meals, meals, she thought, her thwarted, unneeded protecting love and sympathy curdling within her as she remembered all the meals she and her poor Gaston had had to do without. Even in this last week, the week since the tragedy, Milly must have gone on having regular and abundant meals, or she couldn't possibly . . .

: Agatha was deeply estranged. For a long while after Gaston's death she herself had only been able to touch an occasional cup of tea, and a little piece of bread. The first thing real love does, bereft of its beloved, is, she was certain, not to eat. What was there in common, what could there be in common, between herself and such only too evident shallowness?

Milly sat down too, on the edge of the bed at right angles to her, while the flame of the candle, flickering in the draught of the open window, threw a gigantic bonneted head on the wall high up near the ceiling, an unquiet shadow that waved grotesquely. Agatha's profile was turned to Milly, for it pained her too much to look at what Milly had become, and the profile wasn't as completely strange as the full face, because profiles last longer than full faces; in its general scheme it did seem faintly familiar to Milly, as if some elderly aunt with a family likeness to Agatha, one of those likenesses which chill intending husbands, had come to pay a call. But nothing to do with *Aggie*, thought Milly, a sense of loss, tragic and profound, bleakly crawling round her emptied heart—nothing to do with her own sister, the one who used till five minutes ago so brightly, so warmly, to fill her heart.

She smoothed her dress over her knees, and clasped her fingers together on her lap, eyeing them carefully, as though to see that they were behaving properly. But though she eyed them she didn't see them. She saw Agatha; she saw with perfect distinctness this stranger with the voice of Agatha.

My sister—oh, my sister!

"When did you leave Switzerland?" she asked, paralyzed by politeness, nervously saying the first thing that came into her head so as to avoid another silence. The stranger on the chair didn't seem to mind silences. She anyhow did nothing whatever to break them.

"At dawn the day before yesterday," Agatha replied, staring at the chest of drawers.

"But you must be worn out," said Milly, apparently addressing her fingers.

"Not at all," said Agatha, apparently addressing the chest of drawers.

The shadow on the wall gave a violent lunge, and leapt across the ceiling. Milly got up and shut the window.

"I'm afraid you feel a draught," she said solicitously, relieved to be doing something, and struggling with the catch, which didn't fit.

"I never mind draughts," said Agatha, motionless on her chair.

"I suppose there are lots in Switzerland," said Milly, struggling. "All those mountains."

"Of what do you suppose there are lots?" inquired Agatha with bleak patience.

"Draughts," said Milly.

"Possibly," said Agatha.

Ah, but wasn't this nonsense, thought Milly—wasn't this the ghastliest nonsense, talking about draughts, she and her sister, after a lifetime's separation, being polite, being stiff, behaving as though they had never set eyes on each other before, when each was all the other had—all, now, of love and comfort in the world?

But she would, she *would* be natural, Milly thought, she would force herself. . . .

"You've changed, of course," she said, her arms still stretching up trying to fasten the window, for either the catch didn't fit or her hands weren't steady enough to get it to, and anyhow it was an excuse to turn her back. "But it doesn't matter, Aggie"—astonishing how difficult it was to call the stranger on the chair Aggie—"bodies don't matter. Outsides are really nothing."

"They are apt to be symbols," said Agatha, from the chair.

"I don't believe it," said Milly.

"I beg your pardon?" said Agatha, who indeed hadn't heard this, because of the noise Milly was making with the catch.

"No, no, *no!*" cried Milly, turning round quickly, and facing the motionless figure. "Don't talk like that—don't say, 'I beg your pardon' to me—to *me*, just as if —just as if——"

The words died away. She couldn't go on. Acute loneliness overwhelmed her. This frozen stranger, who wouldn't look at her, the mean little room, icy with alienation, tragic with loss. . . .

My sister—oh, my sister! Lost, lost, gone for ever, that dear one the thought of whom, loving and understanding—yes, always loving, always understanding, whatever one did or didn't do, had been like a lit lamp shining along the years. . . .

"Just as if?" Agatha coldly encouraged, as Milly paused.

She made a great effort. All this was idiotic. They simply *must* free themselves from this paralysis of hiding, and if they didn't like each other's bodies they must get past the silly things, through them, round them, to their naked spirits, and to what surely was in both their hearts—the old, dear, warm, simple sister-love.

"Aggie," she began, forcing herself to say the word.

"Yes, Milly?"

"Have I changed so much? Can't you even look at me?"

"You have grown stouter," said Agatha evasively, her eyes on the chest of drawers.

"Yes, yes—I know. One is bound to grow something in twenty-five years."

"Indeed that is true," said Agatha.

"But it doesn't matter. What does it matter? After all, it's natural, I suppose, to fill out. What is *really* important is——"

"Have I?" interrupted Agatha.

"Have you what?"

"Filled out, as you put it."

No; certainly Agatha hadn't filled out. She had done the precise contrary, and entirely lost whatever there had been of her original filling. But was that a reason for congratulation? Again in her voice there seemed to be hostility. Why hostility?

"If," said Agatha, as Milly said nothing, and still keeping her eyes fixed on the chest of drawers, "I seem a sad woman to you, you must forgive me, and try to remember that I *am* a sad woman."

"But aren't I too?" said Milly. "Aren't I a sad woman too? I mean——"

She stopped; for was she a sad woman in the sense in which Agatha, really mourning, was? Was not what she was a guilty woman, who was miserable only because she had been found out?

"I know," said Agatha in a level voice, "that you must be very sad, and I have come all the way from Switzerland to comfort you. But——"

She too stopped; and the room seemed to re-echo with the melancholy of her voice. Even the word comfort, beautiful word of warmth and good tidings, sounded, laden with that odd suggestion of reproachful hostility, like a knell.

Milly crossed over to her, and sat down on the bed again. "It was dear of you—very dear," she said, resolutely taking Agatha's hand. If it had been dark she would have kissed her. That was the right thing to do, she was sure; but with the candle alight she found she couldn't. Kissing was much easier in the dark. Everything was much easier in the dark, she reflected desperately, her eyes wavering away from Agatha's stern profile. But even so, dark or no dark, kisses are things which have to leave off sooner or later, and there you are again. And though the dark was extremely helpful in many cases, if it hadn't been for that candle she would by now have been telling Agatha all about Arthur.

She shuddered. Very awful, thought Milly; very, very awful, to have told the dreadful story to somebody one believed to be one's sister, and then have lit the candle and found a stranger sitting listening. The

candle had saved her. Yes—but only for a moment.
She had got to tell Agatha ultimately. She couldn't go
with her to Switzerland and eat her bread unless everything was clear between them. Besides, some explanation would anyhow have to be given of the manifest
fact that she had hardly any money, and it should be
the true one. No more lies, said Milly to herself.

But first she must get over what Agatha now looked
like—get used to her in her new disguise, learn to see
through it, to find the love behind this strange surface—

My sister—oh, my sister . . .

Stoutly Milly, sitting on the edge of the bed, turned
a deaf ear to the cry that kept on tearing through her
heart. Presently the strangeness would wear off; presently Agatha wouldn't mind Milly so much. It was
evident she was much shocked at Milly's changed appearance, and Milly felt that perhaps she could bear
Agatha's own alterations better if Agatha weren't
having such obvious difficulty in bearing Milly's.
They would get used to each other. They would——

Milly's eyes, wavering away from Agatha's profile,
chanced to fall on the hand she was holding, and remained riveted. What she was thinking came to a sudden end. Her lips dropped open. She stared a moment in
silence.

"Aggie——" she presently breathed, staring, for the
hand Milly was looking at for the first time was a
ruined hand; not merely deformed and spread with
work, and discoloured and scarred by exposure but——

She hung over it.

"Aggie——?" she breathed again, pointing to the
other one, unable to get more words out; for weren't the
hands—could it be that they were the hands of someone
who for a long time hadn't had enough of anything,
not even—*My sister, oh, my sister!*—enough to eat?

And Agatha, her eyes following Milly's pointing finger
and looking down at them and at the face bending over
them, at the complete contrast of the smooth, plump,
unlined face and the shamefully ugly, spoilt hands, was
seized by a sudden desire not only at once to make the
confession she had been shrinking from, but to make
it, so some strange impulse drove her, as exact and as
painful as possible. Curiously, she no longer wished
to make the best of it, she wished to make the worst of
it.

"Work," she said briefly. Adding after a pause, her
eyes on Milly's sleekness, almost as if considering into
which soft bit of her she would plunge the knife, "And
hunger."

§

The candle lit up two motionless figures looking into
each other's eyes. Milly's were full of puzzled horror.

"Hunger," she repeated in a whisper. And then,
again, "Hunger——?"

"Are you not acquainted with the word?" inquired
Agatha, herself surprised at the surge of bitterness that
was flooding her, as if the great volumes of it which had
been accumulating for years secretly in her heart, kept
under and carefully not recognized while she walked,
as she had often insisted to herself, her head high with
pride, her eyes full of angry tears, on her mountain-
side hand in hand with God, were now all being let
loose on Milly.

Was it because up there, where the few scattered
inhabitants also struggled and were poor, there had been
no one to compare her own misery with? Was it because,
though she had always known Milly was prosperous,
not seeing her she hadn't realized how blatant that prosperity really was? The very crumbs from Milly's over-

loaded table would have saved Gaston and herself from those pinches of poverty, those pangs of the inadequately nourished, which had so deeply distressed their later years. True she had had sufficient food during the last few weeks, but it would take more than a few weeks to remove the traces of privation from her body, and never would they be removed, she felt, from her seared heart.

But Milly didn't seem to hear her bitter question, and continued to look at her with eyes of horror. If that were so, her mind was slowly grasping, then Aggie had been—was—desperately poor; and if that were so, and she had come to live with her as her last hope, what was to become of them both?

"Tell me," she whispered. "Tell me everything, Aggie——"

§

Agatha told her. She told her thoroughly, sparing neither of them.

After the first few sentences Milly left off staring at her with those horror-stricken eyes, and slid down to the floor at her feet, her arm round the lean knees and her cheek against the knuckly hands.

It was just and right, thought Agatha unrolling her tale, that this comfortable, cotton-woolled sister should be made to understand for once what life was really like, and what it can force one to do. Evidently she hadn't an idea. Her comfort, both spiritual and physical, was complete.

She couldn't see Milly's face, who sat quite still and silent, her head against Agatha's hands, and very soon, at the memory of all she had gone through with and for Gaston, while everyone else was having an easy time— people like the Botts, and their friends, and relations and hangers-on, even people like the Botts' servants, pampered, and of course over-fed—very soon tears were flowing freely down her thin face.

It really seemed, she said, as if all that was needed for a successful and happy life, happy, that is, on the lower levels, was to be without a capacity for feeling. The moment one felt—fine things, beautiful things, the things, in fact that are immortal,—one became marked down by misfortune, dogged by it. She and Gaston had been dogged; she and Gaston, who cared so much for ideals, who felt so keenly. The most extraordinary things, which happened to no one else, happened to them—she would give a few examples—they seemed almost trivial against the great background of suffering and death, but they all had helped in the weaving of that background: clients, for instance, who had engaged the best rooms ahead, and obviously were indifferent to what they paid, either fell ill or had accidents at the last moment, and never came. One client died in the hotel at the beginning of a promising season, and because he did so immediately after dinner the others were afraid, and left in a body, creating an impression which was hard indeed to remove, and was not lived down for several seasons, that something was wrong with the water or the drains. Once there was a fire; confined, it is true, to two rooms only, but those two rooms were completely gutted, and as they were not insured, owing to lack of money for the premiums, the loss was serious. Misfortune of these kinds went on all the time. Pipes burst; the weight of the snow crushed in the roof; the hens contracted diseases from which other hens were free; the goats failed to breed, and continually perished; the potatoes were preyed upon by blight; great rains came at harvest time, and beat down the rye they had tended with such care; and when the feet of clients tore holes in the sheets, they declared it was the fault of the sheet. Then, finally, there was the war, and with that real hunger began. She herself had been so strong that she was able to bear what Gaston couldn't, and so had mercifully been in a position to do without food better than he, and to nurse him in his illness. She had, indeed, been able to bear everything, thanks to God who had endowed her with as strong a spirit as a body, except one thing—and that one thing was the jeers which would have been flung like mud against her loved husband, the triumphant jeers of that cruel Ern—— that cruel family, the Botts, had they known of her sufferings.

They should have helped her, said Agatha, drawing one hand out from under Milly's cheek to stem the flow of her tears, instead of jeering. Too much worldly prosperity, however, deadens people's souls. If Gaston had had a little capital, quite a little, if he had merely had an occasional temporary helping hand, he would frequently have been saved from his predicaments, none of which were of his own producing. At his death a little help would have spared her the bitterness of having to sell the hotel. As it was, it had been sold for a song, and she had had to accept the post of book-keeper in what had been her own house. Probably what the Botts spent on feeding unnecessary servants would have been ample to put Gaston on his feet and keep him on them.   He wouldn't have grown old and ill with work then; he would have been alive at that moment. She was not speaking of Ernest, for he was dead, but of the Botts as a family. Ernest had done what he no doubt thought was right in separating her from Milly, and she was not criticizing him, for he was dead; but his action had made an outcast of her, and had implied that her husband, than whom no one nobler had ever

trodden God's earth, was a scoundrel. Any woman with
a grain of pride, and she had many such grains she was
glad to say, would have done what she did and concealed the real state of affairs from Milly, who, though
she was her sister, and as such entitled to know the
truth, was also the loyal loving wife of the man who
was keeping them apart, and as such was in the enemy
camp. Not that she wished to speak of Ernest as an
enemy, for how could he be when he was dead? There
existed people, however, who thought of success only in
terms of money, and were incapable of comprehending
the successes of the spirit, which were all in terms of
love. Her marriage had been as successful and prosperous as Milly's, but on a plane which Ernest would never
have understood—the plane where there was nothing
but love.

This was in no sense a criticism, for how could she
criticize one who was dead? But she couldn't help regarding the whole of her bitter misfortunes, and the
wrong-doing she had undoubtedly been guilty of in
writing things to Milly which had not been really true,
(except in a spiritual sense, which would be difficult,
perhaps, to explain) as due to one cause only—the unjust, narrow, and cruel attitude towards her marriage
taken up by—well, by the Botts.

"But I am no longer concerned," she continued, laying the hand with which she had been wiping her eyes on
Milly's shoulder, but withdrawing it quickly because
the shoulder felt so very like a well-stuffed pillow, and
she was forced to ask herself once again whether acute
grief, the kind her own was, and the kind that every
woman's was who loses a loved husband, especially if
she loses him, as Milly had, suddenly and violently,
could ever be encased in such resilient plumpness, "I
am no longer concerned with other people's injustices.

I have passed beyond that, and am prepared to overlook the grievous harm this family has done me, and live— withdrawn from them, perhaps, as much as is polite, yet amiably, in their midst. I came here to help you, Milly—to help and comfort you, and I shall not allow the Botts to prevent my doing so. My duty and my love, now that the barrier separating us is no more, brought me to you instantly in your hour of——"

She was going to say, and wished to say, need; but was there any real need except her own? Alas, that cushiony shoulder, that sleek, smooth portion of cheek she could see, half hidden by hair without a sign of grey in it, on her lap! Emotion and hysteria there had been in plenty on the stairs, but since the lighting of the candle what evidence had she seen of need? A plump, smug, expensive-looking woman, who shrank away from her gaze and said foolish things entirely unsuited to the tragic, the solemn occasion—that is what she had seen and heard, and the fact that she was her sister mustn't blind her to the truth. So she substituted the word widowhood for need, this at least being accurate. "In your hour of widowhood," finished Agatha; and paused.

Milly, on the floor at her feet, said nothing. Her face, except that glimpse of hair and cheek, was hidden, and Agatha, sitting stiffly above her, wiping her eyes with her free hand, struggled within herself as to whether she should leave her motives for so quickly coming to England at the two she had mentioned, and continue to conceal that further motive, the baser, material one.

So she paused, struggling. Why did not Milly say something? Why did she sit there as if she were inhumanly asleep? She was not asleep, Agatha knew, for she could feel the movement of her eyelashes on the hand her cheek held imprisoned beneath it. Why, then, did she say nothing?

"Besides," went on Agatha, winning her struggle and bowing her head, for this bit of truth cost her a very great effort, "I am weary of poverty—weary, weary." Her voice sounded hollow, and incredibly tired.

"See how I confess my weaknesses to you," she said, after another pause. "I will withhold nothing. It is not, I believe and hope, that I am materially minded. I dislike and condemn luxury. All I ask is safety, security. I have a great longing"—she stopped to steady her voice, which she was ashamed to hear shaking—"for freedom from sordid care. I wish to be free from fear. Life is very difficult when one is afraid—afraid of the future, afraid of not being able to save enough to keep one's old age secure from cold and hunger. Under such circumstances it is indeed difficult to retain the freedom of one's spirit, for it becomes absorbed in the most wretched preoccupations. My salary as book-keeper was one hundred francs a month—less than fifty pounds a year in your English money. The new proprietor advanced me the fare of my journey to you. I told him you would repay it. How long should I have kept my post had I stayed there? Have I not told you I am old and broken? How long could I expect the proprietor to have patience and pity? Day and night the question of how long haunted me. Then this happened—this sad death of Ernest, and sad and terrible as it must be for you, if you loved him as I loved my dear husband, it has saved me. I will be absolutely truthful. Love did bring me here—great, great love for my sister in her sorrow, and also duty, the sacred duty of helping and comforting her. But I came, too, to a refuge, to a harbour. I came to what I know is the end, at last, of bitter and hopeless poverty."

There was a silence. Agatha had said her say. She had exposed herself quite naked for the first time in her life.

And Milly, who during the whole of her recital had sat without moving or speaking, presently said, very softly, almost as if she were talking to herself, "You know, this is so dreadful that I can hardly bear it."

"I beg your pardon?" said Agatha, supposing she hadn't heard aright; for that Milly should declare herself hardly able to bear the mere description of that which Agatha during twenty-five years had actually borne, seemed too much of flabbiness and selfishness to be credible.

"Such punishment," murmured Milly, again as if talking to herself.

"I beg your pardon?" Agatha said a second time, sitting up straighter and stiffer than ever. "You mean," she said, "that you regard what Gaston and I went through as punishment? Might I inquire what for? No—do not tell me," she instantly added, holding up her free hand. "I can guess your thoughts, and they are unworthy. How can you, my sister, after all these years bring up that one small, strictly temporary, and in the circumstances inevitable, divergence from rigid convention?"

But Milly didn't answer. She sat without moving. And Agatha felt something wet slowly trickling along her land.

⁑(VII)⁑

TEARS.

"Now what," thought Agatha, looking down at the silent figure, and feeling extraordinarily hardened because of that word punishment, "has Milly got to cry about? It was I who suffered, not she."

In fact, Milly's behaviour was entirely unaccountable. Tears—of sympathy with herself, apparently, that her tender ears should have to listen to such a tale—and then that heartless, unjust word.

But Agatha forgot the tears, forgot the word, when Milly, sitting up after a moment and drying her eyes, told her that Ernest had left her, Agatha, a thousand pounds in his Will.

"I beg your pardon?" said Agatha, staring.

Milly was sitting up now, with her back to her, dabbing at her face with a very much crushed handkerchief.

"Yes," she said, her voice muffled by the handkerchief. "I think—he wanted to make amends."

"A thousand *pounds*?" said Agatha. "You do not mean"—she leaned forward and touched Milly's shoulder—"you do not mean francs?"

"No—pounds," said Milly, busy with her handkerchief. "Will it help you at all, Aggie?"

"Help?"

Agatha drew in her breath.

"Help!" she said again.

Why, a thousand pounds was twenty-five thousand Swiss francs. She counted it up quickly. Why, if she

119

had had only half of that two months ago, she could have gone into partnership with the man who bought the hotel. He had offered to take her in if she could find twelve to fifteen thousand francs—out of courtesy, of course, well knowing she couldn't find such sums; but suppose she had been able to, and had said yes? To be independent, to share in a successful enterprise, to raise up on the very spot of Gaston's failure a monument to his memory, to make his hopes at last come true—compared to that, what could existence in Milly's house at Titford, eating the bread of idleness in an atmosphere thick with Botts, offer her?

A thousand pounds. Agatha sat awestruck. So much money in her whole life had not come her way. Ernest leaving her a thousand pounds, recognizing the wrong he had done her, magnificently making good. . . .

But it had come too late. The hotel was gone. She was pledged to the comforting of Milly. Fate even in its gifts—and this was the first she had ever had, except her youth, which was hardly a gift because it got taken away again, and her Gaston, who got taken away too —continued hostile. Still, how wonderful, how very wonderful, to have a thousand pounds. What a background, solid, golden to her life; what an alteration in her position; what a difference at once in her relations with the Botts.

"See," she could say, when they were rude to her or cold, "your own son, your own brother, recognized he had done me a grave injury, and set it publicly on record that he had in his Will——" and the family, confounded, would be forced to behave.

Very solemnly she raised her hands, as if in posthumous blessing. "I have misjudged Ernest," she said, overcome. "He was at heart a just man."

"Yes," said Milly.

"He repented," said Agatha, "and he made good."

"Yes," said Milly.

"This action of his will entirely rehabilitate me with the Botts," said Agatha.

"Yes," said Milly. "Except," she added after a slight pause, still busy with her handkerchief, "that there won't *be* any Botts."

"How, no Botts?" inquired Agatha.

"I've left them. I'm not going back."

"Left the Botts? Left Titford?" exclaimed Agatha. "Were you then—was it your idea, Milly, to come permanently to me in Switzerland?" And a vision suddenly flashed into her mind of herself and Milly going together now to her mountains, and Milly's money buying back the hotel—not merely a share in it but the whole thing—and a new life opening for them both, full of prosperity, and peace, and capital, and competence, she competently, and to the benefit of them both, manipulating Milly's capital.

"Milly," she said, laying her hand on her shoulder, and this time leaving it there, "was that your idea?"

And Milly said, after a little gulp, as if she were swallowing something difficult to get down, that it wasn't. "I was only going to take you the money, Aggie," she said in a choked voice. "And—and just see you again, because I did so long to see you again, and then—well, then—I was coming back."

"But coming back to what, now that you have left the Botts? No, no, my Milly"—Agatha pressed the shoulder—"no, no, my little sister. Your place is with me. Our futures lie together. Together we will go to those better, purer, simpler surroundings, far away from everything that has distressed you. Hand in hand we will begin afresh——"

"We can't," said Milly, shaking her head. "We can't

do anything hand in hand, Aggie. I've got no money.
Ernest didn't leave me anything. Except for your
thousand pounds, he left everything he had to charity."

§

Sitting listening in silence to Agatha's story, such
acute distress had twisted Milly's heart, such almost
physical pain, that it had been hardly possible to bear.
Be sure your sin will find you out—yes, she knew all about
that by now; but why should it find Aggie out as well,
who had done nothing but be good? Pressing her cold
hands together in her lap, she sent up little darts of
prayers—hardly prayers so much as agonized inquiries:
"What am I to do? How can I hurt her least? Isn't
it very wrong to punish her because of what *I* did?"

But prayers, she remembered, don't get answered;
hers didn't. And, leaving go of them, Milly, who had
made such recent vows to relinquish it for ever, fell back
once more into lying.

How avoid it? By lying, Agatha could be given the
thousand pounds and think it was hers. At least she
should have that. It was the one thing Milly could do for
her. If only it had been ten, twenty times as much!
Apart from this, however, she wouldn't lie. There should
be no lying about Arthur, though she was not any longer
sure Aggie was going to understand about Arthur. How
gladly, how very gladly would she have suppressed him
altogether. But she couldn't suppress somebody who
was likely now at any moment to become Agatha's
brother-in-law; for plain was it to Milly that, penniless,
she must marry Arthur, and as she must do so with what
in an ordinary widow would be indecent haste, nothing
but the truth could explain it. How difficult, though, it
was going to be. Icy doubts slid down her spine as to the
way Agatha might take it. Suppose she was horribly

scandalized? There was that about her appearance and behaviour which suggested rigidity of principle. Grown into rigidity she had—for the impassioned, vivid creature of Milly's youth had been like quicksilver.

Milly pressed her cold hands together. No wonder people didn't tell the truth very often, if only out of loving kindness, out of courtesy, out of a desire to avoid shocking and hurting. Or was it out of fear? Was she once again, as so lamentably often, just simply a coward?

That was it, she was afraid, for at the mere thought of explaining Arthur she found she was in a perspiration. She sighed, and put up her hand to hold Agatha's on her shoulder, because, on hearing of Ernest's gift to charity, it was making movements of withdrawal.

"Does that mean," Agatha was saying, in a voice both appalled and incredulous, "that you are poor, Milly? *You?*"

"Penniless," said Milly. And repeated, in a kind of astonishment at the word, "Yes,—penniless."

"You are left entirely without resources?" asked Agatha, her voice gone cold to match the cold flooding into her heart; for here was Fate, at it again, striking her down at the very moment when she was beginning to raise her head. Milly poor? She herself, by a turn of fortune's wheel, the one of the two with money, and the legacy perhaps having to do for them both? Ah, but impossible. Ernest could not have entirely—— And why should he? Why should he do anything so un-natural?

"It seems queer, doesn't it," said Milly, "after the way I've wallowed for years." And she added, gripping Agatha's hand very tight, "Didn't I tell you, Aggie, that you would have to be patient with me, and—and love me very much?"

"Naturally, Milly, I love you," said Agatha, trying

again to draw her hand away. "It would be strange indeed if sisters did not love each other. But I know from bitter experience that love is difficult where there is real poverty."

"But you said you and Gaston——"

"I said, I said," interrupted Agatha with something which sounded very like exasperation. "I tell you it is difficult, and I fear my thousand pounds will hardly——"

She paused.

"Be enough for us to love on," Milly finished for her softly.

"Be enough for us to *live* on," corrected Agatha. "Surely it is plain that one must first be alive, in order to love."

"No—one must first love, in order to be alive," corrected Milly in her turn. "Which is why"—she seized, tremblingly, the opportunity—"which is why—which is really what—in fact, just that is the explanation of Arthur."

Arthur.

There was a silence. Agatha sat looking down at the back of the sleek head, and the more than sleek shoulders, leaning against her knees.

Arthur. Was not that the name Milly had said on the stairs? Who and what was he? And why should he keep on entering the conversation?

She fumbled in her memory. Perhaps he was one of the innumerable Bott brothers-in-law. But if so, what had he to do with the nonsense Milly had just said about loving in order to be alive?

"Is that a Bott?" she asked.

"No," said Milly. "The exact opposite."

"The exact——?"

And Milly, leaping into the icy waters of truth, and in her agitation letting go of all her grammar, said with a gasp. "He's the man Ernest left his money to a charity because of." And while Agatha was endeavouring to unravel the meaning of this remark, she elucidated further, her voice suddenly quite clear and steady now that the moment had really come and there was no help for it, "He's the man I'm going to marry."

§

It was just on ten o'clock when Milly said this, but not till after two did Agatha leave her, and go down to her own room for what was left of the night.

"I have no more to say," were her last words, as in the dark, the candle having long burnt out, she went away.

And Milly, by this time half lying across her tumbled bed, her arms flung out, her face buried in the pillow, was too much exhausted to do anything but murmur, "I should think not——" which, fortunately, Agatha didn't hear.

"So that's the end of *that*," thought Milly dully, as the door shut behind her she had dreamed of as her sister. "One has to——" the words passed idly through her battered brain—"face facts. Yes, facts are—what one must face—no good pretending things aren't—what they are—simply silly—doing that——"

And slowly sitting up she began, her eyes shut, her head nodding, to drag off her clothes, for she couldn't spend a second night without undressing, and then, creeping under the ruffled blankets of the bed, she dropped like a stone into sleep.

On the floor below her Agatha neither slept nor undressed. To do so, to do these things of routine and a quiet mind, would have seemed to her a betrayal of every right feeling on the night of the discovery that she had been loving and believing in somebody whose life had been a treachery, and all her words lies. That she, of all women, should have a fallen sister, and one who was publicly branded as fallen by the terms of her husband's Will, struck Agatha, apart from its shame and horror, as fantastic. Never, she felt, would she forget the hours she had just passed through. Surely they were the worst of any of the many miserable ones Fate had plied her with? For in the others there had yet been dignity, there had yet been the hope that is at the root of defiance, and the pride of seeing how high one can keep one's head beneath blows. There was no dignity and no pride and nothing to defy in the wretched tale of sordid sinning the person who once was Milly had so cynically unfolded. Yes, cynically; for at one point she had dared compare her behaviour—years and years of adultery—with Agatha's behaviour; she had dared say, when she had listened for some time to Agatha's expressions of horror, words to the effect that after all she, Agatha, had done the same thing with Gaston.

"But he was my husband," Agatha indignantly had pointed out.

"Not to begin with," Milly had actually replied— once more throwing, once more having the effrontery to throw, in her face that brief and unexpectedly inevitable departure from convention which had preceded the sacred marriage of a lifetime. And when Agatha, almost speechless but trying to be patient, pointed out that no one ever is a husband to begin with, Milly, with incredible and indecent flippancy, replied, "Oh—do you really think as badly of women as that?"

What was one to say to such a speech? Poor, unhappy Ernest. Good, wronged man. His patience had been a marvel. His conduct in saying no word, in continuing to extend the protection of his roof and name to the woman he knew was betraying him, was that of a saint. And even this patience, this conduct, Milly, until Agatha sternly silenced her, had been inclined to criticize. The fallen woman criticizing the upright man. What next? Agatha asked herself, at whose feet a pit of unimagined wickedness yawned.

On her mountains such sinning was simply unknown. Like the deciduous trees, it did not flourish above five thousand feet. No one committed adultery up there. There was no one, thank God, to commit it with. A few scattered husbands dwelt there, practically snowbound, each with his lean, hard-working wife, their one concern the business of keeping alive. They did not even drink where she lived, though down in the valley among the vineyards drunkenness, she knew, was prevalent. Down in the valley, among the vineyards, drunkenness; and down in the cities, among the idle and overfed, adultery. Prevalent. It must be. For actually in her own tiny family of two, one of the two had committed it.

Ah, she would take the money Ernest had left her, and shake the dust of these dreadful places for ever from her feet. Back she would go to purity, and leave Milly to her second, her disgraceful, husband. Marry the man she must, of course, for there was no other way of expiating what she had done; but it did seem terrible that God's holy ordinance should be used as a kind of cloth to mop up sin.

From this, however, there seemed no escape. In no other way could the two atone for their sin. Merciful indeed, and yet another proof of poor Ernest's foresight and care, that Milly should be without means, for if she had had any, Agatha believed from several things she had let fall, she would not have married the man, and then no atonement could have taken place. But suppose Milly, having married him, were to be happy?

What would then become of atonement? Agatha could only shake her head at the topsy-turviness of life.

She sat at the window, looking out at the stars twinkling through the branches of the trees in the square, and tried to hope in all things for the best. One must cling to one's ideals; never, however hard circumstances pulled at one, must one let them go. And then she remembered that it was at this very window—in the old days it was Milly's room—they used to sit together when they were young, before going to bed, and build bright castles in the air. How sad life was. How differently it turned out from what, young, one expected. In those days they were sure it was going to be magnificent. There wasn't anything fine and noble they weren't going to achieve. And one night Milly—she could see the small figure in its nightgown now—had flung up her arms towards the light-strewn sky, and cried that she was going to reach right up to heaven before she had done, and catch hold of the very stars.

Alas. Just was her punishment; fitting that it should fall upon her. But—alas, poor Milly. And alas, too, to compare the thoughts with which she, Agatha, had travelled over from Switzerland to the thoughts with which she would travel back again. And most alas of all—yes, tragically alas—to know that she would never now see Milly, the Milly she had supposed existed, again. Finished, that was; and an immense, the longest, chapter of both their lives closed. Henceforth she would be completely alone. The person Milly had developed into was going with her to the solicitor in the morning to fetch the legacy, and it would be their last walk together. After that they would go their several ways; they would say good-bye, and it would be for ever.

She stared at the stars, sitting without moving. The affection of a lifetime, the belief of a lifetime. . . .

The stars became a little blurred.

Perhaps, as there was no question of sleep for either of them, they should spend the few remaining hours together, even if they said nothing, but just sat near to each other. The person Milly had developed into still had good in her. She had been quite ungrudging about the legacy, evidently glad that Agatha should have it. Yes; there was good in her still. Agatha, softened, thought she would go up to her once more, and say, "Milly, this is in all probability our last night on earth together——" and if Milly were again to say, as she had certainly said several times during the recital of her terrible tale, only Agatha, in her surprise and horror, had waved it sternly aside, that she was sorry for what she had done, Agatha thought she would perhaps kiss her. Yes; she would kiss her. Poor, sinful Milly, lying tossing in the room above—she should have one last kiss from her sister, before they parted and saw each other no more.

And lighting the candle, and holding it high above her head, she did go up to Milly's room, opening the door softly so as not to rouse anyone in the house, and crossing over to the bed began, "Milly——"

But there lay Milly, deaf and indifferent to tenderness, deeply, and comfortably, and cynically asleep.

§

Hopeless; quite hopeless she was, thought Agatha, sternly descending to her room again, her softened heart once more frozen hard. Imagine sleeping soundly immediately after a scene so painful, so terrible that it made her sister feel as if she would never be able to close her eyes again! And Agatha, blowing out the candle and stiffly resuming her vigil at the window, felt full of that curious itch of exasperation which follows a thwarted benevolent impulse. She had gone upstairs ready to bestow valedictory love, and it had not been required. She had gone actually prepared to suggest, though not expecting it would be possible for the suggestion to be accepted, that Milly should try to get a little sleep; and there she was, getting a great deal. Hopeless, hopeless,— or, rather, the person she had developed into was hopeless.

Agatha thought her even more hopeless when next morning, having duly bathed her burning eyes in cold water, she came down to breakfast—she had no desire for food, but knew she would have to pay for breakfast, eaten or not—and was met by the manageress with a message from Milly that she had gone out, and wouldn't be back, probably, till twelve o'clock.

What can be done, Agatha, staring outraged at the manageress, asked herself, with such wriggling duplicity? What can be done with a person who says she will accompany you immediately after breakfast on a most important mission, and then slinks away, entirely unaccountably, before that meal, merely leaving word she will not be back till noon? Noon? Half the day gone, the important busy day on which Agatha was to receive her legacy and depart with it for Switzerland; for go back to Switzerland she certainly would, and by the very first train, once she had got her money. Milly did not know in so many words that she was going that day, but surely she would take it for granted that she would get away by the first possible train from the place where she had lost her beliefs, and become acquainted with shame? The first possible train, since the morning trains would be missed while she was at the solicitor's,

would be the two P. M. *via* Laon and Berne. She needed
no time-table. She knew all the trains by heart, having
learned them in those days when there were still people
in England wishing to come and stay in Gaston's hotel,
and who had to be met at the station in the valley by
mules. She had never forgotten them. Life changed,
but trains went on. At nine, at eleven, at two, and at
four, people weary of London and its dirt and sins left
it, and twenty-four hours later stepped out into the clear,
cool calm which was Switzerland. The two o'clock was
the train she had decided in the watches of the night
she would go by, leaving the morning free for the visit to
the solicitor. Now, owing to Milly's inexplicable conduct,
the two o'clock would be missed. Perhaps even the four
o'clock would be missed. Really such behaviour. . . .

Her great eyes, weary from want of sleep, blazed at
the manageress.

"Well, that's what she *said*," said the manageress
petulantly, turning away into the dining-room, where
her one other lodger was waiting to be fed. "*I* can't help
it, can I, Mrs. Le Bon?—Le Bone if you ask *me*," she
added to herself, measuring out Agatha's portion of
porridge with swift practised movements—"figure and
nature and all."

And as she dabbed the plate down in front of the
chair placed ready for her gaunt guest, she thought that
the sooner she took her figure and her nature somewhere
else the better pleased she would be. Except that she
would take her sister with her. That was the snag of
her going. After all the sob-stuff on the stairs the night
before it wasn't likely, she was afraid, that they would
separate; and the manageress not only approved of
Milly, her face, her clothes, her soft voice, and the
gentle manner which made her so easy, she was sure, to
do what one liked with, but locked up at that moment

in the bureau of her private room was Milly's handbag, with four one-pound notes in it, given to her to take care of on her leaving the house an hour before.

The manageress liked being given handbags with pound notes in them to be taken care of. It made her feel safe, and relaxed the necessity of having to watch the front door. How such a real lady as Mrs. Bott came to have a sister like this Le Bone she couldn't imagine. And she decided, her decisions being always rapid and frequently rash, that Le Bone must be a bastard.

"That's it," she thought, a bright and hostile eye on Agatha, who was putting more sugar on her porridge than was either necessary or lady-like. "Not much holy wedlock about *her*."

§

Meanwhile Milly was wandering about London.

It seemed an odd thing to be doing on a day which was going to be too short for all there was to settle in it, but it was forced upon her by circumstances. Agatha, who of course didn't know the solicitor's name and address, had instructed her the night before, in an interval between one set of horrified reproaches and the next, that she was to show her the way to his office directly after breakfast. Obviously, then, Milly had to be well away before breakfast; obviously she must be out of the house before Agatha could join her. For if she joined her and came too, she would find out that the legacy was but another lie, and suffer a very cruel shock and disappointment.

Agatha had had enough shocks and disappointments in the last twelve hours, thought Milly, shaking her head. She needed that thousand pounds far more than Milly needed it, who had Arthur; in fact her need was desperate. And she might refuse to take it because of her

principles—though perhaps, on the other hand, she
mightn't, reflected Milly, clear-sighted now, and without illusions. So she crept with peculiar caution past
Agatha's shut door, and thought that it would be nice
when the need for all this creeping was over. She seemed
to have been doing it now for so long that it was surprising to remember it had only begun about twenty-
four hours before. Anyhow it was a miserable way of
getting about, she said to herself, and she would be glad
when she could bang a door again.

Fortunately breakfast wasn't till nine o'clock at the
Home from Home, the manageress having long discovered that ladies in bed were less trouble than ladies
vigorously roaming about the house, so that Milly had
plenty of time before Agatha would start on her hot-
water can; and the front door being open, for it was once
more the hour of airing, she was proceeding to slip
through it—nice when the necessity for all this slipping
was over—when the manageress, seeming to surge up
from nowhere, waylaid her.

"Why—Mrs. *Bott!*" she exclaimed, much as she had
exclaimed the morning before, on catching her doing
the same thing.

But this time Milly was equal to her. "Sh-sh," she
whispered, pausing a moment and glancing up the
stairs. "We mustn't disturb the others——"

And before the manageress could say anything, and
she had much to say, for the disturbing or non-disturbing
of the others was exclusively her own affair, Milly
opened her bag, took out some loose silver, showed her
there were four one-pound notes still in it, thrust it into
her hands, begged her to take care of it till she got back,
asked her to tell her sister she mightn't be in till twelve,
and was down the steps and round the corner into the
next square like, the manageress said to herself, amazed

by these rapid and purposeful movements in one who the day before had seemed such a mass of inertness, a streak of ink.

Once round the corner she walked more slowly. There was no hurry. The solicitor wouldn't be at his office before ten at the earliest, and it was then only half-past eight. Her mind was very clear, and she idled along, arranging her plans, in a kind of dead calm after the deep sleep that separated her from yesterday. That sleep seemed to have washed her clear of illusions and sentimentality about Agatha. It was as though she had been plunged, drunk, into icy water, and come up sober. She knew exactly what she was going to do—all the small details of the next two hours, the sending of a telegram to Arthur, who must have got back to Oxford from his holiday the evening before, for he had said he would and he was a man who kept his word, then break-fast at an A. B. C. shop which used to be near the British Museum and probably still was, then a walk down to the Embankment, where she could sit and watch the river till ten o'clock, which was the earliest moment, she judged, familiar with the habits of busi-ness men, she could expect to find the solicitor at his office.

These were the things she would do next. After them, there would be the handing over of the money to Agatha, the seeing of her off, for she would be sure to want to leave by the very first train—no, she wouldn't see her off, because it was Victoria she would have to start from, and that was the station for Titford, and she might meet Botts—the saying good-bye to her, then, at the boarding-house, and after that an omnibus to Chel-sea, and the meeting with Arthur at his flat.

Those were the next things.

And after them—well, the best thing to do, and cer-

tainly the cheapest, would be to stay in the flat till she
was married, Arthur—for there should be no more
sinning till they were married—going back to Oxford as
usual. And when the woman who occasionally cleaned
came in and found her there, she would explain, and
say: "Mr. Oswestry has lent me his rooms. We are going
to be married." And the woman, who of course would be
surprised by her widow's mourning, so fresh, so evidently only just begun to be worn, would probably say,
her mouth opening, "Married?" And Milly would say
composedly, "Yes—married."

She walked very slowly through the sunlit squares,
killing time, detached and observant, noticing the roofs
of the houses glittering against the blue sky, and the
rush of a flight of pigeons, their wings glittering too, and
the light on a girl's hair as she scrubbed a door-step, and
the whistling of a boy with a milk-cart, and the smell
of the coffee and bacon all Bloomsbury, apparently, was
going to have for its breakfast, and the whole untiring
zest with which the world each morning lays hold of
its new day. Life had strangely straightened itself out.
Aggie had disappeared, and Agatha had taken her
place. Arthur as a sin had disappeared, and Arthur as
a husband was going to take his place. Just as well,
she said to herself, thinking of Agatha with acquiescence;
nothing like seeing things as they are. And, considering
Agatha, she saw that the lies one tells oneself are even
more numerous than those one tells other people. One
lives and fattens on the lies one tells oneself. For years
she had been nourished by the lies she told herself about
Agatha. And was it Agatha's fault? Foolish, surely,
to blame her. How could she help what she, Milly, was
determined to believe about her? It came to this,
thought Milly, that what one wanted beyond everything
else in the world was love, and one would do anything

to get it, and if it wasn't there one invented it. The least little word, the smallest encouragement, set one off inventing love. Agatha being of the same blood had started it; and what could be more silly than to suppose that love had anything to do with blood? On the contrary—what naturally proceeded from the same blood wasn't love, but claims to it; which, she thought, avoiding a banana skin as she crossed the square to go to a post-office she had caught sight of down a side street, was nothing but upsetting.

Upsetting. A mild word. But she felt so mild—cleared out, empty of feeling, numb. Mere eyes she seemed to be this bright morning, quiet eyes looking straight and recognizing. And among other things she recognized was that however much she had believed she would be turning her back on her sin by going to Agatha in Switzerland and leading a new life, the plain fact was that expiation lay in marrying Arthur. Agatha had been quite right about that, though she needn't have said it in such terrible words. After all, it was what decent people in her and Arthur's position invariably did; it was certainly what he would want to do; and though being turned into an instrument of expiation struck her as an unexpected end for Arthur, who had started off so flamingly as a wonder and a secret joy, yet it was an end that had the restfulness of the finish of a struggle, of a correct solution, and also the great comfort, the real solid comfort, of propriety.

Love must either begin or end in propriety if there is to be any peace, thought Milly, pushing open the door of the post-office. It must, that is, either begin or end in a husband. Happy are those women, she thought, searching for a pen or pencil that would write, happy and blest are those women who start with both. Theirs, surely, is the kingdom of heaven. If she and Arthur had been able to marry when they first loved, it would indeed have been wonderful. Now, having loved, they were able to. *Having* loved. . . .

Well anyhow, she said to herself, borrowing a pencil from the young lady behind the wire-netting, who had never been known to lend a pencil before, but whose rocky heart melted at the sight of Milly's pale face in its shroud of crape, it was the right thing to do, and only in doing the right thing lay peace. Peace was what one wanted after a certain age. Hers was the certain age. She would seek peace and ensue it. Besides, married to Arthur he could tell her at once, instead of having to wait till they met, about his colds.

She smiled faintly as she wrote her telegram. Was that cynical about the colds? She didn't feel cynical; she only felt empty, and as if nothing was really much worth bothering about—gone numb, perhaps, from the reproaches Agatha had piled on her in the night. Wicked as she knew she had been, she hadn't really known how wicked until Agatha, as it were, took the matter up, thought Milly, faintly smiling again at the phrase, so inadequate to the situation. According to Agatha, she was past praying for. Being past praying for, however, seemed to have its points—it did bring relief with it, it did clear the atmosphere. Look how clear and calm the atmosphere now seemed. Also it was comfortable; one gave up, one let go, one rested. Rest was comfortable, and the atmosphere she was now in was certainly restful, for she was delivered from the convulsions and confusions of doubts, and knew that she had to marry Arthur. Another curious and unexpected end for Arthur: he had become the alternative to starvation.

So she wrote her telegram, asking him to meet her at the Chelsea flat that afternoon at three, instead of the afternoon in the next week, which was the one they had arranged to meet on before he left England; and after a moment's thought she added the word *Urgent*, though much disliking using such a flurrying word to Arthur. But then supposing he didn't come? He would be busy, she knew, resettling himself in his rooms after his four weeks' absence, and wouldn't see, unless she put in something like that, why the plan they made last time they met—they never wrote letters—couldn't be kept to. It was to the last degree unlikely that he should have heard of Ernest's death. He didn't read newspapers on his holidays. Besides, if by some chance he did know, he would at once have written to her, the necessity for not writing, which was Ernest, having been removed.

No; he didn't know. But he would when he opened the door, and saw her in her widow's dress. And in answer to his astonished eyes she would nod; and he would then draw her inside, and fold her in his arms, and be so kind and sympathetic, because he knew that death, even when it didn't mean loss, was a tremendous thing, and that no one could be near it without being brushed by tragedy; and then presently he would say, "Well, now we must be married"; and then, habit being strong, and he accustomed to tell her everything, he would talk about his holiday and all he had seen, as they sat on the divan side by side, her head on his shoulder, his arm round her, and how easily and often one caught colds travelling abroad.

And wasn't that a good thing? Wasn't it really right and sane to pass on to something else, to the next thing, and not linger stirring the same emotions round and round? Women, thought Milly leaving the post-office and going in search of breakfast, like to emphasize and perpetuate a situation. They like to put it into capital

letters, envelop it in exclamation marks, and keep it
for ever just where it originally was. It is fortunate for
them that men don't and won't, or life would become an
unending series of violent explosions on the same spot.
After all, one has to get on with one's living—or is it
one's dying? The sore throat of to-day is of more interest
than the passion of ten years back. What one is doing
is important, not what one has done. And—"Aren't
I thinking platitudes!" she said to herself; and concluded that that was probably what one did, when one's
whole emotional content could be expressed by a shrug
of the shoulder.

The A. B. C. shop was still where it used to be, and
still with apparently the same cakes in the window. In
it she breakfasted, taking as long over it as possible, and
the waitress was assiduous and kind. So assiduous and
kind was she that Milly, looking up into her pleasant
young face as she hovered above her, was moved at last
to say gratefully, talking simply out of a heart entirely
simple and empty, "I think people are so wonderful to
each other when they are strangers, and don't know
what they are really like."

But there was no response from the girl; she only
stared at her, her pleasant face gone stupid with alarmed
surprise.

"That wasn't very clever of me," thought Milly,
picking up the bill and giving the girl half of what it
came to. "I suppose one doesn't talk to strangers about
anything except the weather, though they are really the
only people in the world one could talk to with complete
truthfulness."

And she smiled at the waitress as she went away, who
pretended, much embarrassed, to be wiping coffee which
hadn't been spilt off the marble top of the table.

She walked to the Strand, and down to the Embankment, and sat down on a seat near Cleopatra's Needle to wait till it should be time to go to the solicitor.

He was a Mr. Jenkyns, of the firm of Jenkyns and Rowe, whose office was somewhere near there in a street called Essex Street. She knew the address well, having often seen it on letters Ernest had written, and Jenkyns and Rowe were names familiar to her on his lips ever since her marriage. At the wedding Rowe was present, and at the funeral Jenkyns. Rowe had died some years before, and the firm had become only Jenkyns, though still calling itself Jenkyns and Rowe. Rowe she remembered as a kindly, smiling man, but perhaps that was because he was at a wedding. Jenkyns she had never seen. She was sure he would be hostile, and twenty-four hours earlier she would have shrunk from having to face him. Now she didn't care. It was a thing that had to be done, and what did it matter what Jenkyns thought of her? Whatever he thought it couldn't possibly be as bad as what Agatha, her sister, the person who said she loved her, thought. As one of many and much more unpleasant things it sank into insignificance. At least, then, she reflected, watching the shining gulls, there is some advantage in having lots of misfortunes.

And a man, passing at the moment between her and the gulls, paused to look at his watch and blotted them out, and Milly, her eyes necessarily on this obstruction, gazed at it unaware that here, actually, was Jenkyns.

§

It was Mr. Jenkyns's practice, on sanitary grounds, and not because he liked it, to walk every morning to his office in Essex Street from his house in Kensington, and in the evening to walk back again. The result was that he arrived at each end a little cross, for it is a long way,

and the pavements are hard. But he persisted, and was
of opinion that it was owing to this practice that he kept
young. He said so to his wife when, disappointed by
their evenings, she suggested his taking a taxi at least
one way, and on her asking with real surprise, "But
have you?" he, being offended, was silent.

His daily walk led him along the Embankment, and
when he got to Cleopatra's Needle he would take out
his watch to see if he were late, in which case he would
hurry, or early, in which case he would linger, because
he as much disliked the unpunctuality which arrives too
soon as the unpunctuality which doesn't arrive soon
enough.

On the morning Milly was on the Embankment he
found he had two minutes and a half in hand; and feeling for some reason, probably the sudden descent on
England of Spring, a little more tired than usual, he
thought he would sit down. He would not have sat
down if the person he saw on the seat had suggested, as
so many persons on seats do suggest, insects, but the
well-dressed widow in brand-new black, looking like
somebody's ideal client, which she no doubt was, for
widows need solicitors almost as much as solicitors need
widows, inspired him with confidence that near her all
would be clean; so, slightly raising his hat and preparing
to sit, he said politely, "You allow me?" and Milly,
equally politely, replying, "Do," they sat side by side,
and together silently watched the gulls.

It seemed to make a bond between them, watching
the same gulls. At least Mr. Jenkyns felt it did, whose
daily exercise had anyhow kept him young enough to
know an attractive little woman when he saw one. This
was an attractive little woman. And he thought,
glancing down at her heavily craped knees, "Poor
thing." And he added, glancing sideways at her pale

profile with its delicate nose and long dark eyelashes, "Poor young thing." Not a girl, of course—which was fortunate, for Mr. Jenkyns didn't get on with girls—and plumped out, perhaps, rather more than was necessary; yet quite sufficiently young to be arresting and pathetic as so very recent a widow. Thirty, Mr. Jenkyns decided, who used to be thirty himself, and knew that it was one of the pleasantest of one's many ages; and, clearing his throat, he asked her with the equivalent in a lawyer of that which in a doctor is a good bedside manner, with, that is, sympathetic yet controlled *empressement* combined with a suggestion of limitless reserves of discretion, whether she didn't think it a fine morning.

Milly said abstractedly that she thought it a very fine morning; and then looking at him, and perceiving him respectable, with his gloves and attaché case and all, she asked if it were far to Essex Street.

"Essex Street? I'm going there," said Mr. Jenkyns, struck by this coincidence.

"Is it far?" repeated Milly, for this didn't seem an answer to her question.

"That," said Mr. Jenkyns with the prudence of his profession, "would depend on the pace at which one walks to it. It may be done, and has been done, in ten minutes, but I would not advise it. Personally I allow eleven. A lady, perhaps, might require, say, twelve."

"I want to be there at ten o'clock," said Milly.

"Indeed," said Mr. Jenkyns, struck by this second coincidence. And added after a slight pause, during which he considered the claims of caution and decided that in this case it had none, "So do I."

He took out his watch and stared at it, frowning.

"It is now," he said, "twelve minutes—no, pardon me—twelve and a half to the hour. From here, as I said, it takes eleven minutes. But a lady would need twelve. If you will allow me," he continued, "I will show you the way."

"It would be very kind," said Milly.

He got up. So did she. And they proceeded together along the Embankment.

Pleasantly conversing, taking pains to please, pointing out objects of interest—"That," he said, "is the dome of St. Paul's,"—Mr. Jenkyns suited his pace to hers. He would be a few minutes late that morning, he realized, but it was of no consequence. It kept one young, this sort of thing, this walking with and talking to a strange lady. For a long while now he had wished that he might have some sort of little adventure, just as an assurance that he was not yet old. Almost anything would do which fulfilled the requirements of caution. The lady—naturally there would be a lady—must be beyond reproach morally and socially, for he had a profound aversion from anything approaching shady, and also she must be attractive. His profession had brought him into sad contacts, and taught him that the combination is rare. Along the paths of adventure it would be almost impossible to find. Indeed, he found it difficult to imagine the form a respectable adventure could possibly take. And here he had found it, on a seat on the Embankment.

Gratified, and faintly excited, he walked beside Milly, chatting and feeling ten, no, twenty years younger, for he had got to the age when being ten years younger wouldn't have done him any good at all. He asked so little. At his age it was no use, he knew, asking much, and as a family lawyer of the highest standing it was risky asking anything at all. But this lady, should anyone see him with her, could only do him credit as a companion, and no one would ever guess that he didn't even know her name. Indeed he asked very little. He only wanted some nice and pretty woman, who wasn't married to him, to show interest in him, to be aware that he was a man, to listen, to smile. This one listened and smiled very sweetly, occasionally looking up at him when she answered with particularly good and charming deep blue eyes—eyes still liquid, Mr. Jenkyns, observing them sympathetically, opined, with the tears of bereavement.

"You will pardon me," he said, while they were waiting to cross the road, "for speaking of it, but I fear from your dress you are—that you have—no, not yet," he broke off quickly, catching her by the arm as she was about to step off the kerb into what would have been certain death. His wife did that sort of thing, and it exasperated him. It didn't exasperate him in Milly, for she wasn't a wife but an adventure. Also it gave him the opportunity, having saved her, of holding her by the arm, and presently piloting her across into the security of the other side.

"May a stranger," he resumed, his hand still on her elbow in case she started off again, "offer you his condolences?"

"Thank you," murmured Milly, bowing her head.

"A dove," thought Mr. Jenkyns. "A dove." And he let go her arm, when holding it was no longer necessary, with reluctance.

What then was his surprise and dismay to discover, on approaching his office and inquiring of Milly which number in Essex Street she wished to go to, that she wished to go to his number and that she was none other than the disgraced and disgraceful Mrs. Ernest Bott. In answer to his sudden question, light having flashed like an extremely unpleasant sword through his brain, she said she was. Of course. Fool that he had been to be taken in. When she asked, this new-made widow, if it were far to Essex Street, he ought to have guessed at once who she was. Why, he actually had been expecting her. Mr. Herbert Bott had been in to see him the previous day in a state of much anxiety, inquiring if he had seen her or if she had communicated with him, and saying that she would be sure to call soon because she had no money; and he had asked him to hand her over a thousand pounds, the amount to which her legacy entitled her, when she did call. He had arrived with the notes all ready in his pocket-book, and said he wished her to have them at once, and that she would repay him when the necessary formalities for the release of her legacy had been fulfilled, and that meanwhile she must not be allowed to starve.

Mr. Jenkyns considered, and felt it his duty to suggest, that the thousand pounds would probably never be repaid, but his suggestion had been repudiated with heat.

Mr. Herbert Bott had then asked, as a personal favour, that the loan should not be mentioned to the lady as a loan, but that she should be allowed to suppose it was her legacy. He would tell her himself later, he said; and, as he joined to this request a further request that no reference to his visit should be made to his brothers should they call, Mr. Jenkyns was left with the strong impression that here, if this poor client Ernest Bott had chosen to bring a divorce suit, was the co-respondent.

Ernest Bott, then, had been more magnanimous even than his friend and solicitor had imagined. Declaring, "I don't know the man's name and don't want to," he had been shielding his own brother. Natural indeed was it that a man thus wronged should have been unable altogether to resist some slight revenge, and the codicil, in Mr. Jenkyns's eyes, had been the very mildest form of it which a betrayed husband could well take.

He therefore looked at Milly, who had but so recently been charming to him, with real aversion. How profoundly he detested these women who prey and betray. No man was safe from them. They come along with their long eyelashes and little round busts, he thought, eyeing her with deep dislike, and before a man knows where he is he has been flayed of his honour and his happiness.

"A wolf in widow's clothing," he sternly said to himself, looking at her with eyes gone steely.

"I suppose you are Mr. Jenkyns," faltered Milly, aware of the instant and humiliating change in his manner.

The finger of scorn—that was what she was up against for the first time in her life; and she didn't like it. Thus, then, did good men look at bad women; men, that is, who felt they were good, at women they were sure were bad. Now she knew. In spite of her humiliation she was interested, the rôle of bad woman being so new to her. Was this the sort of thing she must expect? But after all, she had been prepared for hostility from Jenkyns. Why did she mind it so much? Perhaps because he had been so very pleasant and kind a few moments before, and so manifestly admiring. She felt whipped.

Icily polite, freezingly stately, the long, lean Mr. Jenkyns held the swing door of the building his office was in open for her, and followed her up the worn stone stairs. Leading her straight into his room, through the room his confidential clerk sat typing in, he said, indicating a chair, "You have come for your legacy?" and without further speech unlocked his safe, and took out the envelope Bertie Bott had left with him the day before.

"I think you will find these correct," he said, handing

them to her and not looking at her. "Perhaps you will be so good as to count them."

And while she counted them with fumbling fingers, for she wanted to cry—absurd, absurd to want to cry because of Jenkyns, she angrily told herself—her head bent over the notes, her veil fortunately falling over her face, Mr. Jenkyns, sitting at his table, took up the telephone and engaged in a long and technical conversation with somebody, just as if she had ceased to exist.

So she had, except unpleasantly, for him. Added to his temperamental dislike of such women, was the annoyance of having been attracted and taken in. Also there was an unaccountable feeling of frustration, as if his drink had been snatched from him. True the drink had not been anything more heady than, say, a cup of tea, but such refreshment as can be got out of a cup of tea had been rudely dashed from his expectant lips.

When she had finished counting, Milly sat quiet. She couldn't very well get up and go while he was still telephoning, nor could she interrupt him to say that the notes were correct; and she sat feeling every instant more like some evil and castigated kitchenmaid. Mr. Jenkyns had much to discuss with the person at the other end of the telephone, and did so leisurely and at length. When at last he hung up the receiver, after an urbane leave-taking which seemed to Milly to last at least another five minutes, he pressed a button on his table, and, as she was opening her mouth to speak, the clerk she had seen typing in the other room swiftly and silently appeared.

She shut her mouth again, and waited. "I don't care," she thought, trying to give herself courage. "What do I care for Jenkyns?"

But she did care.

"Write out a receipt for one thousand pounds," said

Mr. Jenkyns to the clerk, who went swiftly and silently away to do it.

"This," he said to Milly, but not looking at her, and sitting quite still, his elbows on the arms of his revolving chair, his finger-tips joined, and his eyes looking down his nose, "is highly irregular."

"What is?" she asked, her voice a little uncertain, for she was afraid he was going to say something personal and dreadful.

"Handing over this money to you."

"Why?" she asked, recovering her breath.

"Because I have no proofs of your identity."

"Oh," said Milly, considering this. Neither, if it came to that, had she. She had been told she was Milly, and had early accepted it, but how could one prove it?

"You mean—" she hesitated—"you can't be sure I'm Mrs. Bott."

"Mrs. *Ernest* Bott," he amended severely.

"Mrs. *Ernest* Bott," repeated Milly; and reflected.

The result of her reflections was that after a minute she said, "Well, I am."

Mr. Jenkyns was silent. He sat motionless, gazing down his nose.

Then, remembering that her name and Ernest's were engraved inside her wedding ring, Milly hastily pulled off, or rather wrenched off, her left glove, which was tight and resisted.

"Look," she said, offering the ring to him across the table. "There's my name engraved inside it, and Ernest's, and the date of our marriage."

Mr. Jenkyns didn't look; he merely made a gesture of aversion.

"Quite; quite. No doubt; no doubt," he said, much shocked by the tactlessness which could adduce the very symbol of the vows she had broken in evidence that she was indeed his poor client's wife, the very ring which had been placed, full of trust and affection, on the hand that was to betray him. "In a court of law, however, that would be no proof at all."

"But we're not in a court of law," said Milly.

Mr. Jenkyns's mouth seemed to become even thinner and smaller. That was the way his wife reasoned. They were all alike in brains, if, fortunately, differing in morals.

The swift and silent clerk reappeared, laid the receipt on the table, and vanished.

"Please sign here," said Mr. Jenkyns, dipping a pen into ink and handing it to her.

He held it with severe patience while she pulled off her right glove. The glove was tight and resisted. It was tighter, and resisted more, than the left-hand one. New, and of kid, they were a size too small, but had been ordered by the family along with the rest of the mourning, and the family, seeing her small, had supposed her hands matched the rest of her. So they did, but they were plump as well as small, and the plumpness that is comfortable in six and a half goes with difficulty into six and a quarter; also it comes out again with difficulty.

Milly's plumpness wouldn't come out. Mr. Jenkyns, pen extended, his eyes carefully averted, was patient. Milly, struggling, was hot. The glove stuck. Stupid glove—oh, stupid, stupid *fool* glove, she thought, agitated. And while she tugged, flushed and nervous, the notes on her lap fell off on the carpet, and Mr. Jenkyns, forced by convention, was afraid he would have to pick them up.

He found he couldn't bring himself to. No; he couldn't stoop and grovel on the floor at such a woman's feet. So he rang for the clerk.

"Oh, thank you," said Milly, confused and warm, and

trying to get her glove off and take the notes from the clerk at the same moment. She smiled a little from habit as she looked up at him and said thank you, and her smile was kind and sweet.

How good she looked. Mr. Jenkyns disliked her more than ever. That she should look good when she wasn't was an outrage.

"A serpent," he said to himself, his mouth very tight and thin. "A serpent masquerading as a dove."

₊(VIII)*₊*

SHE was back in Bloomsbury before eleven, the thousand pounds, in nine notes of a hundred each and twenty of five, for Bertie Bott had thought of everything and knew she would need small notes to go on with, in an envelope inside the front of her dress. Mr. Jenkyns had not detained her. He watched her stuffing the notes into what he reluctantly thought of as her bosom, with sternness. He made no inquiry as to her address, for in his opinion it was much better that nobody should know it. Let her disappear. Let the family be quit of her. Mr. Herbert Bott had asked him to telephone to him at his office directly she called, alleging it was important that he should get into touch with her; but Mr. Jenkyns had no intention of doing any such thing. Why should he? It was not his way, and never had been, to encourage co-respondents. Get into touch with her! No doubt. An appropriate phrase. But that he should ask him to help him to do so seemed to Mr. Jenkyns rather as if he took him for a fool. And when Bertie rang up just before lunch, and inquired, his voice as anxious as ever, whether his sister-in-law had made any signs, he received the brief reply that she had been and gone; and when he prefaced whatever he was going to say next with a voilent explosion, which sounded at first like a fit of coughing, but which resolved itself into oaths, Mr. Jenkyns sedately hung up the receiver.

Milly walked back to the boarding-house turning her thoughts away from Mr. Jenkyns. He was, as an incident in her life, over, and it was foolish to mind him. Considering how many other things she had to mind, it seemed to her rather odd how much he rankled. But no man had ever been rude to her before, except of course Ernest, and her skin tingled as if she had been slapped. What could be more rude than the sudden change from urbanity, and an obvious desire to please, to that icy, that annihilating politeness? Ernest must indeed have told him terrible things about her to produce it. Well, she wouldn't think of it. Shake him off; shake off Jenkyns, she said to herself, instinctively making a movement with her shoulders as though she were doing it, and finding the same sort of comfort in calling him Jenkyns without Mr. that a small boy finds in putting out his tongue at an unconscious back. But though she held her head high, her eyes were full of humiliated tears. Ah, if she ever met a sinner, how kind she would be, how uncritical! And then she reflected that perhaps she was always meeting sinners, only they had been cleverer than she had, and hadn't been found out.

She got back to the *Home from Home* more than an hour earlier than she had said she would. She was sorry about this, and walked as slowly as possible, being reluctant to arrive; but her interview with Mr. Jenkyns had been short, and here she was, back before eleven.

As usual, from nowhere, the manageress hurried forward to meet her, giving her her bag with many assurances that she would find its contents intact; also, she said, she would find Mrs. Le Bon waiting for her in her bedroom, who would be glad, the manageress was sure, to see her, having seemed a little put out by the message Mrs. Bott had left—"If you ask *me*," said the manageress.

"Have you ever sinned?" Milly was wondering, her eyes on the manageress's face as she mechanically took her bag. "I mean, major sins—the ten commandments —not just being cross. Have you ever done any of them?"

She looked at her in silent speculation, trying to reconstruct her twenty years earlier, which would probably, judged Milly, be about her time for falling out with the commandments.

No; she was sure she had not. But then the manageress would be equally sure that she, Milly, hadn't sinned either, and how much mistaken she would be. Nobody could ever be sure. Perhaps even Jenkyns . . .

Going slowly and thoughtfully upstairs she rejected Jenkyns as a sinner, however, on the ground that if he were one he surely would be less steely. Did sin, then, make one soft? Did it make one generous? Did having sinned incline one to pitifulness, to understanding? If so——

Milly broke off. It was all very difficult. And after a pause of reluctance at Agatha's door, she knocked and went in.

§

Agatha was very angry.

"I was afraid you would be," said Milly contritely, fumbling at the fastenings of her dress so as to get out the notes.

"That you should disappear in this manner when we have such a vital appointment to keep!" cried Agatha, towering over her like a black pillar of indignation.

"I kept it," said Milly.

"You kept it?"

"Yes. And got the money. Here it is," said Milly, extricating the packet. "The thousand pounds," she explained, as Agatha made no movement to take what was being offered.

Agatha stared uncomprehendingly.

"What?" she said. "My legacy?"

"Yes. Here it is."

"My thousand pounds? They were handed to you?"

"Yes. Won't you take them?"

Then Agatha did take the packet, and having got it held it tight in both hands, staring at Milly as though she were frightened, as though she had had a narrow escape from unthinkable disaster. For there, merely tucked into the front of Milly's dress, and carried in that way through the streets of London, a place notorious for its accidents and its thieves, had been her rehabilitation, her honour, her happiness, her life.

"Did you *walk?*" she asked in a low voice.

"Yes," said Milly.

"Milly—you carried this enormous sum openly through the streets?"

"Not openly. I was buttoned up."

"Why," said Agatha, staring and clutching the envelope to her breast, "you might have been run over."

"Well, I wasn't," said Milly.

She went to the window, and sat down dejectedly. She was tired; she was hot; she wished she were safe with Arthur, and the next few hours over. Agatha would now begin to cross-question her as to how she got possession of money not belonging to her, and why the solicitor should, without authority, so incredibly have given it to her; and Milly would be forced to make up some story, and no story that she could make up would be much good. There simply wasn't a story, thought Milly wearily, searching about in her imagination for something plausible. And then if Agatha guessed the truth, who knew but what her pride wouldn't make her refuse such a gift from what she might regard as a tainted source? Milly felt that Agatha would certainly now think of her as a tainted source, and if she did what would happen? The only other alternative to her being cast adrift penniless would, in that case, be help from Arthur, and he too, of course, as a source was tainted.

But she needn't have been troubled, because Agatha forgot everything when she opened the envelope and looked inside. A queer little shiver shook her bonnet—she was dressed ready to go out the instant Milly returned—when first she actually beheld riches. To her a thousand pounds were riches. With the contents of this envelope, she was certain she could conquer the world.

She stood a moment holding her breath as she looked, and then walked over to the bed as solemnly as if she were walking to an altar, bearing in her hands the chalice that was to give her life; and kneeling down, and taking out the crackling notes, clumsily because of her excitement, she spread them side by side on the coverlet with what seemed to Milly reverential awe, and became absorbed and lost in counting them.

Milly sat watching her. She left off wiping her hot face, and leaned forward in the chair, her eyes on the figure by the bed. Even more than Agatha's ruined hands and body did this ecstatic worship reveal what the depth of her poverty must have been. Oh, poor Aggie—poor, poor Aggie, thought Milly, pity and tenderness washing into her heart again. Heart-breaking what poverty, real extreme poverty, could do in grinding away the graces and charities, thought Milly. And grace and charity had been there, Milly knew, well remembering the young, generous body and mind which used to be Aggie's. Too generous she had been, too believing. Excess of faith and hope, excess of the very virtues we are asked to cultivate, had sent her swinging off to the heights with her lover, and excess of pride had

kept her defiantly declaring she was still on them when
she had long sunk down miserably into depths. But it
was magnificent to have stuck to her sinking ship like
that, a splendid piece of courage; and she herself, Milly,
the comfortable coward, the dealer in daily treacheries,
had let her vision of Agatha's qualities, qualities gone
curdled only by misfortune, be blotted out because she
was not very pleasant. Not very pleasant! What, in her
shoes, would Milly herself have been like? Something
worse than not very pleasant, she was only too sure.
Certainly nothing approaching magnificent. Probably
a great groaner, with no pride anywhere about her..

And watching Agatha's blissful absorption, Milly
couldn't help reflecting on the strangeness of the fact
that it was her own sinning which was the ultimate cause
of it. Arthur's adultery with her and Ernest's punishment of her had both ended by making joy possible for
Agatha. It was exceedingly queer. It made one feel
giddy. It was altogether more than her brain could
deal with. Best not to think too much, she thought, realizing that she had rescued Agatha far more effectually
than by the kind of rescue living with her in the comforts of Mandeville Park Road, surrounded by indignant Botts unable to forgive the elopement and the
hotel, would have offered, if Ernest had never found out
about Arthur and she had come into all his money.
Agatha would have hated being dependent; Milly would
have writhed in her perpetually resentful company.
Indeed Ernest had done better than he knew, when he
left her only that thousand pounds. So could she bless
Agatha, and let her go.

"Are they all right?" she asked, when the counting
seemed to have come to an end.

"Yes," said Agatha without turning her head, beginning carefully to put the notes together.

She collected the small ones first, the five-pound ones, and spread them out neatly one on top of the other. Twenty of them. Twenty notes, each worth a hundred and twenty-five Swiss francs. And each of the bigger notes was positively the same as two thousand five hundred francs—two thousand five hundred!—and there were nine of them.

She knelt before them, worshipping. On these crisp bits of paper she was going to be wafted back to where she heart and soul belonged, and buy herself into the management of the hotel. Bought in, the proprietor, before he knew where he was, would be bought out; she wouldn't rest till she had turned over enough for that. Then she would reign supreme. She could do it all—she could, she could. There was nothing she couldn't do, given a chance, given capital. *Madame la Patrone* . . .

It was as though, thought Milly watching her, she were praying, kneeling there, her hands clasped in front of her, gazing at the little pile of notes. Then, folding them and reverentially putting them back into their envelope, she came out of her golden dream, and said, turning to Milly with knitted brows, "But I still cannot understand what your reasons were for evading me this morning, and fetching my money without any authority from me. Also," she went on after a pause, as Milly said nothing, "I consider it extremely wrong, and probably criminal, of the solicitor to have given it to you. In Switzerland he could and would be sued."

"Anyhow you've *got* it," said Milly, turning her head and looking out of the window, away from Agatha's eyes.

"But how was it possible?" she insisted. "And why did you evade me?"

"Oh, Aggie—" sighed Milly, "what does it matter as long as you've got it? I just was up rather earlier than usual, and so I—I thought I'd go for a walk. And then, as I happened to be out, I thought I might as well go and fetch the money, and save time."

A poor story, thought Milly; a thin, poor story. . . .

For a moment Agatha, who was buttoning the envelope into the front of her dress, said nothing. Then she remarked, "I should like to know your real reasons for acting in this manner."

"Oh, Aggie—bother," said Milly, drooping on her chair. "I couldn't explain them if I tried."

"All reasons can be explained," said Agatha, rising from her position on the floor, her distrust becoming deeper every moment—for suppose Ernest had left her more than a thousand pounds? How was she to know that he had not? She was in ignorance, except of what Milly had chosen to tell her. "Unless," she finished, "they are discreditable."

And Milly, silent, wondered whether it mightn't after all be the good who needed to be dealt with uncritically and patiently, rather than the sinners.

§

Fortunately at that moment the manageress knocked at the door. She wished to tell the ladies, she explained on coming in, that lunch was at half-past one.

"I am leaving," said Agatha, much annoyed at the interruption and turning on her with lofty displeasure, "I shall not require lunch."

"Sorry, Mrs. Le Bon," said the manageress crisply, "but if you leave without notice you'll have to pay for the week. I told you last night this house isn't a hotel. It's a private boarding establishment. And the rule is a week's notice or a week's pay."

"I shall pay for what I have had," said Agatha, still more lofty, "and I shall pay no more."

"The rule is——" repeated the manageress, her eyes beginning to emit sparks.

"Your rule is not my rule," Agatha interrupted. "Let me have my bill."

And there followed an altercation which could only be described as unseemly.

Milly from the window looked on, an extremely unwilling spectator, but the other two were between her and the door, against which the manageress stood, so that no one should get through it till she chose. Milly therefore had to stay where she was, and listen. They said rude things to each other—at least, the manageress said rude things, and Agatha, with infuriating iciness, swept them aside and stuck to her guns. Milly, herself so evasive, such an anxious compromiser at the mere scenting of a scene, such a quick giver-up in the face of demands, marvelled at the unflinching determination of Agatha not to be done. She herself would so much rather be done than do. It seemed an outrage on something very delicate and brittle tucked away deep inside one, something that would get hurt much more by winning than by giving way, to fight. But perhaps that was a poor, abject way of looking at things. Several times she tried to pour the oil of her gentleness on these furious waters, but the manageress's voice was too shrill and persistent, and Agatha's too big and booming, for Milly's soft piping to get through. Difficult, thought Milly, reluctantly listening, to live with Agatha. One hadn't to live with the manageress, so she didn't matter, but she had longed to live with Agatha a few hours earlier—how much she had longed! It would have been difficult, she now knew. So much and such ready courage, such excessive quantities of grit. . . . Grit was good, and she admired it, but not such quantities of it. Le Bon—how had he managed? He hadn't managed; he had died.

Yes, but not for a long while—for twenty-five years he had lived with all that grit. What sort of a man could he possibly have been? Wouldn't he and she have been rather good friends? Wouldn't they, after a bit, have been inclined to comfort each other?

Ah, but this was getting worse, the things they were saying—Agatha telling the manageress with scorn that she cared neither jot nor tittle for English laws or police, because she was a free and independent Swiss, and the manageress retorting that she ought to be ashamed of herself for being a thing like that, and actually in her excitement proceeding to add something unintelligible to Milly, but manifestly insulting, about Agatha's parents.

Agatha's, and therefore, her own, parents?

This time Milly intervened more energetically. She got up from the chair she had been sitting on, and went to the manageress and laid her hand, with all the firmness she had, on her arm.

"Don't," she begged. "Please——" and kept on saying it till the manageress heard her.

"Please don't," begged Milly earnestly, having got her attention. "My sister——"

"She your sister?" cried the manageress, glaring with distended nostrils at the unflinching Agatha. "I don't believe it, Mrs. Bott—not for a single instant. You may *think* she is, and I dare say she is in a way, but not a way any of us would much like to mention, if you ask *me*. I should say your father——"

And the manageress, got completely out of control, was on the verge of openly bringing out her theory as to Mrs. Le Bon's birth, when Milly, feeling something awful was coming, stopped her by interjecting that she was paying the bills herself for both of them, flinging her words quickly in front of whatever the manageress had been going to say.

"My sister is going to Switzerland," Milly went on breathlessly, "and has to catch a train that leaves at two o'clock. She couldn't possibly lunch. I'll settle everything with you. Shan't we go downstairs and do it now?"

"Why, you're not leaving me too, Mrs. Bott?" exclaimed the manageress turning to her, softened by this speech, and remembering the four one-pound notes in Milly's handbag.

"I'm afraid so," said Milly, her quick smile, a little anxious now, but inevitably sweet, at once producing an answering glimmer on the manageress's heated face. "I'm so sorry——" Her voice became very gentle, almost caressing; anything, anything to calm people. "I would have liked so much to have stayed. You've been so kind. I shall hope to come back——"

But Agatha sternly put a stop to this scandalous and completely uncalled-for insincerity. Lying, terrible to have to recognize, seemed to be the unhappy Milly's speciality; but why she should stoop to it in order to please and flatter a harpy was past comprehending. "Untruths," she interrupted, with a great sweep of her arm, "nothing but untruths. My sister is not sorry. She would not have liked, either much or at all, to have stayed any longer with you. You were not kind. And she will never come back."

And once again Milly thought, looking at her in flushed and startled embarrassment, that it wasn't the sinners who needed understanding and patience and uncriticalness so much as the good.

§

An hour later Mr. Jenkyns, having just bowed out an important client, was told by his clerk that a Mrs. Le Bon wished to speak to him; and on inquiring if she had an appointment, and being told that she hadn't, he refused to see her.

But the clerk came back, and said she was so urgent in her desire to see Mr. Jenkyns that he couldn't get rid of her. "A widow, sir," said the clerk. "Been waiting half an hour. Says she won't keep you more than a couple of minutes."

A widow. Mr. Jenkyns reflected. He rather specialized in widows, who, when newly made and in the first confusion of disaster, were easy clients, both grateful and guidable; and though he was a man with as big a practice as any in London, yet a new client who was also a widow should not, perhaps, lightly be turned away.

"Does she—er—look——?"

He wished to say opulent, poor widows being worse than none, but said respectable instead.

"Oh quite, sir," the clerk assured him. "Very. Couldn't be more."

Mr. Jenkyns sighed, and fingered the pencil lying by his pad.

"Five minutes, then," he said. "Come in at the end of them, and call me away."

But at the end of three he was ringing for his clerk. "Show this lady out," he said, his thin face much flushed; for Agatha, who prized direct methods more highly than tact, and was also full of distrust, had started the interview unfortunately, severely inquiring of the surprised man, in a room in which severity had till then been his monopoly, by what right and by whose authority he had handed over the legacy Ernest Bott had left her to a third person.

Mr. Jenkyns was so much astonished that for half a minute of the three the interview lasted he gazed at her over his spectacles, speechless. Then anger, thick and hot, surged within him, for the incredible creature was actually threatening him with the law—threatening him, a lawyer, with, as it were, his own law.

When he recovered he made short work of Agatha, who in her turn was rendered speechless by what he told her. No mention at all of her in the Will? The money not her own by right at all, but a present from Milly? "And a very handsome present too," said Mr. Jenkyns sternly, pressing the bell on his table. "If I may make a suggestion, madam, I would bear the saying in mind as to the undesirability of examining a gift too closely."

"Then my sister," said Agatha for the third time, her eyes bigger than ever as she stared at Mr. Jenkyns every bit as inimically as he was staring at her, "fabricated the entire story?"

"To what end I am incompetent to judge," said Mr. Jenkyns, putting some papers together with exasperated movements. "Show this lady out," he added, on the clerk's appearing.

Agatha got up slowly. Deep were her suspicions. How did she know that what this man alleged was true? He might well be nothing but a rascal. Was not the expression "rascally lawyer" proverbial? Had she not frequently enough in her reading come across it? Besides, how unlikely, how incomprehensible, that Milly should divest herself of such a sum, and make her a present of it. People didn't make presents of fortunes. And she remembered her words when she told her of the legacy, and how she had said, and it had seemed most right and natural, Agatha thought, that Ernest in this way wished to make amends for the wrong he had done her.

There was, undoubtedly, something strange and suspect about this lawyer.

"Be so good," she said, towering tall and black on the other side of the table from which Mr. Jenkyns, in the

act of slightly bowing, had half risen, "as to produce
that Will. I desire to see it for myself."

At this Mr. Jenkyns rose completely. He straightened
himself out till he was as tall as she was, and looked at
her in silence, with eyes that were two points of bright
steel.

"Remove her," he then said, briefly, to the clerk.

§

It was now nearly one o'clock. At two the train for
Switzerland left. Agatha stood uncertain on the pavement in Essex Street, a kind of black Cenotaph, on
either side of which washed the indifferent flow of
passers-by. There wasn't much time to decide in. If what
that man said was true, and there was something about
his wrath at the end which convinced her it was, pride
demanded that she should return to the boarding-house,
fling the packet of notes at Milly's feet, for ever relinquish all idea of happiness, and go forth penniless to
struggle for what still might be left to her of existence.
After all, she was used to suffering. Oh, yes, she hoped
she knew how to suffer as well as anybody, she thought,
with an upward jerk of her chin. Or she might take out
one of the small notes for her fare—Milly was careless,
she was sure, and not the kind of person who counted
notes—and go back to Switzerland and throw herself
on the mercy of the hotel proprietor, and get reinstated
in her miserable post. Base? To take the note and not
tell? No, because it was merely a temporary taking—
ultimately, from her painful earnings, to be repaid.

She stood in a tumult of indecision. Traffic washed
round the island she made. Her hand, held tightly
against her chest, pressed the packet of notes. How
could she bear to let them go, and with them every
hope? Ah, how—how?

She walked a few steps up the street, and stopped again, and again pressed the notes against her chest, and again the passers-by divided on either side of her and streamed along, the ceaseless flow of absorbed, indifferent, busy people.

Mr. Jenkyns himself, on his way to lunch, was one of them, but he wasn't indifferent, for on catching sight of the motionless figure he immediately crossed to the other side, and there held on his way indignantly. "Pah," said Mr. Jenkyns to himself—a man not at all given to exclamations of the kind; but the expression seemed to describe his state of mind. He had a desire, unusual at that hour, to have a bath. After the encounters of the morning, first with that woman who had all but made a fool of him, that scandalous widow of poor Ernest Bott's, and then with her outrageous sister, he felt he needed a bath. There should be some soap invented, he thought as he hurried along, which washed off irritation; some Cuticura of the mind . . .

And Agatha continuing up the street, mechanically grasping the front of her dress, felt that not since Gaston's death had such desolation been hers. If she had only refrained from insisting that Milly should tell her the solicitor's address! Milly had tried not to tell her, and the more she tried the more Agatha had insisted— naturally, for such reluctance, such distressed reluctance, merely confirmed her suspicions that something was being hidden from her. And so something had been; and now she knew what it was; and it was the precise contrary of what she had been suspecting; and it destroyed her.

For how could she keep this money? Quite apart from what it represented—the contemptuous gesture, a kick almost, a parting kick from the outraged husband to the unfaithful wife, her principles would never allow her to take money from anyone fallen. Impossible. She could not even imagaine such a thing. A Magdalen's money. Better crusts in gutters than prosperity and honour at such a price. The wages of someone else's sin—how could she touch them? And Milly had known she couldn't and wouldn't, and therefore had invented the story of the legacy.

Kind of Milly? Kind to wish her to have the money? Yes, she supposed it was kind. Yes; it did seem quite kind. But if Milly had been virtuous, if she had remained a chaste wife, there would have been no need for all this complicated and lie-entangled kindness. The wages of someone else's sin—she couldn't touch them; but the punishment for someone else's sin appeared to be hers alone. Milly could go to the partner of her guilt, and they would marry, and perhaps even be happy, and anyhow cease to feel guilty. She would be comfortably provided for, and for the rest of her life, as in the past, not have a care; while her sister, who had never done anything but strive to live nobly——

Two tears slowly forced themselves from Agatha's eyes, and trickled down her face. She had had too much to bear. She was most weary of bearing. Now it was all to be begun again. . . .

And the passers-by—for she was in the Strand now, being jostled and noticing nothing—stared, seeing this weeping woman; and some were sorry, and thought fleetingly, "Poor old thing."

§

All the way to Bloomsbury Agatha wrestled with herself, tears on her face, and at her side walked her two bleak angels of Pride and Principle. By the time she had reached the boarding-house she had won her battle, and made up her mind. What was right had once more, she thanked God, got the upper hand with her, and she would acknowledge Milly's good intentions and give her back the packet, merely asking for a loan of one of the five-pound notes, so that she might at once travel back to Switzerland. There should be no secret taking of any note, and there should be few words. Indeed, there was time for nothing but the utmost brevity if she was to catch that train—and catch it she must, thus as quickly as possible closing this tragic chapter in her tragic life, this ill-fated attempt to bring love and comfort to a sister who for the past ten years had existed only in her imagination.

Neither to the right nor to the left would she look; neither at the hopes with which she had come, nor at the desolation in which she would go back. That way lay despair. Head up, mouth firm, thoughts nailed to the actual moment—this was how she was going through the rest of her life. "I refuse to be beaten—I *refuse* to be beaten," she kept on repeating to herself, her hand pressed against her bosom, where lay, warmed now by her warmth, the little bundle which held the possibility of the fulfilment of all her dreams—"Like a child," she suddenly thought, pressing it closer; and immediately was ashamed of such extreme absurdity.

Proudly, for she had won her battle, she turned the corner into the square, and up to the very last moment, when she was in the hall of the *Home from Home*, she was repeating, her head high as she walked past the servant at the door, "I refuse to be beaten——" Then, at the actual instant when she opened her mouth to make her brief speech of thanks to Milly, who came out of the dining-room hesitatingly, as if afraid to meet her, at the actual instant when her hand was preparing to draw out the packet of notes and give them up, she was beaten.

Her hand wavered. The words she had prepared refused to be spoken. Instead of drawing out the notes, she pressed them fiercely and hard against her chest. And looking at Milly, and drawing a long breath, her great eyes very wide open, her face defiant, she said, "I did not go to the solicitor after all. I feared—I came to the conclusion it might make me miss my train."

§

At the station, at the last moment, when porters were shutting doors and late passengers were scurrying about in confusion, Agatha, sitting straight and rock-like in the corner of her second-class compartment, and until then of the fewest possible words and a stony impassivity, suddenly gripped the window-sill with her cotton-gloved hand, and said in a queer voice, "Milly."

Milly was standing outside the door, vaguely looking along the platform, so as to not look at Agatha. She had come to see her off after all, no longer caring whether anybody from Titford saw her or not. Agatha had lied: speciously, recklessly, with the splendid and defiant despair of a God-fearing child driven into a corner, and Milly's heart was full of love. Poor, poor Aggie—what desperate fear and misery lay under her lying! But on no account must she notice any tenderness, or she would suspect that Milly knew, and be crushed by humiliation. All Milly had said, on receiving the lie square in her face, —and she had to say something after recovering her breath,—was that she was very glad Aggie hadn't gone that long way and tired herself out before her journey; and then, averting her eyes, she had pretended to be busy fastening her cloak and pulling on her gloves.

"I'm coming with you to the station," she said.

"Pray do not," said Agatha, very stiff and grim.

In the taxi—they were obliged to take a taxi, the time being short—they hardly spoke, each looking out of her own window. At the station there was a rush to get the ticket, and no talk was possible. Now, Agatha established safely in her corner, and Milly on the platform at the door, and the minutes of the rest of their time together this side of eternity rushing along till at last they were only seconds, they still said nothing, they still averted their eyes.

Once Milly remarked, watching with apparent interest the activities at the farther end of the platform, that she thought the crossing would be good, because there was so little wind; but Agatha didn't even answer.

Then, just as she was thinking, "But this is dreadful —another moment and she'll be gone for ever——" she heard that voice behind her saying, "Milly."

She turned quickly. Agatha was looking at her, her face working strangely.

"Milly——" she began.

"Yes, Aggie?" said Milly.

"I wish to say—I would like to say——"

She gulped, and looked speechlessly at the face in the window-frame.

Then she did get it out. "Bless you," she finished suddenly, her face all twisted.

In an instant Milly was on the step of the carriage, her arms round Agatha's neck.

"Bless *you*?" she whispered, drawing her close.

Then Agatha suddenly began kissing her wildly. "Milly, Milly——" she gasped, wildly kissing.

"Stand away there, please," shouted the guard.

⁂(IX)⁂

I̶T̶ ̶W̶A̶S̶ the established custom that Arthur, on the afternoons of their meetings in Chelsea, should be at the flat
a little before Milly, watch from behind the window-
curtain for her appearance at the corner of the street,
and open the door for her the instant she was on the top
step. This had been arranged at the beginning, when
they were both terrified lest she should be seen, and it
had become a fixed habit. Automatically Arthur took
up his position, and automatically the door opened,
with him behind it, not showing himself till she was inside. Then, at the beginning, what a falling into each
other's arms, what an enraptured silence and close
clinging! Not now, of course. Years pass and holds
loosen. Naturally, Milly told herself, reasonable and
sweet, when first Arthur's hold became definitely looser.
Ecstasy can't be kept up for ever; something much better takes its place—infinitely better, she assured herself;
and then sat and wondered what it was.

When he began to loosen, Milly, instantly aware of it
and delicately taking her cue from him, loosened to
match; but for all her apparent equal loosening the
second stage in loving had nevertheless been entered
into, the stage in which it is the woman who is the fonder. She was very fond; so, fortunately, was he, but not
as fond. He loved Milly dearly, but she loved him
more; and it was she, now, who brought and arranged
the flowers. Then, as the years passed, the third stage
was reached, when nobody brought flowers, and they

had quite settled down into comfortable, secure, equal
affection, without fuss or bother of any kind. The door
still opened as if by magic, but that was just habit, and
there was no magic waiting behind it. Composedly, unhurriedly, it was shut when she was inside, and composedly, unhurriedly, pleasantly, they smiled at each
other. Anybody might have seen them; anybody might
have heard them.

"Well, dear?"

"Well, Arthur?"

"I all but missed my train to-day. It actually started
a minute before its time."

"Really? I hope you didn't get hot hurrying? How
is your cold, darling?"

That was the sort of thing. Naturally, thought Milly;
for sin too settles down, and becomes indistinguishable
at last from virtue. Everything settles down. Naturally,
she thought.

On this occasion—the very last, she realized, of the
many occasions on which the journey had been made—
Milly, who usually went to King's Road from Victoria
in a taxi, walked. And she walked for two reasons: first,
because it was early, and Arthur's train, the one he
always came by, with a restaurant car enabling him to
lunch comfortably on the way, didn't get to Paddington
till three, and then because, on paying for the taxi from
Bloomsbury she had been reminded by the emptiness of
her bag that the manageress, refusing to be satisfied
with less, had got her four one-pound notes. After paying the taxi there was very little left in the bag—two
shillings to be exact, a threepenny bit, and five pennies.

Therefore she walked. And it occurred to her with
some surprise, for she hadn't thought of it till then, that
Arthur would have to begin at once paying for her needs,
and feeding and lodging her—yes, and clothing her too;

for even a registrar's office, a place accustomed to the
absence of sentiment, might think it tactless if she were
to be married in fresh widow's weeds. Arthur's first
present to her as his betrothed would have to be a
complete new suit of clothes.

Not that he would mind; nor would she mind asking,
for being used to having money, being ready herself to
give, she was also simple and unconcerned in taking.
And he wouldn't mind either her having been left with
only a thousand pounds. He cared nothing for money,
and would merely applaud the gift of it to her sister.
Besides, he had recently become Senior Tutor of his
College, with a house and garden attached to the position roomy enough for a large family, and he was well
able to support a wife. She had pointed this out smilingly to him—sometimes she was less sensible, and
tried to make him say things—when at her request,
she went down to be shown his new possession and have
tea in it, and he had answered, "Indeed, yes," and
hadn't said, as he always was saying at the beginning,
"Ah, if we could only be married!" Naturally, thought
Milly, one ends by putting impossibilities out of one's
thoughts; and this impossibility had now so long been
out of Arthur's that he failed to notice the obvious opportunity of referring to it. Instead, he began to tell her
of a fragment recently discovered at Naples, which appeared to belong to an inscription in honour of
C. Duilius, the victor over the Carthaginian fleet in
260 B.C. Naturally, thought Milly, who knew he was
just then much interested in Duilius.

Into this house she was now after all going; and walking by roundabout ways, for she had time to fill up, to
Chelsea, the first stage of that going, her thoughts, a
little sleepy in the relaxation succeeding the tension of
Agatha's departure, idly wandering, she remembered

that the garden had an apple-tree in the middle of its
grass plot, and she saw herself sitting through many
placid May days beneath this tree, dreaming as sweetly
as the dreaming spires themselves, while Arthur, in his
languidly charming voice, read to her of what he was
at the moment interested in. And, as her mind dwelt on
this vision of peace, she couldn't help wondering where,
then, what with Aggie gone away blessing her, and
Arthur, all kindness, taking her into his life legitimately,
expiation came in.

It didn't seem to come in anywhere, thought Milly,
her face still burning from that last desperate kissing,
her heart, released now because of it from unkindness,
comforted and quiet. Aggie had blessed her. Their bitterness and disappointment with each other was wiped
out. Still there was love between them in their thoughts.
And what a debt she owed her very severity! For it
was because of her shocked conviction that the only
amends Milly could make for her sin was to marry
Arthur, that her path at that moment was so straight
and clear. Aggie had sobered her. Those frenzied ideas
that Arthur must be fled from, that if she married him
Ernest would for ever be rising up accusingly between
them, were so many twisted cobwebs she had swept
from Milly's brain. Arthur to be fled from? Milly, relaxed, wondered at herself for having thought so. Why,
he was all she had now in the world, her one link with
some sort of love, some sort of warmth. Also he was the
only person she really kissed; and every woman had to
have someone in her life she really kissed, else she
starved. That was what was the matter with Aggie,
over and above her poverty—that she had nobody really
to kiss. And as for the frightened nonsense about
Ernest's memory worrying Arthur and herself, if at any
time it were to cross their minds it would be greeted,

she knew, by Arthur, who had never felt any hostility towards Ernest, and who would be sure to be genuinely sympathetic over the manner of his death, with the kindliest, "Poor fellow"; and no ghost, however obstinately set on haunting, could stand up against that gentle welcome.

Really, she didn't see quite where expiation came in. Life with Arthur, far beyond sight and sound of the Botts, would be nothing but restful. In Oxford no one would dream she was a person with a past, for the Botts were not in touch with Oxford, having all been educated, as Ernest put it, privately, and it would be impossible just from her appearance to guess she had got such a thing. How was it, wondered Milly, considering her case, and slowly advancing westwards through the sunny streets like a slightly torpid beetle—she was suddenly immensely tired—how was it she was being let off so lightly? Why, lightly wasn't the word; entirely was the word. For there was no punishment anywhere, and her plans for expiation were all confounded. Peace, security, affection were going to be hers. Coals of fire were being heaped on the heads of two sinners. Justice was staying its hand. Mercy was having its way unhindered. And again, her eyes half shut, and swaying a little as she walked, she saw herself under that appletree, being read aloud to through the summers of the future, or, in the winter, as in the Chelsea studio, being read aloud to by the fire. It used to be Keats and Shelley they read together, she remembered, dreaming of the past as she walked, hardly seeing the streets she was going through, or the polite, kind people making way for her; Keats and Shelley it used to be, in the first fervours. Ah, the wonderful time, that beginning time! She hadn't realized how wonderful till it was over. He was like a boy, shaken and torn out of the groove of

middle age by love, and she was so glad to be dragged
back with him by his passion to youth. Ah, sweet,
absurd time. . . .

Well, never mind; they were still so fond of each
other, and everybody was bound to grow older. They
had begun to grow older when, after Keats and Shelley,
came Milton and Blake, and were definitely older when
he tried to teach her Italian, and make her read Dante.
Gradually all the poets were left behind, and the excava-
tion period set in. History was what was studied in this
period, and great books were lent to Milly to read, for he
liked her to share his interests—books she took home
with her, and had to hide as carefully as if they were
some kind of enormous love-letter. For seven years now
the reading aloud had been of excavations, and she
didn't suppose he would emerge from them again.
Nothing except ancient Greece and Rome seemed really
to rouse him any more, to bring him back to life; and
just as she had inaccurately picked up poetry because
he had loved it, and inaccurately picked up Italian
because he had wanted her to learn it, so had she picked
up what was needed of facts connected with excavations
to be able to give him the comfort of believing he was
being intelligently listened to. Even—she smiled a little
to think of it—even she reacted satisfactorily when he
wished to talk to her of telamones and heroons; taking
him in, of course, but after all one had to be one's man's
companion as well as lover, and if one were ignorant
one must manage somehow to pretend one wasn't. Yes—
and one had to be his mother too, soothing headaches
away, pillowing him on one's bosom when he was tired
and needed a bosom—fortunately in whatever state her
brains might be, every woman had a bosom—brewing
him hot drinks to stave off his oncoming colds, being
sorry for him, petting him. Perhaps only in this relation-

ship had she had no need at all to pretend, she reflected; it came very natural to her to be a mother. If Ernest and she had had children, she probably wouldn't have wanted to get away that day of dissatisfaction and rush up to London, and then she never would have known there was such a person as Arthur.

But wouldn't that, honestly, have been a pity?

Ah, yes, yes—to have missed love, not to have known love. . . .

"What? She really thought that? She really thought it would have been a pity not to have committed adultery?

Milly was startled. Of course she didn't mean that. Of course she——

Well, she couldn't go into it now, she said to herself, pushing these questions on one side; for here she was— here was the corner of the street off King's Road, and there, halfway down on the left, she could see the familiar door.

Her heart began to beat a little faster as she turned the corner. This was no ordinary meeting. Great events had happened since the last one. The occasion was solemn with death, serious with the close of an epoch, hopeful with the beginning of a fresh one. At least, she thought with a feeling of gratitude and rest, there would be no surprises for her in the man she was going to marry; she knew him so well, so completely, that she could tell beforehand almost the very words he would use, and what he would do, and how he would look. Now, for instance, to-day, in another minute, when he opened the door and saw her in her widow's dress, she knew exactly what his face would look like, all sorry and all—she was going to say glad, but put the word pleased instead, as perhaps more accurately descriptive of Arthur's mild reactions these days. And she said to herself, with a feeling of having got safe into harbour, into calm water, how, after ten years of love, there are few things a woman doesn't know about her man; in fact, she amended with a small smile as she went up the steps, there are none.

But for the first time during the ten years of love, Milly was mistaken.

§

To begin with, the door didn't open; she actually had to knock.

Such a thing had never happened before.

She knocked, and waited, and knocked again. The street became interested, but no one came.

Then she remembered that he, watching from behind the curtain, couldn't possibly guess that the shrouded figure on the door-step, the strange widow, was Milly. Stupid of her to arrive with her thick veil over her face.

She put it up, and knocked again; and the street became still more interested, and still no one came.

Inside she could visualize Arthur, astonished at this visit from a stranger, turning away annoyed and perplexed from the window, determined not to show himself, to lie *perdu*, till the creature on the steps, the impudent widow, had gone, hoping to goodness she would go before Milly arrived, and putting her down as some charity collector, or someone frankly begging.

Well, she must bring him to the window again, so that, her veil now thrown back and her face turned towards him, he would see who it was; and once more she knocked, loudly, persistently; and the street became absorbed.

He did come at last—not to the window but straight to the door, outraged that anyone should dare go on making such a moise. She heard the irregular, limping footsteps, and immediately afterwards the door was flung open, and Arthur, indignant, appeared.

"Milly!" he exclaimed, his brown eyes wide with amazement. Then, "*Milly*——" he repeated, his voice dropping, a strange expression taking the place of amazement, an expression she found she didn't know— she who had been so sure she knew them all.

He forgot to shut the door. He stood gazing at her clothes. "Are you—is it possible——?" he said in a low voice; for Arthur, though short-sighted and generally unobservant, did know a widow when he saw one,— besides which Milly, as a widow, was impossible to miss. Of her class she was, perhaps, owing to the Botts' tradition, the most perfect specimen.

He looked at her in dismay. The expression on his face, which she had never seen before and couldn't place, was simple, stark dismay. She, however, passed quickly from wondering about it to wondering, in her turn, at his appearance. What was the matter with Arthur? Bronzed from his holiday as he had never been after any holiday, he not only looked amazingly well, but he produced an unusual effect of cleanness, though he had always been clean, and of awakenness, though he had never been sleepy. Curiously on the spot too, he seemed; come back to the present. And even his voice, naturally languid, was in some odd way brisked up. Also, incredibly—her lips dropped apart when she saw them—he was wearing spats.

She stared. She was so much surprised that she forgot all about her own appearance.

"How *well* you look, darling," she said, a little hesitatingly, her eyes rising from the spats to his face. The strange expression was still on it. It didn't go at all with the rest of him, especially not with those optimistic spats. What was it? she wondered. In anyone else, she would have said it was——

Her thought stopped short. He was motioning her inside. Of course; they were still standing on the steps, in full view of the street.

She went in, and he shut the door. In the little space partitioned off from the studio by a curtain, he said, laying a finger for an instant on her sleeve, "Milly—— Why? What has——?"

"Ernest," she said, nodding slowly, brought back at once to the seriousness of the occasion; and, her eyes on his face, she waited to be taken in his arms.

But Arthur's behaviour was as strange and unusual as the rest of him. He didn't take her in his arms; he stood looking at her in silence, the expression she couldn't place more marked than ever; and all he said, after an appreciable pause, though he said it with evident feeling, was, "God."

This outburst too was entirely unlike him, and surprised her afresh. God? She couldn't remember his ever having said such a thing before.

"I knew, darling," she said softly, "that you would be much shocked——" and as he said nothing at all to this, but in silence was holding the dividing curtain aside for her to pass through into the studio, she passed through it.

He followed. Still no sign of any of the things she had been so certain he would say and do, and always that expression on his face which in anyone else she would have said was—— But of course it wasn't; it couldn't be.

"Darling——" she began, taking off her heavy bonnet and laying it aside.

He interrupted her. "When, Milly?" he asked abruptly.

"Friday," she answered.

"Friday? This last Friday? Less than a week ago? But—why? Why should he——?"

"An accident," she whispered; and again Arthur, after staring at her a moment in silence, burst out strangely and abruptly, and said, "God."

Milly leaned against the table. For some reason her legs were shaking. The long walk, perhaps, she said to herself, from Victoria, on top of the long walk that morning to Essex Street and back. But why didn't Arthur kiss her? He always did kiss her—affectionately and kindly, when she arrived. Why didn't he to-day, of all days? He must know she couldn't have been anything but deeply wretched; he must realize that what had happened meant their marriage.

She put up her hands with a nervous movement to smoothe her hair, ruffled from the wearing of the bonnet, and discovered it wasn't only her legs which were shaking, but her hands too.

This surprised her. Her hands had nothing to do with walking. Why should they shake? Here she was with Arthur, safe with Arthur. . . .

But was she safe with Arthur?

Suddenly it seemed as if a door in her heart blew open, and an icy wind rushed through it. Quickly she shut it, banged it to again, leaning against it with all her might. Oh, nonsense . . . oh, nonsense. . . .

He was standing in front of the empty fireplace, his elbow on the mantelpiece, looking at her; and his brown eyes, so kind always, were full of—what? Distress; extreme distress, decided Milly. Evidently he was more shocked by Ernest's death than she had supposed possible. She had expected some shock, but not this. Perhaps he was one of the people whom death, any death close enough to be realized, appalled. She hadn't known this side of him, because there had been no death within measurable distance of him during their intimacy, and the subject had hardly been mentioned in their talks, except generally. If so, if this was it, and he was simply horrified, and his horror was increased a thousandfold by the sight of her dreadful clothes, naturally he shrank from her, naturally he couldn't bear to take her in his arms.

Rapidly Milly gave herself explanations, but even while she gave them she was aware that they didn't hold water. There was something else the matter with Arthur. At least she knew him well enough to know that. And again she leaned with all her might against the door in her heart, which the freezing wind of desolation was trying to burst open.

"Darling," she said at last, her voice trembling—but why? Wasn't he Arthur? Wasn't she Milly?—"it has all been sad and horrible, but it isn't *going* to be. Some day"—she tried to smile at him, and her mouth merely twitched—"some day there'll be—we'll be——"

Her words petered out. She stood looking at him. Then she said, suddenly, desperately, quickly going over to where he stood, "Arthur, why don't you kiss me?"

He stared down at her. He was so tall, in spite of his stooping shoulders, and she was so short, in spite of her high heels, that when she was close to him she had to crick her neck almost so as to look up into his face. She did so now, holding on to his coat with both hands to steady herself, for he made no attempt to put his arms round her; but there was such distress in his eyes, such evident trouble, that it was she who put her arms round him, letting go his coat, holding him to her breast.

"Don't, Milly—don't, dear," said Arthur in a low voice, gently loosening her arms; and the door in Milly's heart blew right open, and swift, icy fear tore through it.

She stood away from him looking at him, her arms hanging by her side. Fumblingly she said, as though she were trying to find him in the dark and were faintly calling after him, "Arthur——?"

"Listen, Milly," said Arthur, trying to be very matter of fact, and failing, "I have a good deal to say to you."

He took her hand, but there was no heart in the way he held it, all loose.

"A really extraordinary thing has happened," he went on. "A thing, I suppose, that doesn't happen once in a hundred years——"

And another expression came into his eyes, blotting out the first one, an expression she knew she had seen before in them, but a long time ago, such a long time ago that it must have been when——

"What—thing?" she faltered, as he paused, suddenly flushed, she could see, beneath his sunburn.

He looked down at her, loosely holding her hand; she looked up at him, and the expression on her face brought dismay back to his.

"Perhaps," he said helplessly, dropping her hand and turning away, "we had better sit down——" and his glance wandered vaguely round the room, in search of a suitable spot.

There was no suitable spot; none, that is, suitable now in his eyes. The room had a divan in it, and a table, and a gas-ring for making tea, and a sink with a tap. They had never needed more furniture. On the divan they had loved, and then, as years passed, merely sat peacefully among its cushions; and sometimes, while he was reading aloud, she would slide on to the floor and sit at his feet, leaning her head against his knee. But Arthur had no knee now for Milly's head, and nothing would have induced him to go with her on to the divan, because that had happened to him which, in his ignorance, he thought never did happen, or only once in a thousand years, and he had been fallen in love with by a girl. He, fifty-five; he, amply old enough to be her father.

The girl had had great trouble in getting him to believe it. It was only with the help of her mother, who at last had had to take him aside and point things out, that he had been brought to see what was so evident to everybody else. Then, in his turn, he had fallen in love—deeply, helplessly, with the irresistible heavy falling, the stone-like swift drop, of the elderly when faced by radiant, worshipping, willing youth; and to her, to the girl he was going to marry, the slim wonder with the mouth like some lovely fruit and the lithe movements of a boy, he owed it that he should keep off divans. Besides, the bare idea revolted him. Strange to say—and it did cross his mind as strange, remembering how habitual the caressing of Milly among cushions had so long been, and how even more habitual the being caressed among them by her,—the thought of the divan, and its cushions and its caresses, now revolted him.

He didn't want to touch her, or be touched. A moment ago, when she put her arms round him, it had made him feel most uncomfortable, and curiously ashamed as well as sorry; yet last time they met, five weeks before, they had stood on that very same hearthrug, saying good-bye in almost identically the position, and with no feeling at all on his part except that it was natural.

"Well, I can't help it," he thought—irritably, because he was so much worried, so much taken aback by Milly's unexpected widowhood, and so genuinely sorry that he was going to have to hurt her. "*Conceive* Ernest's dying at such a moment!" he said to himself, distressed and exasperated, and still looking about the room for something satisfactory for them to sit on.

"But Arthur—" said Milly, "tell me—what thing?"

"There's nothing to sit on," he said impatiently, as if he couldn't tell her anything unless he sat.

"Why not the divan?" she asked.

"No, no," he said quickly; and then her last uncertainty, the little shred she was still holding on to, disappeared; and she knew.

§

Coming up in the train that day, and indeed whenever since his engagement Milly crossed his mind, Arthur had told himself that, being reasonable, she would understand. Obviously she couldn't marry him herself, Ernest being alive, and surely, then, it was natural that in the fullness of time, and after long years of devotion to her, he should marry and settle down. She might even be relieved, he thought; glad not to have to make any more journeys to Chelsea, now that she was older, and presumably more easily tired.

But Ernest had done, poor fellow, what no one would ever have dreamed he would do, and Arthur was much afraid that Milly would expect to marry him. Naturally she would expect it, seeing she didn't know what had happened to him in Rome; and equally naturally she was going to be terribly hurt by what he had to tell her.

Not, mind you, he said to himself, still looking about for chairs which weren't there, all these thoughts passing through his mind in a kind of extremely disagreeable flash—not, mind you, for the only reason which could justify marriage, passionate love on both sides, the love which was transfiguring his own life and so marvellously restoring him to youth, but because she would think it the right thing.

In her case, of course, there could be no love as Arthur at that moment understood it. She was forty-five; a middle-aged woman. And middle-aged women, Arthur said to himself, who was ignorant, have finished with that sort of thing. He hadn't thought of her as middle-aged before, time having slid along for them both unnoticed on the smooth wheels of use and wont, but he remembered that she was the first time he had emerged sufficiently from the intoxication he fell into, on discovering he was loved by youth, to be able to remember anything. Then he remembered Milly, and her age, and everything about her, with extreme clearness; and it seemed to him natural, in his desire to believe it was natural, that a woman so old as that would be glad not to be bothered with even the mildest, most shadowy of lovers.

Surely for years now he had been a most mild lover; surely it would be the easiest thing in the world for them to proceed from the pretence of being lovers to the reality of being friends? Friends were what one-time lovers should be when both were middle-aged, and he and Milly would always be the best of friends, and never would he forget how much he owed her, at a lonely period of his life, of comfort and peace.

He was very fond of Milly; very fond of her indeed. She had made an immense difference to his life. But he was now fond of her only as a friend. She must know that, though undoubtedly there had been a season of love, even of passionate love, between them, for a long while past it had been mere affection; and mere affection wasn't enough to marry on. Imagine, thought Arthur, used to his regular life alone, imagine taking a woman into one's house, letting her loose among one's habits, living with her all round the clock in the closest intimacy, on a basis of mere affection! One only married, surely, because one couldn't help oneself, because one had fallen in love, because if one didn't, if one didn't seize this strange, intoxicating opportunity of becoming young again at the touch of youth, of being magically made alive, of being restored to poetry, to beauty, to eagerness and excitement, to all the things one used to feel and for such melancholy ages had felt no longer, one would just crumple up slowly into what one had already begun to be,—a limp, boneless, indifferent old man.

Incredibly but genuinely, this girl he had met in Rome loved him. How refuse such a gift? It would be like turning one's back on life itself. Of course he was old for her, ridiculously old; but since she didn't think so, and only laughed when he talked about it, why should he mind? It was most extraordinary, a girl like that loving someone old enough to be her father, thought Arthur, who was ignorant; and just as extraordinary was it that he, of the age of the riper fathers, should have fallen as utterly in love as if he were twenty, he thought, continuing ignorant.

He couldn't help being rather proud of this—of knowing that he still was able to fall in love, and that he had; while as for his pride in her, it overwhelmed him. To be seen in streets and picture-galleries and tea-shops with this girl manifestly concentrated on him, drinking in all he said, and so pretty, so adorable, that everyone looked at her, made him glow with a kind of hot pride. No one had ever looked at Milly when he and she walked along King's Road in search of a taxi. Hers was the kind of charm—and he hadn't forgotten that she had been of much charm—which only becomes apparent on closer acquaintance. She had never been a woman to attract notice in a street. But a man, he discovered with much surprise, likes to be able to be proud of the woman he is walking with and taking care of, likes to know it isn't only himself who thinks his companion desirable, likes to see other men's eyes become interested as she passes, even though he may wish, in return, to fell them to the ground.

Foolish? Probably. But to have such feelings showed one was alive, and better to be foolish and alive than wise, indifferent and semi-dead. He had been wise, indifferent and semi-dead so long now, he recognized; resigned to dullness, petrifyingly comfortable. And this enchanting child had flashed into the gathering shadows, this shining thing of untouched innocence and eager worship—she thought him distinguished, bless her, she thought him brilliant—calling him forth, like some bright angel of the Resurrection, to renewed life, and youth, and love.

Refuse it? Refuse to listen to that clarion call from heaven? Who would?

No one, of course; no man in the world, he said to himself.

But then—what about Milly?

"That's it," thought Arthur, leaving off looking about the room for what wasn't in it, and turning a rueful and distressed gaze on Milly. "That's the difficulty."

§

She was standing quite still, her eyes on his face.

"Poor little thing," he thought, very sorry, asking himself what one did on these occasions, what one could do to avoid hurting. "It's awful if she's going to mind. I wish to God——"

But what he wished to God he couldn't have said; certainly not that this hadn't happened to him, this miracle of new life.

And to give himself courage he asked himself why, after all, should Milly want to keep him—supposing, that is, that she did? Illumined by his recent experiences, he saw now how poor and dull a lover he must have been for years past, what a habit he had got into, started perhaps by her ready sympathy and soothing ways, of talking about himself and his ailments—never about her and her ailments, and she must occasionally have had some and not felt well,—taking for granted that the things which interested him, his work, what he was reading, were also the only things which interested her, and if they hadn't been the only things, if she in her turn had begun to talk of interests of her own, he wouldn't have listened, he couldn't have listened, he would simply have been bored. Why should she want to be bothered any more with someone so unsatisfactory? Still, Ernest being dead, he was much afraid she——

He looked at her very ruefully; and she, looking at him, was thinking, "So this is it. This is what Fate has been keeping up its sleeve to hit me with."

§

As if it had been a dream, Milly remembered her walk from Victoria and how she had thought she was being let off lightly, and how she had wondered where expiation, or any opportunity for its practice, came in. Lots of opportunity now . . . lots of opportunity now . . . sing-songed in her head, swung through it backwards and forwards, idiotically.

It struck her that she must be making a silly sort of face; she could see by the expression on his that something had happened to hers, and she made a great effort to pull herself together. It would be indecent, she told herself, to wince, to let him see her wincing. And of what earthly use was it making them both wretched? One wretched person was enough. And he looked so unhappy, standing there in his poor, happy spats; he looked like—she gulped down a strange, gasping laugh—

some poor baby who has got into trouble with—yes, its mother.

"I think," she began, trying to smile—why won't one's mouth do anything but wrench itself into a ghastly grin just when one wants to look most natural? She was sure it must be a very ghastly grin; what else could it be with that ice in her heart?—"I think, Arthur," she nodded slowly, trying to smile naturally, "that you've fallen in love."

He was so much astonished that he could only stare.

"And that," she went on, "you want to get married."

He stared, his mouth open beneath his rather ragged moustache. Milly smiling? Looking quite pleased? Was it going to be all right after all?

"Isn't that what you've got to tell me?' she asked. "Arthur"— she laid her hand on his sleeve, but withdrew it quickly because of the way it was shaking— "isn't that the extraordinary thing? But why extraordinary?" And anxious only to wipe the troubled look from his face, she added softly, "Darling."

His thin face flushed. That word—it was all right, then. At the bottom of his heart he had been sure of it. Ernest or no Ernest, Milly wouldn't fail him, wouldn't ever do anything or want anything that wasn't sensible and kind.

"My dear!" he exclaimed, his face lit with relief and gratitude. "My dear, dearest friend—you don't mind?"

"Mind?" repeated Milly, insisting to her mouth that it must go on smiling, dragging it by force of will up at its corners. "Mind?" she said again, to hide the sob she was strangling.

She turned on herself ferociously, menacing the soft thing inside her which was trying to disgrace her.

"You've got to *behave*," she furiously cried out to it. "You're not to start whimpering. What's the good of you, anyhow, if you can't when you're in a tight corner *behave?*" And she held out her hands to him, smiling very hard, and said, "Why, it's *wonderful* news!"

Arthur drew a deep breath. Flushed up to his forehead, his face all gladness, he gripped the hands she was holding out, and said with profound conviction, "From the first you've been the best friend a man ever had."

"Have I?" said Milly. "I'm glad I've been something."

And then to cover it up—for it had slipped out, and certainly she had no intention of being bitter—she was going quickly to say something else, anything else, when he interrupted, holding her hands very tight, beaming down on her—Arthur, who hadn't done anything approaching beaming for years.

"How did you know?" he asked. "How on earth could you guess, Milly?"

"What—that you've fallen in love?"

She drew her hands out of his. "Oh, well—really, Arthur," she said; and achieving another smile, and bending her head while she blinked back the tears from her eyelashes, she pointed to his spats.

("I've cried enough," she said sternly to herself, blinking the tears back. "I've done nothing but cry lately. I won't any more. I will *not*." While as for that soft part of her which wanted to say useless, regrettable things, she wasn't going to let it; she simply was not going to let it. Oh, she knew the sorts of things it would say if she gave it a chance—the squashy, fool things with tears in them. Tears? She had had enough of tears. Or perhaps, even, betrayed by the ridiculous desperation of her situation, appeal. Appeal? Good God, no; for ever *no*.)

"Really, Arthur—" she said, her head bent, pointing, "your beautiful spats."

"Yes,"he said,looking down at them and smiling too,
an ashamed, boyish smile. "Yes. I hardly know why
I——"

He looked up from them to her, grateful, happy,
letting himself go to his relief, foolish, proud of being
foolish—in fact, fatuous. His young love admired these
spats. She had said, and it much diverted him, that she
always considered spats the mark of a gentleman. He
would like to tell Milly that; it would amuse her.
Couldn't he tell Milly that? Presently, perhaps——

And Milly thought, in bleak wonder: Arthur fatuous.
Her scholar, her serious, absorbed man.

With an absurd stab she remembered that he had
never worn spats for her. "He wasn't so old, though,
then," she said to herself in a flash of insight; adding, lit
by another flash, "nor was I as young as—as I expect
this one is."

"I suppose," said Arthur, rather sheepish and apologetic, but feeling very safe and comfortable now with
Milly, "the idea at the back of my mind must have been
to improve myself."

"I suppose," she said, able to smile again, "it was.
Though I don't admit you need any improving."

"Ah, Milly, you were always a flatterer," he said;
and he thought with gratitude how simple it was being
after all, and how perfectly naturally everything was
panning out, as Sylvy—his young love's name was
Sylvia—was so fond of saying. He even wouldn't now
mind sitting on the divan with Milly, just as two old
friends, and nothing in it, while he told her all about
what had happened—well, not quite all, perhaps, but
the main features. And Milly was astonished at the ease
with which she was able to take him in, how he saw
nothing, how completely satisfied he was at once, without the least further search or doubt that all was well

and he free to be happy. But at this moment he was only wanting to be taken in; if he were not able to believe, if she could not do him this last service of lies, how miserable he would be—and no good done to anybody. Also, he was in love; no good shrinking away from the words; and a person in love, as she well knew, doesn't look very attentively at other people.

"But, Milly," he said, after all not quite so blind, so satisfied, as she had just been thinking, and insisting on taking her hands again, "why do you look so pale? I've never seen you so pale, dear."

"Oh, that's because of Ernest. And—and everything," she reassured him quickly.

"My God, yes—of course," exclaimed Arthur, remembering Ernest. For the last few minutes he had quite overlooked him. Poor fellow. At that moment Arthur was truly sorry for anyone who was dead. Rough luck indeed to be out of a world brimming with the most gorgeous miracles.

"It must have been terrible, dear," he said, subduing his voice to the proper concern. "What a time you must have had, you poor little thing. You must tell me about it—" for decency demanded that before he told her his own happy story she should tell him her sad one.

Yet not sad really, he thought, except for Ernest; not sad for Milly, once she had got over the first inevitable shock of death. Because Ernest, poor fellow—and probably because he couldn't help it, Arthur thought, indulgent in his happiness to the whole world—had been a trying husband, and now Milly would be free, besides having all his money to do what she liked with. A desirable position. She would see how desirable presently. But meanwhile he must certainly comfort her. . . .

"Tell me about it, dear," he said, carefully damping

the happiness out of his voice; and again she was what
he knew she was, to be relied on utterly for understanding and common sense, and, guessing how difficult it
would be for him that day to tune himself down to
commiseration, she wouldn't let him, but declared she
had had enough of sadness, and wanted now to talk of
happy things.

"I'll make tea," said Milly, to whom a way of at least
relaxing for a few minutes while she had her back to
him over there in the corner, of not having, for a moment, to smile, had occurred—"I'll make tea while you
tell me. I haven't had any lunch, and I——"

"No lunch, Milly?" exclaimed Arthur, almost as
much shocked at this as he had been by her widow's
dress—no, that is an exaggeration; but he was shocked.
"How came you to have no lunch?"

"I think I forgot," she said, preparing to withdraw to
the corner where the kettle was.

Arthur, however, limped off to it himself. "You sit
down," he said, waving her towards the divan. "I'll
make it. You shall have it at once. At once. No wonder
you look like a ghost. So wrong of you, dear," he went
on, busily filling the kettle, dusting the cups with his
handkerchief, shaking biscuits out of an ancient tin,
amazingly active for one who had long been torpid,
"so very wrong of you, at a time when you need all your
strength. Now where have those matches got to?
Where on *earth* have those matches got to?"

He was just what he had been ten years ago, she
thought, dropping on to the divan, alive, eager, making
tea for her, excited and happy, returned, as he had then
returned, for even ten years ago he had been middle-
aged, to youth, to boyishness. And watching him, she
said to herself, "Only love does this for a man. Last
time it was love for me. Now——"

She shut her eyes, her head leaning back on the cushions, her mouth relaxed. Darkness was in her heart; dreadful questions crept about her mind—what next? where? how? And her body seemed nothing but deadly, leaden fatigue.

"Milly," said Arthur, hunting, "there were matches here last time, weren't there? Didn't we have tea?"

"I expect they're on the shelf," she said without moving, her hands limp by her side, her eyes shut. "Why don't you let me do that?"

"Why should you?" Arthur answered, lighting the spirit lamp, measuring out tea—ready to do everything for her, she thought, except love her. Love her? How could he love her if he didn't?

"You know," said Arthur, busy and making a great clattering, "I always made our tea"—and this was so remote from the truth that Milly smiled almost naturally.

"Not always," she said.

"Well, very often," insisted Arthur.

§

The tea was made, and they both sat on the divan— Milly at one end, propped against cushions, Arthur at the other, rather awkward on the low edge, for divans are uncomfortable things unless one gives oneself up to them. Between them, like Siegfried's sword, was the plate of biscuits.

Now, he thought, he would begin and tell her all about it. But he didn't like to, somehow, unless she helped him to start. So he waited, restraining his eagerness, while she drank her tea.

"You're to eat every one of these," he said, pointing to the biscuits.

"I couldn't," said Milly, shaking her head. Even the

tea made her feel as if she might be sick, while as for those biscuits——

‹ "They do look rather nasty," said Arthur, peering at them. "Mouldy, aren't they?"

"I think they've been here for years," said Milly. "Like us," she added, smiling at him.

"Yes—it has been a long time, hasn't it?" said Arthur, clasping his thin hands round his even thinner knees, and dying to begin his story. "But it was nice, dear, wasn't it? You're not sorry?"

"I think it was very nice," said Milly pleasantly.

"And after all," said Arthur, "life has to go on. If old things didn't come to an end new ones couldn't begin."

"I hope, Arthur dear," said Milly, smiling across the biscuits at him, "it's not me you're describing as an old thing?"

"You, Milly? My dear, I was thinking of epochs," he said; but, looking at her as she sat against the cushions, taking up a good deal of the divan—she sloped it down, and the plate of biscuits kept on sliding towards her—he thought that compared to some people she certainly wasn't young, poor Milly. Still, why should she be young, and why should he call her poor Milly? She hadn't, he was sure, the least wish to be young again, or anything but what she was—a dear, good woman, a staunch friend to whom one could always turn in moments of need. While as for being poor, her situation, with Ernest removed, was about as agreeable as he could think of. Rich and free and a great dear, bound to be surrounded by people devoted to her—what could be more satisfactory, more generally enviable? Yet—poor Milly. Perhaps it was all that black stuff she was wrapped up in. Such a heap of black she looked piled up on the divan, and on top of it a little round, white, puffy face. . . .

And suddenly she was blotted out by a vision shooting up before his eyes like a spray of light—Sylvy, his young love, in a blue frock as he last saw her, with the sunshine on her bright hair, so slender that she would almost, he had told her, be able to be pulled through her own wedding-ring.

He stared at Milly without seeing her. On his face was the same expression that she had seen a few minutes before, when he told her something had happened to him that doesn't happen once in a life-time pride, wonder, extreme tenderness; and Milly recognizing it, and remembering how it had once been there for her, thought, "Why should I stay here and be tortured? I won't. I'll go. I'll get away—anywhere——"

But the only result of her sudden movement to get off the very low divan was that she broke her cup. It shook off its saucer, and fell on the bare boards, and broke, and made a pool of tea.

"There," said Arthur, picking up the bits and wiping away the pool with his handkerchief, "now we've only got one left."

"I'm so sorry. But we don't want them any more, do we?" said Milly, sitting still again, caught, obliged to stop where she was and listen. And wasn't it the only thing to do, to listen, to hear him out, if she were not to betray what she was determined never to betray, and show herself to him as one needing pity? Pity! Poor Arthur. How miserable he would be, and she herself how shameful—clinging, and calling out.

She set her teeth, and sat quiet. In these cases, she was dead sure, all that was left to be done by the one who minded was to pretend that she—surely most often a she—didn't mind; and to pretend so well that she was entirely believed.

"That's true," said Arthur. "Shall I break the other one, so that no one else will ever be able to drink out of it?"

"How romantic," smiled Milly.

"Well, I feel romantic," said Arthur. "We've been happy here, after all."

"Very," said Milly.

"Though I do think," he went on, remembering how for years he had held her down among the ruins of Greece and Rome—to Sylvia he hadn't so much as mentioned them; with her he was reading Keats and Shelley—"I do think I must have bored you terribly."

"Only sometimes," she smiled.

"The fact is, I get so much wrapped up in what interests me," he said apologetically, "and I'm afraid when I get hold of a hobby I ride the wretched thing to death."

"With me on the pillion," she said. "But I liked it," she added quickly, smiling. "And it was very educational."

"Educational! I don't know that——"

He broke off and got up, carrying the fragments of the cup to the sink.

"Shall I really break the other one?" he asked, over his shoulder.

"The other what?"

"Cup."

"No. Take it to Oxford with you as a memento. A Present from Chelsea for a Good Boy." And Milly, now that he wasn't looking, leaned her head back on the cushions again, and whispered to herself, "Oh, I'm tired, tired—oh, I want to go home—oh, why can't I go home. . . ."

"Milly," said Arthur, his back to her, his long thin

fingers piling the broken bits of cup one on top of each other in the sink, "tell me frankly—do you think me a fool?"

"Why, dear?" she asked, her eyes shut. "For wanting to break the other cup?"

"No. For marrying."

"Dear Arthur—why should you not?"

With a movement of his hand he scattered the little pile he had made, and came back and stood before her.

"She's only nineteen," he said, a sort of ashamedness struggling with pride and wonder on his face; and Milly looking up at him thought, "What can possibly be younger than the not young, when for any reason they return to being young?"

She felt very old, and dismally, wretchedly lonely. "That's just the right age for you," she said gently, holding out her hand.

"You don't think so really, of course."

She sighed. These efforts . . . oh, it was more than . . .

"But I do, Arthur," she said. "Won't you sit down and—tell me about it?"

"It seems so——" he touched her crape sleeve, and hesitated. "It does seem rather—with this just having happened to you——"

"Oh, but please," said Milly.

"You know, if I had had an idea——"

"But you hadn't. Sit down and tell me."

"If I had had an idea," he persisted, his hand on her sleeve, wanting to say the right thing, the kind, decent thing.

But he couldn't. He found he couldn't pretend that Ernest's death would have made a difference if he had known it, because he knew it wouldn't have—not once he had met Sylvia.

"Please——" begged Milly. "Won't you sit down?"

§

Now Arthur was a humane man, and would not willingly have hurt anybody, least of all Milly, his one really close friend, his one comfort during otherwise lonely years; and therefore, beginning his story, he picked his way carefully among words. But pick as he might, small ecstasies burst through, and little jabs of happiness. He did his best to present Sylvy—

"Sylvy?"

"Yes. Her name is Sylvia, but I—her mother calls her Sylvy."

"Oh."

—he did his best to present Sylvy in a sober light, as a good, intelligent girl, with a most sensible mother, who would make an excellent wife, he thought, being intelligent and brought up carefully by a most sensible mother—he dwelt with insistence on the sensible mother, obscurely feeling that her sensibleness made the whole thing sensible—besides becoming less young, of course, every day, and also she would be a good mistress, he believed, for his house, which really was, as Milly had seen for herself, a good deal more than he could manage alone; yet, try as he would to be thus sober—and he tried so hard that he perspired—Sylvy danced and laughed and sparkled through his words like the thing of light she indeed was, and Milly saw her dancing, heard her laughing, and suffered.

"Absurd I am—*absurd* I am," she told herself, doing her best not to suffer. "I, at my age, still wanting to stick. Is it possible? Is it credible? Why can't I give him up nicely—really nicely, not just pretending? I've had him for ten years, and I've often and often been disappointed in him, and secretly impatient, and not liked his having all those colds. But then——"

She stared at the thought an instant, before turning her mind away from it. It was, *He's all I've got.*

Faintly she said, noticing that he had stopped, "Go on, Arthur——"

"Aren't you well, dear?" he asked, struck by her whiteness.

"Yes, I'm quite well," said Milly. "Go on. She sounds—" she managed to smile naturally enough to satisfy him—"your little girl sounds so—so nice."

Nice. He liked that adjective. It exactly described the impression he wished to produce of a good girl, who would make a good wife, and no nonsense about the marriage, just reason and sense.

He held out his hand across the plate of biscuits. She put hers into it, still smiling.

"You know," he said, for after all it was true, "for years I wanted to marry *you.*"

"I know," she answered, giving his hand a friendly little squeeze before drawing away her own. "And we weren't able to. Go on."

Arthur went on; and inevitably, as he proceeded, his words grew warmer, grew less able to hide his pride and amazement that this should have happened to him. He did try. He thought he was succeeding, really doing it very well, keeping as much to facts as possible; but the facts themselves were so marvellous, glowing so hotly that his face was flushed as red by them as if he were toasting it at some great fire. Sylvy—that child—loving him, bringing him back to life. . . . He, modest man, couldn't get over it. If Milly only knew how wonderful she was! But of course he didn't say this; he was most careful, most tactful; eliminating, so he thought, every trace of excitement.

Leaning forward on his elbow closer to the barrier of biscuits, he kept to the safer facts, such as his stock blindness, and how her mother positively had at last to take him in hand and make him see what everybody else in the pension had long ago seen, and how Sylvy herself had told him afterwards that she had been quite ashamed of—well, of liking someone who never even looked at her. But how natural that was. Didn't Milly think it natural that he should never have dreamed——?

"Very natural," agreed Milly; and asked herself whether, when men were older, they often became like this. Or was it only Arthur, bewitched, caught in a spell, caught perhaps—who knew?—by the mother?

"Is there a father?" she asked.

Her father, Arthur explained, was dead; and her mother, left a widow with a young family on her hands and the eldest only nineteen, was of remarkable courage and resource. She was determined, she had told him, to do her very best for them whatever it might cost her of self-denial, giving them every possible advantage, however much she herself had to do without things; and one of the advantages she considered indispensable was educational travel in foreign countries—which was how she came to be in Rome with her eldest daughter, and, miraculously, in the same pension as himself.

He made friends with her before he even saw her daughter, though for a whole week the child had actually been sitting opposite him at every meal. Didn't Milly think that most extraordinary?

"But you saw her mother, for you said you made friends with her."

No, Arthur explained, he hadn't seen her mother either, till she came up and spoke to him. Then he saw her, of course. He wasn't much good at seeing, as Milly knew, if he happened to be thinking of other things. She, kindly soul, noticing that he was always alone at meals, made friends with him. She had read in some paper of his appointment as Senior Tutor of Zebedee, and asked him if he were the same Arthur Oswestry, and was much interested, because one of her nephews was there.

They soon were friends. She told him she was having a pretty stiff struggle to keep things going, and it was a great comfort and relief to her, she frankly confessed after it had all happened, to know that her eldest child, at any rate, was safely provided for.

"I gather, then," said Milly, " that they are poor."

"They are. Completely so," said Arthur.

"Do you mean really completely? Have they only got two and eightpence in their bag?"

"I don't know about two and eightpence," said Arthur with a slight impatience, for the question seemed irrelevant, and as if Milly were not listening to him with real seriousness, "but they haven't much. I expect it would seem nothing at all to you. Even to me—Mrs. Finch-Dawson told me, of course, how they stood—yes, that's their name, Finch-Dawson—it seems very little. How the poor soul has managed at all is a mystery. And that child always so prettily dressed——"

He broke off, he saw it, he gazed at it, the enchanting figure, the dear, delicious blue-frocked figure, with the sun shining on its bright hair. . . .

Milly made a small movement, and then sat still again.

"When do you suppose——" she said, "when do you think of being——"

"Married?" said Arthur.

She nodded.

"Well——"

He cleared his throat, and became carefully matter of fact, while before his eyes quivered bliss.

"Well,—as the house is all ready, and badly needs

someone to look after it, we thought, her mother and myself—and Sylvy thought too—that it ought to be—well, rather soon, perhaps."

There was no hurry, of course, he went on, but that was what they rather thought. He was only just back, as Milly knew, so that no actual decision had as yet been taken. They had all travelled home together, and to-morrow her mother—and Sylvy too—were coming to Oxford to spend the day with him and have a thorough look round. Fortunately—they were much pleased with what he had told them of the house, and Sylvy was especially pleased about the garden and the apple-tree, and said—he turned his face away, because he felt it was betraying too great a happiness—she would do all her sewing there, she being, he was glad to say, a properly brought up young woman, and good at that sort of thing. It was nice to think, he continued, of all those rooms going to be filled, and the place soon cheerful with children's voices——

"Children?" echoed Milly, faintly.

"She has dozens of small brothers and sisters," said Arthur, reddening, turning to her rebukingly, shocked by what she was evidently supposing, and that she should think him capable of such execrable taste; and he hurried on, with a slight feeling of estrangement from her, of disappointment, to praise the behaviour of these children, so well brought up, those he had seen, and so very good-looking. Their looks, indeed, were unusual—the mother's too; while as for Sylvy——

He stopped. He wished he could tell Milly. He wished he could let himself go to the one person he was accustomed to talk freely to, and who always understood and sympathized, about the sweet beauty of his young love.

Couldn't he? Damn tact, thought Arthur, glancing

at Milly to see if there were any encouragement in her face for him to go on. But on looking at her he was seized with compunction. "I'm tiring you," he said, struck a second time by her extreme whiteness, her drooping attitude of evident fatigue.

She sat up quickly, and began smoothing her hair. "Oh, no," she said. "But I do think perhaps——" she looked round vaguely—"I'm afraid I ought to be going."

"It's only half-past five, dear," he said, jerking up his wrist watch, "and we never leave before six. But of course if you——"

"I really think I ought to go, Arthur," said Milly, who could bear no more. Why should she stay there being tortured? He was absolutely happy, completely secure and satisfied that she was pleased about it all. Helped by his readiness to believe, she had done her part very well. But she had done it. It was finished. Let her go.

She made definite movements towards the edge of the divan. But here was a difficulty: it was so low that she never could get up off it unless he helped her, and it was his habit to take her by both hands, and, with a great pull, pull her on to her feet.

The impetus invariably sent her straight into his arms, and for some reason the sudden jerk to his breast had always amused them. It was so sudden that she arrived each time with an effect of surprise; and then they laughed, and, laughing, kissed.

The laughter, it is true, had long become a smile, and the kissing absent-minded on his part, or as often as not just an affectionate pat; but, as she couldn't get off the divan unless he pulled her, pull her he still did, and the pull, which had to be a hard one, inevitably landed her against his breast.

She glanced at him. Had he forgotten she couldn't move unless he helped?

He was staring straight in front of him, his elbow on
his knee, his fingers absently tugging at the ends of his
straggly moustache. In spite of his sunburn and his new
tie and his spats, he looked to her after all what he was;
a delicate elderly man, thin of cheek, stooping of
shoulder; and his sudden return to youth and its excitement only made him seem more brittle, more frail.

"Oh, I hope she will always love him, always be kind
to him," thought Milly, who had loved him so much.

He was staring, Milly knew, at Sylvy, and she herself
had vanished, and the room and the present moment
had vanished, in dreams of happiness. If she could
have got up off that divan alone and crept away he
wouldn't notice, she thought, he would go on sitting
there, lost in dreams; but she couldn't move, not
decently, without his help. It would be possible, she
supposed, by rolling off on to the floor, though she had
never tried it, and scrambling to her knees, somehow to
get up, but what a spectacle! And he, jarred out of his
dreaming by these strange convulsions, looking on in
astonishment. . . .

Milly shuddered away from the picture. "I'm afraid,
Arthur," she said—at her voice he came to actuality
with a start—"you'll have to—do you mind helping me
off this wretched thing?"

He got up at once. Some crumbs of biscuit, he saw,
were on his trousers, and he briskly brushed them off
before holding out his hands.

"Not too quickly," she said, at all costs wishing to
avoid that sudden fling against his breast.

Arthur, however, was quite awake again now, and
he remembered perfectly what had been the invariable
finish to the pulling up. He hadn't thought of it when
he told Milly to sit on the divan while he made tea; he
had forgotten the peculiar difficulties of that seat for a

person of her weight and figure and present age, and he was as anxious as she was to get her off it decorously, and keep her, at the end, at arm's length.

Slowly, therefore, and with caution, he drew her to her feet. It was much more difficult to draw her up slowly than to do it with a heave and a rush, and the veins stood out on his forehead. Milly really was extraordinarily heavy, he thought, for somebody so short; at one moment her weight very nearly pulled him off his balance, and he was within an ace of toppling forward on to the divan in a supremely undignified and awkward mix-up. But he just managed not to; and very red, and breathing rather hard, he got her safely on to her feet.

For an instant they stood looking at each other, he panting, she very pale. Then she thanked him with a polite smile, and went to fetch her bonnet from the table where she had laid it. The monstrous thing, when he had finished wiping his forehead and turned and saw it eclipsing her, her hair disappeared inside it and nothing but a bald white face and two heavy eyes to be seen, brought home to him once again what he had kept on losing sight of in the absorption of his own affairs—the fact that Milly was in trouble.

"My dear," he said, his eyes suddenly worried, "I hate to think of all you must have been through while I was so unaware and happy."

"Dear Arthur—you mustn't," said Milly.

"But I do. And I'm afraid, till you get straight and all the unavoidable business part of it settled, you've a dreary time ahead of you. But you *will* get straight, dear. It will come right. And they've always been very kind to you, haven't they, those Botts?"

"Very kind," said Milly.

"I wish I could help you through it," he said, looking

down at her with kind, troubled eyes. "But I'm afraid"
—he smiled—"our past rather disqualifies me from
appearing among the Botts. Milly——" he stopped
short, struck by a sudden thought, and took her hand.

"What, Arthur? Tell me quick, because really I
can't stay any longer."

"Yes, of course—you must have so many things to
see to, poor little thing. But, dear, you don't mind——"

"Oh, I've *told* you I don't mind!" she interrupted,
trying to pull her hand away. "And that I'm pleased,
I'm glad. Let me go, Arthur——"

"I'm not thinking of the present," he said. "What
has occurred to me is that perhaps you mind our past."

"Mind our past?" she repeated.

"And may have thought it needs—rectifying."

She could only repeat, "Rectifying?"

"I don't know," said Arthur, his face much troubled,
"because I never thought of it as wrong. But I'm not
so sure that you didn't. At the beginning I know you
did. You don't still think so, do you, Milly? You see,
don't you, that we only didn't marry because we
couldn't? You're not worried about it, dear, are you?"

She assured him with earnestness that she wasn't.
"I long ago got over all my prejudices, dear Arthur,"
she assured him. "And one of us, at any rate, is going
to marry and settle down respectably," she added,
smiling.

But he still stared down at her, his forehead puckered.
Was that true, he wondered?

"Anyhow, you're well off," he said, "and won't have
to bother about money. Really, dear, it's a great comfort to know that—the very greatest comfort. Good
God, how anxious and distressed I should be about you
if it weren't so!"

"Darling Arthur, you needn't be," said Milly; and

instinctively she put up her free hand to smooth away the puckers from his forehead. She had always done this when he had been worried about anything; she couldn't bear to see him troubled.

But Sylvy flashed between them, and Arthur drew back.

So did Milly. "Oh, I'm sorry——" she said quickly, her hand dropping at her side.

"It's only——" began Arthur, feeling a fool; but really he couldn't endure anything approaching a caress from anybody just then, except his betrothed. A ferocious chastity had come upon him. He was Sylvy's. Such as he was she wanted him, and such as he was he was altogether hers.

"I must go," said Milly, terribly ashamed, desperately wounded, looking round for her bag.

She picked it up from the table, and went towards the door.

"I'm coming with you to the station," said Arthur, following her. "I'll see you off. We needn't mind being seen together, now that poor Ernest——"

"Oh, but now there's—Sylvia," said Milly, pausing a moment, before getting the name out.

So there was. Arthur paused too, his hat and stick in his hand, his eyes troubled again as he stared at her. It hadn't occurred to him that Milly would be someone he couldn't well explain to Sylvy. To her mother, perhaps, no, even to her mother he couldn't explain Milly—not well, that is. Sylvy, dear innocent, wouldn't understand, but her mother would perfectly understand; and suppose, she, being one of these unworldly women, suppose she said that he was not, then, a fit husband for her daughter? Why, if she said that, thought Arthur, he was sure he would give up, immediately grow old, and die.

"Yes," he said, staring at Milly, and seeing her in a new light, the light Sylvia's mother would probably see her in, "that's true. I'm sorry, Milly."

Perhaps after all then she wouldn't, as he had hoped, be able later on to become Sylvia's friend; perhaps after all it would be too difficult. He hadn't thought the thing out properly. It might mean having to pretend to Sylvy. And most clear in his mind was it that he would never, please God, pretend to Sylvy.

He stared at Milly, very sorry. It was a pity. They ought to have gone on being dear friends, the other thing forgotten—as indeed he had forgotten it, hardly able now to believe it had ever existed, so completely was it gone. Civilized people, thought Arthur, should not make such a fuss over these things. Civilized people, he was sure, didn't. But there was that about Mrs. Finch-Dawson which convinced him he would find her, on subjects such as these, incompletely civilized. Perhaps naturally so, with a large young family depending on her for safety, and five of them girls. Naturally, however, or not, it was the one aspect of that sensible woman which Arthur found less excellent. Women— older women—were frequently, he feared, retarders of civilization. Why should not people be present friends, even if they had been—surely the more that they had been—past lovers? He didn't know many women, it was true, but he did know Mrs. Finch-Dawson; and she, in her certain attitude towards Milly, if Milly were explained to her, was undoubtedly a retarder.

All this passed through his mind, as in silence he stared at Milly. Was he not going to see her again, then? Was she departing, poor little black thing, to her bothers, and he not know any more what was happening to her?

"You'll write, dear, won't you, if you want anything —if I can be of the least——"

"We never did write."

"Because of Ernest. But now——"

"Now we can't because of—Sylvia."

"Do you mean to say," cried Arthur, addressing the universe generally, "that because a man was fond once of a woman he must never——"

"Oh, Arthur!" gasped Milly, wincing at the dreadful word "once."

Tremblingly she pulled her veil down to hide her face. "What's the good of talking?" she said. "What's the *use?* I must go. Good-bye. No, don't bother—I can open it——"

And she pushed the curtain aside, opened the street door, and with a shaky, "Bless you," was gone.

He stood a moment without moving, his shoulders drooping, his hat and stick in his hand, looking at the curtain still swaying from the pull Milly had given it.

It was a devil of a business after all, this breaking off, this finishing. And no sense in it.

:(X):*

HURRYING away from the studio for ever, Milly turned into King's Road and waited at the nearest stopping-place for the omnibus which went to Victoria. She was going back to Titford, to face the Botts.

Before she got to the corner of the street she knew it, lashed into clarity of vision, illuminated by it into the farthermost recesses of her consciousness. Gone now definitely out of Arthur's life, separated from him as completely, and far more dreadfully, than if he had been dead, her exhausted emotions, unable to react any more, dropped into numbness, and her mind was whipped free of that foolish, long-drawn-out dream of being loved, and of trusting, and of supposing she mattered.

She didn't matter. Accept it, accept it, she said to herself. She was of no consequence whatever to anybody; there was no one now in the whole world who would care if she were happy or unhappy, ill or not ill, alive or dead. If she were run over at that moment and killed, as Ernest had been killed, who would mind? The Botts would be relieved; and Arthur, after saying, and meaning, "Poor Milly," would proceed with his happiness. Perhaps Aggie—but Aggie was so far away. Besides, why pretend? Aggie might well be relieved too—probably would be, set free from having to be grateful because of the money, rid for good of an immoral sister.

Well, it was a detached condition. She sat in the corner of the omnibus, being swayed and heaved towards

Victoria, bleakly considering it, this condition swept clear of love—also swept clear of love's illusions, the most persistent and comforting of which for ten years had been the conviction that there was someone thinking often of her, missing her, counting the hours till he saw her again. And, passed beyond feeling, become merely a brain perceiving, Milly realized without emotion that Arthur hadn't done any of these things, not after the first weeks,—neither thought of her often, nor missed her, nor counted hours.

Incurable romantics, women were, she reflected dispassionately, forced to see clearly by the sheer pressure of her desolation; incurable romantics, eternally yapping after love, and more love, and yet more love. But only after love as they considered it ought to be, and were sure that somewhere, if they could but hit on it, it was. Naturally they never did hit on it. The man wasn't born who could go on satisfying them for ever. Just at first he outdid them, because in everything, if he were sufficiently moved, he could always outdo a woman equally moved; but it couldn't be kept up, not at that pitch. And the trouble with women, she thought, relentlessly pursuing her frigid dissections, was that they insisted it should be kept up, and exactly at that pitch, and, when it wasn't, they stuffed out what was left of it with their own illusions, and then, some day, there they were—"Like me," she thought; though it didn't seem to concern her.

Nothing seemed to concern her. She regarded her being, as she put it, there, impartially. One had to be somewhere. If women chose to go in for love-making outside marriage, as she had chosen, sooner or later they would be where she was then—going away from nothing, going towards nothing, being carried along in some sort of dreary vehicle like this omnibus, shut up with strangers who all had left their lovers for the last time, or were going to leave them on some future day, shrugging their disillusioned shoulders, their brains full of icy light.

"Rather horrible," she reflected, critically. But she didn't mind its being horrible; she wasn't touched; it didn't seem to concern her.

Clearly the crowning cowardice of her life had been that shameful flight from the Botts. Whatever they had thought of her, and said to her, and done to her, she ought to have stayed and submitted. Dignity, and repentance for her sin, both demanded it. And so did ordinary humanity; for to run away like that, leaving her humiliated relations to find out from servants that she had gone, stabbing the family, as she well knew, in its most sensitive spot, was plainly a cruelly cowardly thing to have done. It took from the Botts their last doubt, supposing they had had one, of her guilt and of the justice of Ernest's Will; it definitely branded her. Well, she was going to undo as much of that as she could. It was true that she was driven to go back to them, with only two and eightpence in her bag, but if she had had her thousand pounds she still now would have gone, and said, "Here I am. I've been wicked and disgraced you, and I'm sorry. Tell me what you wish me to do, what is the best thing for you that I should do, and I'll do it." And whatever music the Botts should see fit to make she would face it, however furiously it crashed about her ears she wouldn't shrink away.

At least she would take her punishment standing up —only, strangely, it seemed no longer to need courage, the facing of the Botts, the taking of her punishment; this too didn't seem to concern her. She would be there, her body would be, and they would pour out their indignation and contempt, and she wouldn't feel it. It

was her mind which recognized the need for making
good, for decency and an end of lies; her heart, stunned
unconscious, was indifferent. What did it matter? In
Titford with the Botts, working out her punishment, or
away from Titford and the Botts, somewhere alone and
forgotten, there would be the same dead routine of life
to be gone through each day, the waking up, the dressing, the feeding, the sitting, the walking, the undressing,
the sleeping—over and over again, buttoning only to
unbutton, tying only to untie, putting in hairpins only
to pull them out, and everywhere, wherever she was,
she would be there, the ageing fool. "And," thought
Milly, the corners of her mouth for the first time in her
life cynical——

"Didn't you say Victoria, mum? 'Ere we are," interrupted the conductor.

"Oh, thank you."

She got out.

"—and," she continued, when she was out, "all this
is evidently the sort of thing a woman thinks when her
man has thrown her over. She should, of course, be
ashamed of herself, and she isn't. She should give herself
a shake and start afresh, and she can't. One single man,
one Arthur, blotting out hope—really amazing, really
quite contemptible," thought Milly. Could idiocy go
farther? An Arthur, as against the whole of life. Yet it
was what happened to women, to all that immense long
category of fools who let themselves become absorbed
in some particular person, betrayed by their maternal
instincts, those instincts which dressed themselves up
in so many tender and lively names, while all the time
they were ruthlessly intent on being nothing less to the
object they had fastened on than God Almighty—dis-
pensers, that is, of happiness, insisters on dependence,
absorbers of freedom.

She crossed the street.

Deep in thought, she was all but run over. What she was thinking, her mind turning away from Arthur and everything to do with him, was that at least she wouldn't be a burden on the Botts, because in the house in Mandeville Park Road there were jewels, as well as fur and laces, legitimately hers, either given her by Ernest, or bought by her out of her ample allowance, before Arthur was ever heard of; and these she would sell, and on the proceeds, after she had stayed in Titford long enough to stop its tongues, and when and if the Botts were willing to let her go, she would withdraw and live frugally somewhere till she had found something to do. Surely there was something in the world that she could do? If she took lessons? If she learned? "It's a pity," thought Milly bleakly, arrived at the opposite pavement and unaware how narrowly she had missed extinction, "that one doesn't die in time."

She went into the station.

The omnibus fare had been twopence, and the first-class ticket to Titford would, she knew, be one and threepence—she couldn't, returning, travel third class as she had done escaping, for now she had once more to consider the Botts,—so she would have enough left out of her two and eightpence to take a taxi from the station to Mandeville Park Road. Not yet was she composed enough to meet people she knew in the streets of Titford, and she was, besides, so tired that she felt she would never get there at all unless she drove. Silence; darkness; to be alone;—these were what she would best like to find waiting for her. But whatever the day still held she wouldn't try to avoid it, and should she find the house full of Botts she would meet them calmly, and should she find it empty of servants, they having either left or gone off for the evening enjoying themselves, it wouldn't trouble her. Her latch-key was still in her bag, and she would let herself in and put herself to bed in the bedroom she had been so much frightened of, and which was, after all, only a bedroom like any other —a place to rest in, and forget the yesterdays, and not think of the to-morrows.

She took her ticket.

In the chill light of the common sense which had replaced every other emotion, it was with contempt that she remembered how she had imagined that bedroom haunted by Ernest's malevolent eyes. Panic does queer things to one's brain, she thought, coldly wondering at her own folly. Ernest had no further power. He had vanished, and was nothing now but a rather—not very, "Don't let's pretend," thought Milly—pitiful memory, a memory of lost opportunities, of all the missed occasions on which she might, by keeping straight, have avoided goading him into baseness. She would sleep in that room as well as in another. It would make no difference to her. Sleep. How blessed. Oh, how profoundly blessed. If only it were time, already, to sleep. . . .

She emerged from the booking-office; and, proceeding in the direction of the platform the Titford train started from, immediately ran into George Bott.

§

"Ran into" is hardly the right expression, for both were walking so slowly that it might be said they sauntered into each other. Both knew there was no hurry, the train not starting till six thirty-five, and both were reluctant to go on to the platform before they need, because neither wished to meet, unnecessarily, any of those numerous business men and their wives who lived in Titford, might return by this train, and were accus-

tomed to think highly of the Botts. Milly, if asked,
would have said that she preferred never to see anyone
who had ever thought highly of her again; while as for
George, he and his family were just then particularly
desirous of keeping themselves to themselves.

"Good God!" ejaculated George, when he saw who it
was that he had all but walked into, stopping dead,
and staring at her through his horn-rimmed spectacles.

For two and a half days now, he and the rest of his
family had been concentrating on presenting a united
front to the world. It was a front of almost unnatural
composure; and behind it, since the reading of Ernest's
Will, and, more fiercely, since the discovery of Milly's
flight, raged a particular desire to keep themselves to
themselves. At first Titford, sympathetically considering
the bereaved family, took it for granted that it should be
serious, that it should avoid contacts, that it should be
of few words when it was met in railway carriages, during the first days, almost the first hours, after the burial
of a brother. Except when proceeding on their lawful
occasions, no Botts were anywhere to be seen; and this,
too, Titford sympathetically took for granted. But, it
presently having become known through the usual
channels—tradespeople calling for orders which couldn't
be given—that Mrs. Ernest, the newly-made widow,
had disappeared, and disappeared without either having been seen disappearing or any word left as to her
return, Titford, in spite of the statuesque composure of
the Botts, began to ask itself what could have happened;
and they, waiting in a condition of raw suspense for
this inevitable moment, were at once made aware, by
unmistakable small signs, that it was upon them.

In anxious conclave the unhappy family had considered measures for staving it off. Meeting together on
each of the painful evenings, they had done their best

to think out steps which might yet be taken to shield Milly, and therefore themselves, from scandal and disgrace. During Wednesday, the day of her disappearance, they did succeed in persuading the bewildered and half-rebellious staff at Mandeville Park Road that their mistress had gone up to town on business, and would be back to dinner—and they succeeded because there were Botts, that day, who themselves believed it. It was not to be expected, Fred Bott told the crowding servants,—he was the first to recover his presence of mind when he and Alec and Bertie called that morning to inform Milly of the plans they had made for her welfare, and were faced by a house in upheaval—it was not to be expected, he said, that a lady in the first grief of so sudden a widowhood should remember to give orders or leave messages; and the maids, calmed by the authoritativeness of him who was the wealthiest of the brothers, besides having discovered for themselves that their mistress had taken no luggage with her, were ready, though still puzzled, to believe these words of Mr. Fred's, and settled down to their usual duties, and tidied the house, and made preparations for the evening's dinner.

To that dinner Milly never came; and Alec Bott, telephoning at nine o'clock—the family had decided that he, as the eldest, should do the telephoning, it being desirable to avoid indiscriminate and agitated calls,—received the news that she had never come with such evident consternation, with such an entire inability to conceal his amazement and alarm, that the maid at the other end hastened to inform her fellow-servants of the way the old boy—thus she spoke of him—had got the wind up. And the next day, when Alec's wife went round with her suit-case directly after breakfast, prepared, according to the latest hasty decision of the shattered family, to stay in the house till something more definite could be arranged, they met her in a body, demanding a month's wages and their immediate departure.

Fred had had to be telephoned for. It had needed all his authority and conciliatoriness to induce them to stay. Lightly he touched on the legal aspect of their leaving like this—but very lightly, because he saw they were in no mood to be cowed. Insolence trembled visibly on the cook's lips. He felt that they had somehow scented the approach of scandal, and it revolted him, it simply revolted Fred, to know that one of his family, a Bott by name if not by blood, and certainly always treated kindly and affectionately, had put herself in a position, and accordingly the family as well, in which servants could sniff.

Sniffing servants. A nice thing to be exposed to. They had been listening at the door, he presumed, and they had heard that confounded Will read, and no doubt the ensuing family argument. And he cursed Milly in his heart as he stood there facing a heated cook, a pale parlourmaid, and a lesser fry of capless and apronless rebels, all intent on getting out of a house they quite evidently believed to be of little credit to them, when he ought long ago to have been in his office.

Somehow he persuaded them to stay; at least till they had cleaned up thoroughly, and set the house in proper order. He appealed to their sense of fair play, he flatteringly alluded to their years of excellent service, he hinted that wages would be increased during this time of extra hard work, and he assured them that their mistress, detained in London on business, would very shortly be back.

How much he hated himself and them for this having to cajole; what a job for an important business man.

"Look here, Cook," he said, detaining her when the others, still rather disposed to murmur, had straggled out of the room, "you're a sensible woman, and one of the best cooks I ever came across, bar none—just see that they all get busy, like good girls, so that Mrs. Ernest will find everything ship-shape when she gets home. We don't want to add to her troubles, do we?" And he pressed a note into her hand.

It was only a one-pound note. He would have liked to have made it a fiver, he thought, but was afraid she might imagine he was afraid. And he took his sister-in-law aside, Alec's pious wife Ruth, who had stood by trembling, for the sole purpose before he went to his office of relieving his mind by cursing Milly.

"Indeed it's all very unpleasant—very unpleasant indeed," said Ruth, trembling away from the words he used. She was sixty-five, and much shattered by this her first approach to rebellion in the lower classes, and, in her own, to what she feared she must call actual vice.

Alec, too, was shattered; Bertie was in what his wife, watching him, called a state; the whole family was shaken to its foundations; and George, the most phlegmatic of them all, was shattered in his quiet way as much as any of them. On each of those anxious mornings, Wednesday and Thursday, they went up to their offices with stony faces and troubled hearts, and on each of those anxious evenings, Wednesday and Thursday, they returned to their agitated homes more troubled than they had left them—except George, whose trouble took on a different colouring the second of the two evenings, when, heavy with gloomy thoughts after long hours of work badly done, preparing to return to a home he knew he would find seething more than ever with questions to which the only answers possible were unpleasant, there, at Victoria Station, he barged

into the cause of the whole beastly business—Milly.
No wonder then, that stopping dead and staring at her
through his horn-rimmed glasses, his ears—he was a
pasty man, and showed such rare emotion as overtook
him only in his ears—gone crimson, he ejaculated,
"Good God!"

This was unlike George. He didn't often say things
like that, but he was shaken out of his customary
phlegm.

It was Milly who seemed to have any phlegm there
was about. Stodgy, she looked, thought George, staring;
stodgy, and—yes, sleepy. Mooning along, she was, when
he came upon her, and when he stood still and exclaimed
she didn't seem at first to see him,—not very clearly,
that is, and said tentatively after a moment, with an
effect, somehow, of shading her eyes, "George?"

"That's right," said George, wishing with all his heart
it wasn't. Why couldn't it have been one of the others
who had barged into her—Fred, or Bertie? They
would have made a better job of it than he possibly
could. What on earth ought one to say to her? And
ought one to say anything at all to her? Hadn't she——?
Wasn't she——? Oh damn, thought George, again
shaken out of his phlegm.

"You going down by the six thirty-five?" he plunged.
Here she was, anyhow; it was Milly, all right—or
rather all wrong, and he couldn't not speak to her. But
he did wish he knew what one said on such a confounded
unpleasant occasion.

She concentrated her mind on his question, her brows
drawn together. George, she was thinking; George.
The first notes of the music she had come back to face.
The, as it were, prelude.

Bowing her head, she accepted him. "Yes," she said,
"I'm going home."

And George thought, "Home. That's good. Home, indeed!"

He went on staring at her, searching for something to say. The situation was beyond him. Why he should have been picked out for this job, a quiet, unworldly chap like himself, he failed to understand. The only thing he could think of to do at the moment was to buy her an evening paper; so he beckoned to a passing news-boy, and did.

"Thank you," said Milly, as he put it into her passive hand.

"Something to read in the train," explained George.

"Yes," said Milly.

Again he stared at her in silence. What on earth Providence was up to, fixing on him like this, when any one of the others would have been a thousand times——

"Shall I carry that thing for you?" he asked, noticing she had a handbag, and seeing it as something to tack a remark on to.

Milly looked down, and noticed too that she had a handbag. She gazed at it, faintly puzzled. Usedn't there to be a suit-case there as well? When she went away that time—hadn't she been carrying a suit-case? And going up the steps in Chelsea, she seemed to remember. . . . Then, where——? Tiresome if, finding it in the studio, Arthur took it into his head to send it back. Ridiculous as well as tiresome if the last word of their loving was to be a returned suit-case. That curtain was rung down now. It would force her to laugh horribly if it had to be hauled up again, and lo, in the middle of the empty, dark stage, a suit-case.

"No, thank you," she said. "It's quite light."

Again he was silent. Then, continuing to stare at her, not wanting to, but fascinated, he emerged sud-denly once more from his phlegm, for he too, like his brothers, had been fond of her, and burst out, "Hang it all, Milly——"

And, as he paused, she asked, her eyes wide open and fixed on a point just below his spectacles and not looking as if she really saw him, "Why?"

Oh, well—if she was going to brazen it out. . . .

Scrutinizing her, however, more closely through her veil, he thought he saw that she didn't look very brazen; she looked pale and puffy, and extremely unwholesome, but not brazen. Then, if she weren't, why did she behave callously like that? Callous did seem the word to George; it wasn't right, he was sure, just to be stodgy and apathetic on such an occasion, and say "Why?" like that.

Once more he wished that it were Fred or Bertie tackling her, instead of himself. He was no good at all at making out what women were after, or what they were feeling, or what, if anything, they intended to convey, nor had he a notion of the proper line to take with a returning prodigal. He hadn't met a prodigal before. In his orderly life there had been no such person. This one had certainly given his family more anxiety, and caused it more unhappiness, during the last two days than a decent family should be called upon to bear. Yet, knowing that it was a great thing, whatever she had done, to get her back, and his part having been cast by an inscrutable Providence as first welcomer, he much wished to say and do the right thing. Scandal, as to his brothers and sisters, was loathsome to George. Beneath his stolid exterior he was as anxious as any of them to hush up all that might yet be hushed. With Milly fled, there was no possible means of hushing up anything; with Milly actually in their midst, able to be produced, and looked at, and talked to, some way ought to be found even now, and would be found if they laid their heads together, of making things seem, at least, to be all right. Yes, it was a great thing to get her back; no doubt about that. And he would give a good deal to be able to hit on the right thing to say to the woman.

What he really wanted to know—waiving the question of guilt, as to which the Botts, after having hesitated, some of them, the day before, were now of one mind—what he would very much like to know was, seeing that she had come back, why had she ever gone? Obviously it was a flight, it wasn't an ordinary going. Then why, having taken all that trouble to disappear, placing the family in a devil of a fix, doing the very thing of all others bound to expose her and hold up her relations to public shame, why was she here now, ticket and all, waiting to come down by the six thirty-five?

George was deeply perplexed. To a plain man such conduct was inexplicable. And as though she knew the very words of his thoughts Milly said, her puffy face expressionless, her voice monotonous, her eyes fixed on a point just below his spectacles, "I expect you were all surprised I left so early that day."

"Yesterday," amended George.

"Yesterday?" repeated Milly; and added after a moment, accepting it, accepting the incredible fact that it was indeed only yesterday. "Yes—yesterday."

"We were very much surprised," said George shortly. Surprised. A good word that, he thought.

Then sudden, acute alarm seized him, for what would he do, what on earth would he do, if she started confessing to him, here, in the middle of Victoria Station? He knew what she had done, and he didn't want to be told its wretched details; it would put him in the most confoundedly awkward fix if she began. Women should shut up, or tell other women, or priests or somebody, but not him.

"Nice day, hasn't it been," he said, desperately stemming what he feared was going to be the tide.

But Milly didn't seem to hear that; she appeared to be thinking of something else, her eyes fixed on that point below his spectacles. "I went to get the money," she said, after a moment.

"What money?" asked George.

"My legacy."

"Your legacy?"

"Yes—the thousand pounds Ernest left me. I went to the solicitor."

"Well, *we* could have told you that was no good," said George, relieved more than he could have supposed possible by what seemed to him the naturalness of this explanation.

He filled out his chest with relief. Not a confession. Perhaps he'd get her home after all without that happening to him. Idiotic, of course, to rush off like that, making things look blacker than ever for herself, but then she was a woman, and women did do idiotic things —great Scott, yes, and didn't they! Besides, her nerves were probably in a poor condition—must have been, what with Ernest's accident and the being cut off in his Will, and her conscience all rotten. In any case, thank goodness it was a natural explanation, and one the family would be able to understand.

"You should have asked us, Milly," he said, so much relieved that his voice was quite kind, "then you wouldn't have had the journey for nothing. These things take time. There are formalities——"

But, just as he was feeling able to be kind, he remembered that she had been away two days and a night. For

a moment he had forgotten that. A journey from Titford
to London to see a solicitor doesn't take two days and a
night. The explanation wasn't, after all, likely to soothe
the family, and didn't, after all, relieve him.

He stared at her, on the verge of asking how she had
managed to be so long about it, but refrained. It
might be true that she had tried to get the money, but
she must also have been with her—well, he hardly
liked to say her what. It wasn't his business, nor had he
any wish, to stir up the mud of Milly's secrets. Disliking
that particular kind of mud very much, George was of
opinion that it really was peculiarly shocking of Milly
to have gone rushing off to her what d'you call him
with poor old Ernest hardly in his grave. No doubt was
in his mind that part, if not all, of this absence had
been spent with the fellow. He hoped that at least they
had only talked. True, she didn't look as if the visit
had been much of a success; but, on the other hand,
neither did she look, nor had she ever looked, like a
woman who went in for that sort of thing.

Angry and upset again, he said, "Why didn't you ask
one of us? It would have saved you a useless journey,
and saved—well, a good deal besides."

"But it wasn't useless," said Milly. "I got it."

"Got what?"

"The thousand pounds."

"You got it? How?"

"From Ernest's solicitor. Mr. Jenkyns. It was there
ready for me."

George could only stare. It seemed inexplicable. That
thin-lipped, tight-jawed Jenkyns, who had so evidently
disapproved of the lot of them, who had behaved, in
fact, as though they were all tarred with Milly's own
wretched brush, must have advanced her the money.
Yet he didn't look like a chap who advances money.

Still, a woman must know whether she has got a thousand pounds or not.

He stared; and the fantastic idea shot through his mind, the one fantastic idea of his life, that perhaps it was Jenkyns himself who was Milly's what d'you call him.

"I hope," said Milly, her voice very small and tired, "no one worried too much because I went off like that."

"That's putting it mildly," said George.

"I'm very sorry," said Milly, sighing; and, as she spoke, she made an odd, sideways movement, as if she weren't quite firm on her feet.

He caught hold of her arm. "What's up?" he asked quickly, a vision of Milly fainting, and his having to do something about it, rising before his troubled eyes.

He gripped her arm tightly. He was no good at that sort of thing, he told himself, much upset; he hadn't a notion how to cope with a collapsing woman in a railway station. "What's up, Milly? Not got the staggers, have you?" he asked anxiously.

She reassured him. "I only lost my balance," she said, drawing away from his grip. "I think my heels are rather high."

"They would be," thought George. Aloud he said, severely, because he had been frightened, "You're tired—that's what it is."

"Yes. I'm tired. I think I'll go and sit in the train. I expect it's in by now——" and she began moving slowly towards the platform the six thirty-five started from.

George went with her. He hesitated a moment as to whether he oughtn't to offer her his arm. Did one offer one's arm to a—to somebody who had——? But though he was in doubt about his arm, he wasn't in any doubt that it wouldn't do for them to be seen separate,

not travelling in the same compartment when they were
going down by the same train; so he walked by her side,
keeping his eye on her, ready to catch hold of her if she
started tottering again. She looked very white; as if
she might do anything in unreason—be sick publicly,
or something awful like that.

To his relief she didn't do anything, nor did she speak
again; and walking along the platform with her, in spite
of his eyes being carefully lowered, he somehow managed to see how many people there were on it whom
they both knew, and, aware of a hush of interest as they
approached, was thankful indeed to have got Milly in
tow, to be taking her home. Silently they walked, both
looking at the ground, while everybody on the crowded
platform made room for them, those who didn't know
them, impressed by their deep mourning, as respectfully
as those who did. Silently they presently sat facing
each other in two corners of the railway carriage,
George pretending to read his evening paper, of which
he didn't see a word, and Milly not pretending anything, but simply sitting. Silently they got out at Titford, George gravely inclining his head to those ac-
quaintances who, pushed in at the last moment, had
unwillingly shared their carriage and had spent the
journey being unobtrusive; and silently they walked up
the stairs together, and into the station yard.

A melancholy pair they looked—like two unhappy
but rather grand crows, George's clothing, in its way,
being as handsomely sombre as Milly's. Those who saw
them were much pleased, so well did they fill their rôles;
and there was, besides, a genuine feeling of gladness at
seeing Mrs. Ernest reappear, and by her reappearance
putting a stop to the ugly whispers that were going
round. How miserable she looked, too, poor thing. The
onlookers couldn't help feeling gratified to see her so

utterly crushed by her bereavement, for it gave them
the assurance that the world's heart must still be in its
right place if its widows felt their losses like that. Nobody, of course, greeted the sable pair; tact was shown
in every possible way; and the place might have been
deserted for any obstacles George and Milly encountered in their progress up the stairs.

Outside the station George said, "My car is here.
Perhaps you had better let it take you ho—— to
Mandeville Park Road."

Milly acquiesced. "Thank you," she said.

But George wasn't going with her; not he. He regarded his job of first welcomer as finished, and badly
wanted to be rid of her. So, after handing her in with
suitable solemnity and care, conscious that they were
being watched, he said, standing at the door, that he
would go straight home himself in a taxi, because he
had promised his brothers to meet them at his house at
seven o'clock.

Milly acquiesced. "Thank you," she said again; and
as she was driven away, and George dropped out of
sight, she fell to pondering over the question, as one
ponders over a question laboriously in a dream, whether
it would be possible to offer the chauffeur a tip of one
shilling,—which, with three pennies, was all that she
had at that moment in the world.

§

In the end she didn't remember to give him anything.

The parlourmaid, capless, came running to open the
door when she heard the car, and Ernest's Pomeranian
was there too, yapping.

This was the dog, Milly remembered, which had
yapped at her that morning long ago when she thought
she was going to escape. Odd things one thinks one is

going to do. Escape? Nobody ever escapes. Absently she stooped to pat him. He backed away growling, and the parlourmaid rebuked him.

"We weren't expecting you, m'm," said the parlour-maid, apologizing for everything—the dog's growls, her caplessness, Milly's own behaviour in going away without saying a word.

"I ought to have let you know," said Milly vaguely, her eyes on the contents of the hall—the suits of armour, the grandfather clock, the terra-cotta baskets of ferns, all there, each in its same place, after the æons of time since she saw them last. Faintly the smell of Ernest, his coats and mackintoshes and cigars, floated round her nostrils. She put out her hand, and steadied herself by holding on to the hat-rack. She had got what George had called the staggers again.

"Yes, m'm. We was quite worried about you, m'm. And Mrs. Alec——"

"I want to go to bed," said Milly, holding on to the hat-rack.

"Yes, m'm. Early, m'm?"

"Now, please."

"Yes, m'm——"

"And I don't want any——"

But who was this, coming slowly and reluctantly out of Ernest's study, a red spot high up on each cheek? Wasn't it Ruth?

Yes; it was poor Ruth, to whom this unexpected appearance of Milly was the last dreadful straw to a miserable day. Why, she asked herself trembling, when through the window she saw who it was sitting in the car, should she be the one of the family selected to cope with so distressing an encounter? She couldn't cope with it. She was too old. It was unfair. But, after a brief struggle forcing herself to carry out what appeared

his own. Nora might be noisy and super-healthy, but she was straight. It cut the bottom out of a man's life, George said to himself walking home and slowly turning over in his mind all that had happened, if his wife wasn't straight.

The other brothers were also having a kind of second wind of appreciation of their wives—except perhaps Bertie, who never had liked his very much,—and Fred that very day had bought Mabel a new pendant, and Alec was thinking of getting Ruth something—perhaps a new garage, which he badly needed, the one they had being inconveniently small; while those men who were the husbands of the five Bott sisters were glad enough to have steady women at their backs, and not to have to bother wondering what they might be up to.

"It does a woman no good to be too attractive," one of these men, commenting on the situation, remarked to his wife—unguardedly, and as he might have spoken to a brother; and it was things like that, remarks of that sort, which the women of the family, now that Milly had become what the Bible called a hissing and a reproach, found themselves unable to stand. Attractive, attractive; what was attractive? The husband who had used the word—unguardedly, and as he might have spoken to a brother—said that he didn't know; nor, he said, now that he came to think of it, did he know why the word had occurred to him. They were busy men, the five who had married Botts, and couldn't be bothered with the discomfort of quarrels at home. At all times they were ready to placate their wives.

George, walking home to his, decided he would have dinner before he told her the news; but Nora, her hair blowing up in the wind, ran out to meet him, having been watching for him from the dining-room window, and told it him herself. They all knew it. In the brief

period of his walk from the station not only had the
parlourmaid at Mandeville Park Road telephoned, but
directly after that Ruth had telephoned, and since then
everybody had been telephoning to everybody else, all
asking each other if they had heard.

"Such a relief!" cried Nora, warmly embracing him.
"Porge"—for some reason she insisted on calling him
Porge, and it was no use asking her not to, because she
still did—"isn't it exciting!"

"You talk as if it were a sort of picnic," grumbled
George, whose coat was being helped off him; and it
wasn't any use asking her to let him take it off by himself, because she could no more stop being active than
a squib, once lit, can stop crackling round. Lit into
energy by excessive health, Nora couldn't let George
alone when he was within reach. Sometimes he thought
he would prefer a wife who was—well, not ill, but occasionally a little less well, though he knew this wasn't
a nice thought to have.

"And isn't it?" cried Nora. "Isn't it what we've
all been praying for for two mortal days? You're not
going to be glum *to-night*, Porge?"

"Look out," said George; for they were in the hall,
and servants were probably listening.

Nora, however, couldn't look out—not if all the
servants in Titford were listening could she at that
moment restrain herself. Seizing him by the shoulders,
and twisting him round so that he faced her, she again
exhorted him on that night of all nights not to be glum;
and George, facing her, was unable to resist saying, for
now that it was over he somehow felt proud, "I brought
her back."

"You?" cried Nora. "You did it?"

She stared close into his eyes in her astonishment.

George nodded. "I sent her to Ernest's in the car. I walked," he said, looking modest.

Nora was so much lost in astonished admiration that for a moment she was dumb and immobile, her hands on George's shoulders, staring close into his eyes. *Her* man getting a move on; *her* man being the one of the family to net Milly and bring her safely back, while these others, the smart ones, Fred and Bertie, who talked such a lot and made themselves out so important, did nothing at all.

"She was coming in any case," George, being honourable, found himself forced to admit. "Just by chance I met her at Victoria."

"But it was *you* who persuaded her to come back— I know it was!" cried his wife, flinging her arms round him. Sometimes he thought he would have preferred a wife who hadn't any arms; and there was a bit in the Bible they read out in church about everlasting arms which made him glad he didn't believe in heaven.

"Let go, Nora," he said, trying to disentangle himself, "I want to go up and wash."

"But I must hear everything—*everything*," she cried, kissing him.

George didn't like being kissed. He liked women who received, rather than who gave: women who waited. But there it was—Nora was a frequent kisser, and one had to put up with it.

"After dinner," he said, succeeding in getting loose, and going upstairs.

She followed him, talking all the way, holding on to his coat, pulling herself up by it two steps at a time. George sometimes thought it was a pity he had married someone so much younger than himself. He was sixty, and she was forty. Forty, it is true, sounded as if it were a quiet age, but it was nothing of the sort, he had discovered.

"Ruth's coming to dinner," Nora informed him breathlessly—not breathlessly because of the stairs, for she was as active as a lizard, but because of all the words that were wanting to come out at once. "She rang up to ask. She says there's no need for her to stay with Milly now she's come. She says Milly has gone to bed. I couldn't get anything else out of her. And the others are coming round after dinner with Fred and Bertie— Mabel and Edith are. So are Joan and Mary. Maud rang up to say she may be late—that *telephone!* It's been going without stopping. I never heard anything like it. Maud said she may be late because of Edward's knee, but she'll turn up as soon as she can. Everybody's coming. Maggie can't, because Bee's worse this after-noon, and we didn't ring up Katie because she's stuck at Denmark Hill, and it would only make her miserable to know about it all and not be able to leave mother. And anyhow it's no good stirring up mother—she'd want to pounce on Milly, and carry her off before any-body's even seen her. What a *mercy* our house happens to be in the middle, and easiest for them to meet at! Porge, isn't it exciting—fancy Milly turning up again! And fancy *you* being the one to—— Did she say any-thing? Did she tell you who the man is?"

But George, having reached the landing and got into his dressing-room, turned with his hand on the door-knob, remarked, freeing his coat, "One moment, Nora ——" and shut her out.

§

During dinner not much could be said because of the servants. Even Nora, once the servants were in the room, moving about before her eyes, realized that and

watched her words, while Alec's wife Ruth, still shaken
by her unexpected encounter with Milly and the shock
of her fainting—the servants had got her up to bed, and
she had come to after a while, so that there was no sense
in staying—could hardly be got to talk at all. She
hadn't thought it necessary to mention the fainting.
She had desired the parlourmaid not to alarm the
family by reporting it. It was over, so no use fussing.
Besides, Milly had brought it on herself, and one
couldn't feel much sympathy with people who brought
things on themselves. Nervously she crumbled her
bread, and when she tried to drink she spilt her wine.
She was sixty-five, she reminded herself, and ought not
to be called upon to mix with unpleasantness. There
seemed to Ruth little use in being an old lady, in having
struggled up to the age of sixty-five, if one were still
going to be dragged into unpleasantness.

George, at the head of the table, felt there were remarks which ought to be made for the benefit of the
servants if only one could think of them; remarks
about Milly—casual, easy references to her, giving the
servants the proper cue for their own opinion. He was
sure Fred and Bertie were saying the right things at
that moment for the benefit of theirs; he felt that not to
mention her was a mistake, as the servants knew Ruth
had just come from seeing her; but he wasn't used to
this sort of thing, he could only find his way about, as
befits a decent man, in straightforward transactions.
Milly was a great deal more bother and worry than any
living woman was worth, he resentfully thought. Still,
he had a feeling she ought to be mentioned.

"How do you think she's looking?" he suddenly
burst out, addressing Ruth; and Ruth, who was at that
moment being offered pudding, started so much that
she dropped the spoon into it.

The room seemed to hold its breath. Was it George's fancy, or did the servants really slow down in what they were doing, and become almost immobile?

"Who?" asked Ruth nervously. Really George was most annoying. Why couldn't he let the subject alone while servants were present?

"Milly," said George, determined to say it so naturally and casually that it came out with a roar.

"Oh, yes. Very well, I think. No—tired I mean," said Ruth, bending her head over her plate, and wondering how old a woman had to be, then, before she was allowed to stand aside and keep out of unpleasantness.

"Poor old Milly," said Nora eagerly. She longed to talk about her, to hear what Ruth thought, what Milly had said, what she looked like; and here she was obliged to sit quiet and wait interminably, because of the servants. "If only *dogs* could be trained to do things!" she thought passionately.

"She'll be all right in a day or two," George said with vague heartiness, drumming a tune on the table with his fingers; and then he remembered that a widow is supposed to take more than a day or two before becoming all right.

A flush appeared on Ruth's delicate elderly cheek as she tried to eat her pudding. It had been so very painful, meeting Milly like that all by herself, without Alec or anyone to help her, and then having to see her flop down on the floor. It didn't seem right that she, of the whole big family, should be picked out to fill such a part. All her life she had shrunk from anything not nice, all her life she had turned her eyes away from ugly things, and had carefully brought up her children to do the same. She had long now been a grandmother, and she couldn't help feeling that touching pitch wasn't a

game for grandmothers. In obedience to the family's
wishes she had gone to poor Ernest's so that the servants
might have some authority over them, willing, as always,
to fulfil her obligations as the wife of the eldest son,
anxious to do what Alec and the others thought right,
though it had been sad enough being all day in poor
Ernest's deserted house; but she shouldn't have been
left there to bear the brunt of Milly's return and fainting unaided, she should never have been put in such a
position. George knew she was there; why, when he
sent Milly round in his car, did he not come too? She
was very sorry for Milly—very sorry indeed, as she was
sorry, she hoped, for all women who went astray, but
she didn't wish to be with her. Not yet, in any case. Not
till something definite had been decided as to what they
were going to do about it all. And certainly she didn't
wish to be with her by herself, and have to see her
dropping down at her feet in a heap.

Afterwards in the drawing-room, when the servants
had brought coffee and at last been got rid of, she told
George she thought she ought not to have been left in
the lurch like that, without an idea of what to say,—
still not mentioning the fainting, so as to avoid useless
fussing.

"That's how I felt at Victoria," said George, filling
his pipe; an inadequate reply to her just complaint,
Ruth felt, but George had always been irritating.

"I wish to goodness *I'd* been at Ernest's when Milly
got back!" exclaimed Nora.

"What would you have done?" Ruth asked with a
slight shiver; for Nora's vitality invariably made her
feel extra frail and old, as if she were sitting in a draught
—and not any ordinary draught, but her last earthly
draught of all.

"I'd have kissed her," said Nora.

"Kissed her?" echoed George, turning to stare.

"Really, Nora," shivered Ruth, drawing her fur closer about her.

§

Yet this, later on, when the brothers had assembled in George's drawing-room, and their wives were all there, and three of the five married sisters were there too, was roughly the attitude they ended by deciding should be adopted. Not actual kissing; that wasn't necessary. But the kindliness which in happier circumstances would find its culmination in a kiss was from every point of view desirable.

Ruth, frail and old, and still after close on¹ fifty years of marriage believing husbands knew best, was willing to follow any line she was instructed to, once it was made clear to her that it was in Alec's view right. She saw what they all meant, she quite understood that private feelings must be pocketed in the interests of the family's good reputation, and she also remembered that Christ had forgiven women like Milly. Therefore she submitted, and sat quiet by the fire holding her fur close round her chilly shoulders, saying little, resigned to obedience; and gradually there emerged from the tangle of voices the authoritative voice of Fred, who took hold of the meeting and firmly outlined what the family had got to do, and what it perfectly well knew in its heart it had got to do.

Open kindness was the proper, the only attitude, he said; and Bertie heartily agreed, and so, after a moment, did Alec and George. Escaped, through Milly's unexpected and unhoped-for reappearance, from the disaster of an unhidable disgrace, they were going to take no risks—and stand no nonsense of opposition from the women, Fred went on, looking round; and Bertie nodded agreement, and so, after a moment, did Alec and George.

The one thing to be done with Milly, he declared, was what Walter Walker had suggested the other day— take her into their homes, and be kind to her. As kind, said Fred, eyeing the women, as if they were really fond of her; as kind as if they couldn't be happy without her. Anyhow for some months they must do this, till suspicion had lulled. Then, when things had blown over, perhaps she could go to Denmark Hill and look after the old lady for the rest of her days, as their mother had suggested. But not now; not at first. After this last straw of her running away she must be in their actual midst, apparent to everybody, gradually, as the period of mourning lightened, being drawn into ordinary life, being seen in church, being seen by callers, being seen taking exercise, being seen—this was the crux—with *them*, and not only with them, but cherished by them.

Visibly cherished Milly was to be, however great a strain it might put upon them. Their children were to see it, their servants were to be forced to notice it. And as for expense, it was absurd to fuss about that, he said, looking severely at the women. What did a guest cost? Milly, after all, was only going to be a guest, and before she had begun to cost anything she would be moving on to the next host, he added with a grin. Besides, she had her thousand pounds.

Fred and Bertie, supported by Alec and George, who were both glad to be given a lead, looked round the room at the seven women, as who should say, "You dare make difficulties!" But not one of the wives and sisters, now that this was really upon them, so much as murmured. Since that first shock of the reading of the Will they had been through a great deal, and were ready to adapt themselves to necessity. Like Ruth, they were willing to submit to what their husbands and brothers decided, and even Bertie's wife Edith was thinking, as she listened to Fred, that nothing should be shrunk from which could stop people's tongues. Hateful to be questioned by her daughters, one of whom was being courted by the senior curate of St. Timothy's, who would certainly shy off marrying into scandal, as to what Aunt Milly had really done; revolting to have her sons, cynical enough as it was, becoming aware from hints and looks that aunts, too, weren't always what they seemed. Besides, she, with the others, was intensely relieved that Milly had come back, and in her relief, like the others, ready to do much which in a calmer moment would have seemed impossible.

So that the resolution to take Milly into their homes, each in turn, and make much of her, was no longer opposed, and only when it came to discussing details was there any further argument—details, for instance, such as how long the visits were to last, who should be the first host, whether it should go by age, whether the four brothers should begin one after the other, or whether the married sisters should be intercalated.

The married sisters protested at this suggestion. They didn't wish to be intercalated. They considered the men of the family should all come first, regardless of age. And anyhow they would have to ask their husbands.

"Why aren't they here?" Fred inquired.

Well, really Milly couldn't be said to be anything to do with the husbands of the sisters of her deceased husband, Maud, the eldest of the sisters, declared.

There was a silence. They all looked at Alec. He, aware that they were looking at him, pulled at his beard and said nothing.

"What about it, Alec?" asked Fred, seeing that he remained silent. Alec seemed to be showing signs of not wishing to be the one to begin taking Milly. Yet he was the eldest; clearly it was his duty.

"What about it?" Fred asked a second time.

Then Alec, clearing his throat, explained that he knew he was the eldest, but that he couldn't help it, and that Ruth had lately been feeling her age. Also, he explained, Ruth was, he was glad to say, and as they all had long been aware—he looked at her affectionately, and she smiled at him—a particularly religious woman, and perhaps a religious woman—not that the others were not religious, but Ruth made rather a point of it—well, he meant to say that perhaps a particularly religious woman oughtn't to have to be the first to have a—well, Milly in her house.

He stopped, an undefined idea possessing his mind that Milly might be purer after having passed through the sieve of other visits, and more fit to stay with his wife; but he couldn't get it clear enough to put into words, and he sat with his long fingers buried in his beard and his thin shanks crossed, wishing to goodness the wretched woman had never been born.

Ruth, by the fire, looked gratefully at him, and drew her fur still closer round her throat, coughing a little as an involuntary testimony to her frailness these days of being sixty-five. Besides, having already encountered Milly and gone through that fainting scene, and without being prepared for it either, which made it so much worse, she felt she had done her share for a while, and should be put at the bottom of the list. She too obscurely thought that by the time Milly had been on a few of the visits she would somehow be more purged.

"You're not feel ingcold, dear?" asked Alec solicitously, prizing his wife; and Fred too, prizing his, turned to Mabel at once when she made some inaudible observation, with an affectionate, "What's that, old girl?"

and George, prizing his, but not given to easy words, showed his appreciation of virtue by stooping and picking up a liqueur chocolate she had dropped on the carpet, and cleansing it of fluff with his handkerchief before handing it back to her.

Only Bertie remained untouched by the general warm-up of affection. He didn't like Edith very much at any time, and he saw no reason why he should like her any better because poor little Milly had gone off the rails. On the contrary, it made him like her less, her thin-lipped, superior virtue annoying him. Also he was apt to be unfaithful, and resented having to feel that he wronged her. Flushed, and full of the port he had drunk after dinner to assuage his worries, he sat away from her and close to his brothers. He was extremely worried about Milly, and had been immensely shocked by the discovery that she hadn't kept straight. Milly not straight? It seemed unbelievable. Yet no other construction could be put upon her action in bolting,—she bolted because she couldn't face the family, and she couldn't face the family because she was as guilty as Ernest had insinuated in his beastly Will.

Bertie was unable to make up his mind whether he condemned her, or whether he wasn't glad that the poor little soul had had some happiness in her dreary life with that sneak Ernest. But what had happened to her in London? What unexpected catastrophe had forced her to come back? That tale she had told George and Ruth about going up to fetch her legacy, that was just eyewash. Well, she got the money all right from Jenkyns, he was glad to know, and George and the others might beat their brains till they were blue as to how it came to be given to her—they'd never find out. That chap Jenkyns was a scoundrel, but a close one. A mean scoundrel too, not ringing him up as he had promised, when Milly called. If he had been able to have a word or two with her then, he might have helped her a good deal, he might even have saved her from this ghastly being whitewashed by the family and clasped to its heart.

Unfortunate little Milly, he thought; it seemed to be her fate to have to deal with mean men. The chap who let her down—why was she back again if he hadn't?—he must be a pretty mean brute too; and Bertie was so much worried about her that he had had to drink more wine than usual at dinner, and looked more flushed even than he actually was, sitting between the silvery Alec and the sallow Fred.

He was the only one of the family who wasn't thankful that Milly had come back. Far rather would he have had her stay away, for then at least he could have presumed that the fellow she had carried on with was doing the right thing by her. Bertie couldn't understand how anyone should not do the right thing by Milly—a little soft thing like that, and so kind always. How could any man behave so rottenly? He had himself always been good to the women he had had anything to do with—in that way, he meant. Perhaps he hadn't been very good to Edith, but then she—— What was that? What was George saying?

George was saying that Milly was already in possession of her legacy. "She told me she went to Jenkyns, and he gave it to her," George said.

"That's odd," remarked Fred.

"Very odd," said Alec, drawing his fingers slowly through his beard.

"I wonder how she managed that," said Fred, thoughtfully.

George stared at the carpet. "Well, I think he must have advanced it," he said. "Jenkyns must have."

There was a silence. The women were silent, because they didn't see why Milly shouldn't be able to get her money as soon as she liked; but Alec and Fred were thinking that she must have got round Jenkyns, for no man advances a thousand pounds to a woman who has no claims on him and perhaps won't pay it back, unless he has been got round; and if Milly could get round that grim-mouthed solicitor, was there any limit to her wiles?

Unpleasant thought. The last thing they wished for their own peace was to have wiles practised on themselves. Let loose in their homes, what mightn't Milly do if she gave her mind to it? And though of course they personally would remain adamant, their wives might imagine that they hadn't, and then——

"I think I'll ring up Jenkyns," said Fred.

"I wouldn't do that if I were you," said Bertie quickly.

"Why not?"

"Best let things be," said Bertie, pouring himself out a glass of whiskey and soda. "No good beginning to stir round in Milly's past actions. If you take my advice, our line ought to be to make a clean sweep of her entire past, especially her immediate past, and start fair on a basis of—well, to put it rather like a parson, of hopeful confidence."

"Perhaps you'd better be the one to begin with her, then," suggested Fred sarcastically.

"Oh, no——" Bertie's wife intervened. "Why, we're the youngest of all. Bertie is, I mean. We couldn't possibly come out of our turn."

"And by the way," Bertie went on, distracting their attention from Jenkyns and the legacy, "I made inquiries to-day, and my solicitor thinks those words in Ernest's Will—you know, 'My wife will know why'—those words are defamatory, and he's going to apply to have them omitted from the order of probate. He says it's pretty certain the judge in the Probate Division will regard them as inserted to air a grievance, and will rule they're not to be published."

"I thought Wills were sacred," said Nora, who had been thrilled by this sentence in Ernest's, and didn't want it suppressed.

"Not any parts of them that the judge rules are unjustified or injurious," explained Fred, greatly relieved by Bertie's news.

"But this wasn't unjustified," said Edith.

"And therefore can hardly be called injurious,' said Maud.

"Well, it's going to be left out anyway," said Bertie shortly. "And we can all bless our stars that Ernest's craving for post-mortem punishment has been frustrated."

"Yes—I think we must all be glad of this," said Fred, looking round. "It makes it much easier to save Milly from scandal." And, since Alec agreed, and said, "Indeed we must," and George nodded, the wives and sisters were obliged to appear satisfied too.

But they didn't like the way, the wives and sisters didn't, Bertie talked of poor Ernest, and never would. On the day of the funeral it had been disgraceful the way he spoke of him, and now listen to him using such ugly words. Edith ought to make him behave better; Edith oughtn't to let him get out of hand like this. And Edith, watching Bertie with narrowed eyes, was suddenly invaded by a dreadful suspicion. "I wonder," she thought—and it must be said she struggled hard against thinking it—"whether Ernest's reason for not divorcing Milly was because he knew the man was——"

But she couldn't go on. She mustn't, she simply mustn't let an idea like that, so horrible, so completely destructive of her peace, get a footing in her mind. "Out with it," she said to herself, pushing it away with might and main; and asked Nora, for she felt ill, if the window could be opened.

There was an interlude, in which they fanned Edith and opened the window.

Directly they opened the window, Ruth, by the fire, began to cough.

"You see?" nodded Alec, when she had stopped sufficiently for them to hear what he was saying. "I must get her away. To Brighton, or somewhere. I've been thinking of it for a long time." And he added, tapping his own, "Chest."

"You're shirking, old man," said Fred. "You only don't want to fill your proper place as eldest of the family, and be the one to start in on Milly."

Upon which Ruth interrupted again with a worse fit, a fit that shook her thin body, and was really distressing to listen to.

"She's had this cough all the winter," explained Alec when she left off for a moment, taking no notice of Fred's words, "and I think, considering her age——"

"Well, then, Maud—what about you?" Fred asked, looking at his eldest sister. "There's no reason why one of you girls shouldn't be the first. After all, it's much more of a woman's job than a man's. Suppose we begin with the eldest sister, as the eldest brother won't?"

"My dear fellow, it's not a question of *won't*," began Alec, backed up by more coughing from Ruth.

"You're joking, Fred," said Maud severely, when Ruth stopped. She was frowning at Ruth as much as at Fred, for coughing is an irritating noise. "Edward would never allow it. What has he got to do with Milly and her miserable affairs?"

"Yes—and we're not even called Bott now," Joan, another sister, pointed out.

"We ought to be last of all," said Mary, the third one. "After all of you have had your turns."

Nora leaned forward eagerly. "Why not George and me begin?" she asked. "I'd *love* to have Milly."

The others stared at her shocked, except Bertie, who would have liked too to be the one to welcome Milly.

"Really, Nora," Bertie's wife recovered enough to say; and Ruth too, feebly because of that last fit of coughing, said, "Really, Nora."

"My dear, we can't have her out of our turn," said George, frowning at his wife. "If Alec won't——"

"Can't," corrected Alec.

"—there's Fred comes before us."

"Yes. I think that as I shall be taking Ruth away at once," chimed in Alec, "you and Mabel must step into my shoes, Fred."

"Gracious," murmured Mabel, faintly.

Fred looked round at them from beneath his thick black eyebrows. Mean of Alec to get out of it. He might have taken Milly with them to Brighton—indeed, that would have looked rather particularly natural and well.

But he knew when Alec had made up his mind not to do a thing no power on earth would move him; and feeling that it was up to him to set an example, he decided that he would shoulder his burden with at least an appearance of alacrity and goodwill, and show them all how the thing ought to be done.

"Right," he said, bringing his fist down on the table next him, the one with glasses and whiskey on it, and making them jingle, "I'm game. Aren't you, Mabel? We'll begin, then. How long are the visits to last, did we say? Three months?"

"Gracious," murmured Mabel again, faintly.

"Well, say two months. What? Not so long? Oh, nonsense. Six weeks, then. What—not even that? All right—a month, then. But not a day less than a month each. We'd hardly get into our strides under a month."

So it was decided that each of Milly's visits should last a month, and that the first one, to Fred, should begin the next day.

"Gracious," was Mabel's helpless comment, as they led her home.

§

That evening, at half-past eleven, the telephone rang outside the drawing-room door of the house on Denmark Hill, where old Mrs. Bott, who needed little sleep and stayed up till twelve every night, was playing patience.

Her youngest daughter Katie Noakes, who was staying with her for a few days, ran out to answer it, while the old lady, going on with her game, waited placidly to hear the news.

News of some sort it was bound to be, these agitated days since poor Milly had taken to her heels—and there, upstairs, was the best spare room all ready for her, and the bed made, and no Milly to sleep in it. Such a pity. Why not stretch her poor tired little body out in those nice cool sheets, and know that nothing was going to hurt her, instead of rushing about thinking she had to try and get away from something or other? A spell seemed to be laid on these misguided children, preventing their seeing and understanding how simple things really were. They only had to kiss each other and be friends. But some of them had got an idea into their heads that they were going to be scolded, and the rest of them had got an idea into theirs that it was their duty to scold. Well, she could tell them, only they wouldn't listen, that no good ever yet came from scolding. Just cobwebs, these ideas were; unhappy cobwebs; the stuff that dreams are made on, thought old Mrs. Bott, putting down a card, who knew her Shakespeare even better than her Bible, and in her heart preferred it, because she didn't care about foreigners.

"Well, Katie?" she said, not looking up, her hand hovering over the cards, as her daughter reappeared.

"Milly's back," said Katie breathlessly.

"What—here?" she asked placidly, her eyes on her game.

"No—she's at Ernest's. Nora rang up. She's to go to Fred's to-morrow."

"She isn't coming here, then?"

"No—they want to have her with them in Titford."

"Ah," said the old lady, putting down another card. Then she added, "You've all been wrong about poor Milly, you see."

"Yes—that's the idea," said Katie, much flushed, and beginning at once to adopt the attitude prescribed to her by Nora in the name of the others.

"I hope you'll try to make it up to her," said the old lady, finishing her game.

"Yes—that's the idea," repeated Katie, comforted by the fact that she, as the youngest sister, was at the very bottom of the list.

⁑(XII)⁑

THE Fred Botts lived in the most expensive part of Titford, where all the houses were big and all the gardens were grounds. They had a billiard-room, a suite of reception-rooms, an oak lounge hall with a galleried staircase, and a Winter Garden. Also they had a butler, and dressed for dinner. No other Botts had a butler, though several dressed for dinner, but the Winter Garden had somehow led up to him, and when Fred first embarked on giant ferns it was only a question of time before he proceeded to a butler.

Mabel, wispy and insignificant, and at all times of a faint heart, was crushed by the butler. Her lunches alone, with him waiting on her, were nightmares. It seemed so awful, she thought, to be watched by a man from behind. One's back was so helpless. It had no eyes in it. And he disapproved of her, she was sure, and offered her the food as though it were reproaches. Awful to lunch, most of her days, alone with the butler. In the silence of the room, while he, behind her chair, waited to remove her plate the instant she laid down her knife and fork, she could hear him breathing, for he was one of those butlers who breathe. He did it down her neck, too, when he bent over her with dishes, and made the straggles of her hair, which never would keep pinned back out of the way, wave about unpleasantly. She suffered. Also, having been for years in the service of a bishop, he had somehow forced family prayers on her, to which Fred and the boys wouldn't come; and how her voice shook and trembled when she read out bits of Bible and whole collects before the semicircle of stony servants, headed by the butler looking down his big nose.

· Mabel feared him. He was a man of the highest principles for his employers. She knew in her bones that his god was respectability, and his standard bishops. How was she going to break to this virtuous man that he was to wait at table for a whole month on poor, shady Milly? She had no doubt whatever that he knew all about Milly; she was certain, from many unmistakable signs, that the Will, the flight, and the reasons for both, had been thoroughly discussed and judged in the servants' hall.

Dejectedly, Mabel walked home from George's, Fred's arm supporting her, and with a sunk heart and a distracted mind listened to his instructions. If only somebody else were going to be the first to have Milly! Horrid of Alec, whose duty it was to begin, to shuffle out of it. It did seem hard that it should fall to her, the one of the family who had the high-principled butler. And it wasn't only the butler: Rosemary, her severe daughter, would be home before the end of Milly's month, a girl of austere piety who was spending her Easter in Jerusalem, and wanted to become an Anglican nun. What about her? Wouldn't she ask questions? Wouldn't she want to know why Aunt Milly suddenly was poor, and had to stay with them? Whatever else the family could hide it couldn't hide the fact that Milly was poor. Her clothes would gradually grow shabby; her tips would certainly be small. Perhaps she and Fred, thought Mabel, her forehead corrugated with anxious thought, had better do the tipping for her, in case she should disgrace them by its meagreness. She

could say, after Milly had left, "Mrs. Ernest asked me
to give you this. . . ."

And then there were the boys. One was married, but
two still lived at home, and were back from business
every evening to dinner. What about them? They had
heard the whispered anxieties of the last two days; they
had—she had noticed it—pricked up their ears, though
saying nothing. Were they going to be persuaded, fine,
intelligent young fellows that they were, that all had
been well between their Uncle Ernest and Aunt Milly,
and that it had been pure philanthropy impelling him to
leave his money to charity? Oh, she hoped, she did so
much hope, they wouldn't ever know which charity it
was! There oughtn't to be such charities, not with young
men about in the world. Why should wicked women be
rescued? And to have one of them coming to stay with
her as an honoured guest, a guest, Fred was commanding
as they walked—she did wish Fred wouldn't command
quite so much, and then leave her to do the obeying as
best she could—who had to be petted, threw her mind
into complete confusion. And Fred was so determined,
so sure it could and should be done. Manlike, he would
fetch Milly next day, drop her on his door-step, and then
go off to his peaceful office, leaving the burden on his
wife's shoulders.

She walked homewards with dragging footsteps.
What did he know about that burden really? What
did he know, for instance, about the butler? He only
saw him in the mornings and evenings, whereas Mabel
had him all day, and all day was under his voiceless
disciplines. Being rich was nice, of course, but not if
it led to butlers, thought Mabel, faced by the necessity
of having to inform this particular one of Milly's arrival.
She hadn't minded the other stages in her progressive
splendour; had rather liked them, in fact, once she got

used to them; but the butler she couldn't get used to,—
not to this particular one, who looked at her down his
big nose as if she were only about three feet high. And
it was never the least use trying to tell Fred her troubles,
for he wouldn't listen; directly she began he went deaf,
and stayed deaf till she stopped. Yet often there were
things, real things, as now, which. . . .

"You'd better give your orders to-night," said Fred,
cutting across her whimpering thoughts as he opened the
door with his latch-key. "I shall fetch her round directly after breakfast to-morrow."

"But suppose," faltered Mabel, with a last dim hope,
"she won't come?"

"Come? She's got to come. She'll *come* all right,"
said Fred.

"Oh, Fred——" began Mabel, faintly.

"Now then, old girl, buck up," he briskly encouraged,
who himself wasn't feeling much bucked. He hadn't
bargained for having to be the one to begin; he had
taken it for granted Alec would be the first host, and
wasn't as ready for the part as he would have been if he
had had more time to think. Mabel would have to work
out the details, he decided, and get things going on the
right lines next day while he was in the City. Pity she
didn't take to the idea more enthusiastically. After all,
it was a woman's job tackling Milly, not a man's. He
only hoped Milly wouldn't start any tackling game herself though, he thought uneasily as he hung up his hat,
remembering how she must have tackled Jenkyns the
solicitor, getting that advance out of him. Suppose,
instead of supporting the family's efforts to whitewash
her by behaving herself, she began to exercise her tackling powers on himself and his sons? There was no
limit, he understood, to what a woman, once fallen,
wouldn't do. Being a nephew or a brother-in-law wasn't

a protection; and to have a soft little thing sidling up to a man, after dinner, say, after a good dinner, when one's wife happened not to be in the room. . . .

"Run along, old girl," he said to Mabel, giving her an unusually affectionate good-night kiss, quite clinging to her, in fact, a minute. "I'll go and tell the boys their aunt's coming."

And he went into the library, where he knew he would find his sons, who being, like himself, more absorbed in money-making than pleasures, spent most of their evenings at home.

"Your aunt," he said, going over to the fire and standing looking down at them, "is coming to stay with us to-morrow."

"Which aunt?" asked Percy, the eldest boy, without raising his eyes from *The Financial Times*, and also without enthusiasm, for he had eight of them.

"Your Aunt Milly."

"Oh, well—it might be worse," he mumbled, going on reading.

"I thought new-made widows stayed at home," said Dick, the younger boy.

Then Fred explained the philanthropic zeal of their Uncle Ernest, and how his desire to benefit charities had caused his widow to be without a home to stay in. He explained in outline rather than in detail, adding some general observations on the impossibility of ever knowing the secret places of any man's heart, and how one's own brother sometimes turned out, as in this case, to have had ideals and enthusiasms nobody would ever have suspected.

"Rough luck on poor old Aunt Milly," remarked Dick, when his father had finished.

"Yes—that's what *I* think, not being a philanthropist myself," said Fred. "We must make it up to **her,**"

"Do you mean financially?" inquired Percy, his eyes still on his paper.

"Kindness," said Fred.

"Kindness! Well, that's cheap, anyhow," said Dick.

"And easy," said Percy, turning the pages. "I always liked Aunt Milly."

"Yes. She's not a bad old thing," agreed Dick.

"But why did Uncle Ernest——" began Percy, looking up.

"I told you. I've been telling you for the last ten minutes. When philanthropy gets hold of a man——"

Fred broke off and took out his watch. "I'm going to bed," he finished abruptly. "I've had a heavy day, and I'm tired."

§

Milly arrived next morning about twelve. Fred, who went for her at nine, had to wait all that time while she packed, sacrificing his valuable morning from fear that if he didn't actually stay in the house till she was ready and take her to Mabel with his own hands, she might once more slip through the family's fingers.

But Milly offered no resistance. She came like a lamb. She was in bed when he arrived—the parlour-maid had some yarn, to which he didn't listen, that she hadn't been very well the night before,—but got up at once on hearing he was there wishing to speak to her. At first she seemed taken aback when he told her they wanted her to stay with them in turn, and didn't appear quite to get the hang of it, Fred thought; but presently, after looking rather stupid for a while, she grasped it all right, and said the proper things about kindness. They didn't look at each other while he explained, and she thanked; they looked, he out of the window, and she at the fire. But it was he who insisted that she should pack every single thing that was hers personally, and not just take away some of her jewels, as she suggested —"The more you have," said Fred, looking out of the window, "the less you'll want."

"Yes. I understand," said Milly, looking at the fire.

"My God, how slow she is over that packing," thought Fred while he waited, every few minutes taking out his watch; had she no idea of the value of a man's time at that hour of the day? Long after he had settled with the cook, and through her with the rest of the household, which was to receive a generous indemnity and clear off that same day, Milly was still up in her bedroom, packing. It really was too bad of her, he said to himself, to keep him hanging about like that. And what annoyed him even more was that for the first time in his life she made him feel shy. Why, when she came into the room, he hadn't been able to meet her eyes. Most annoying; and so cramping. If she had looked more like what they now knew she was, if she had been bold and defiant, or crawling and hang-dog, an obviously unchaste woman caught out, he would have known what to do, and been perfectly capable of dealing with her. But she looked so infernally good, thought Fred, much put out; she looked just as modest as ever, and was exactly the same little quiet dove-woman he had always had quite a fancy for, with the added claim on his heart strings of a white face and heavy eyes. It wasn't what he had expected, and it threw him out of his stride. Also, he couldn't help thinking, suppose their suspicions, or rather their certainties, were baseless? Suppose they, and Ernest before them, had done the poor thing an outrageous wrong?

The bare thought afflicted Fred, and set his mind off into a kind of stutter. He recovered, however, on re-

membering how she had taken to her heels, and stayed
hidden two days and a night. If she were innocent, she
wouldn't have done that.

Yes—but she had come back. . . .

Oh, hang it all, Fred exclaimed, frowning; and in
any case, guilty or not guilty, she was a fool, who had
all but wrecked the family honour, and still might do it
if they didn't look out.

But when she came down at last, ready to go with
him, black and shrouded and acquiescent, and again
said something polite about his and Mabel's kindness,
he found himself feeling shy again, and touched, and
uncertain, for heaven knew there wasn't very much
kindness in this business.

This would never do, he thought, pulling himself together. It was what had happened to Jenkyns. He
too must have felt touched and uncertain, and it had
ended in his parting with a thousand pounds. Fred, as
a rich man, knew the exact value of a thousand pounds,
and didn't at all like the idea that in his turn he might
be so sorry for Milly that presently he began to part,
perhaps, with money. True she looked like the last
person in the world to try to get anything out of anybody; but see how she had taken them all in already.
They would have to be extremely cautious with her this
time, and take good care that——

It was an immense relief to him when he at last could
hand her over to Mabel, his Mabel, the woman he knew
all about and who was exactly what she seemed to be.
She was waiting for them, according to his instructions,
on the door-step, and directly he saw her his shyness
vanished, and he felt able to play his part of cordial
host.

"Well, here we are," he called heartily over his

shoulder to Mabel, as he helped Milly out of the car; and Mabel said, coming down the steps, very red and nervous and holding out a limp hand, "Oh—Milly. Yes. How nice. How are you? I—I'm so pleased." And, catching Fred's eye, she hastily bent forward, and pecked at the crape veil.

Fred's heartiness increased. Escorting Milly into the house he told her, the butler hearing it, that she was to treat the place and everything in it exactly as if it were hers. "We only want you to feel at home," he said— so heartily that the oak rafters rang. "Mabel and I just want you to rest here and get fit again, and do what you please. Liberty Hall, you know—eh, Mabel?"

And then he actually patted Milly's shoulder, for the benefit of the butler, and looking at his watch remarked hastily, "Well, so long, ladies," and hurried out to the waiting car, leaving Mabel to her fate.

"Fred!" she called after him, running down the steps, "Oh—*Fred!* You'll be back to dinner? You won't be late?"

But Fred, having done his part, opened his *Times* and became absorbed in other things.

That was the last Mabel saw of him through the window of the departing car, absorbed in his *Times;* and she slowly went up the steps again, and there in the hall, patient, waiting to obey, was Milly, and there too, waiting to shut the door and looking down his big nose, was the butler.

What a pair to be left alone with—what a *pair*, thought Mabel in much agitation, her knees seeming to have water in them instead of bones. "Please, Smith," she faltered, meek as always when speaking to the butler, "will you see that the luggage is taken up to the mahogany room?" And, after a hesitating look at Milly, according to her instructions she began to try to pet, and forced herself to go so far as to take her sinning sister-in-law gingerly by the arm.

"Shall we go upstairs?" said Mabel. "You'll like to take off your things after your——"

That was what one said to visitors arriving—"After your journey," but she stopped, because she remembered Milly hadn't had a journey.

"It was very kind of Fred to fetcn me," murmured Milly. "And it's very good of you both to take me in."

Mabel's hold on her arm became slightly less loose, and she drew her quickly towards the stairs. Take her in? Of course it was what they were doing, but it sounded as if she were in need of a refuge; and Fred had impressed on her, during the better part of the wakeful night she had just passed, that the servants were at all costs to be made to understand that the visit was voluntary. As though they would believe that. As though they weren't perfectly aware of the true meaning of it. Still, Fred wouldn't listen when she told him so, but she did hope that at least Milly would be careful what she said before them, and especially what she said before the butler. At luncheon, for instance— Mabel had read a book on etiquette which laid down as imperative that one must always say luncheon when what one wants to say is lunch—they would be in his presence and hearing for half an hour, and it would be ghastly if Milly talked as though he weren't there; too ghastly if she said anything that was true. She must ask her to be careful. She must remind her that——

But ought Milly to need reminding of the dreadful cloud she was under? Wasn't she the last person in the world who should ever, for a moment, forget it? And Fred said it was on no account to be mentioned, the cloud wasn't; it was to be ignored, blotted out. How could that be done if Milly herself alluded to it? Not directly alluded to it, but sideways—like this she had just said about being taken in? Taken in! With the butler standing there listening. . . .

"We *love* having you," said Mabel desperately, her small black eyes, staring anxiously out of her flushed face, making her look like a worried shrimp.

She drew her pale guest up the stairs; and the butler, watching grimly from below, said to himself that it was a pretty state of things, this being required to see after the luggage and attend to the wants of somebody dressed as an afflicted widow and yet no better than she should be. White sheets were what *she* ought to be in, thought the butler,—white sheets, and excommunicated from the church. His lordship would have made short work of such as her.

The butler—his name happened to be Butler, and he much objected to having been re-christened Smith by his new employers, for the bishop had called him by his own name without making the least difficulty, merely replying to the not infrequent query of strangers as to why he called his butler Butler, "Because he *is* a Butler," —the butler indignantly went to do as he had been told. But when at lunch-time Mrs. Ernest, as he supposed he must still describe her, reappeared without her bonnet and veil, and one could really get a good look at her, her hair so neat that it was a lesson to his own so-called lady's untidy poll, her face grave and quiet just as it should be, and her brow pure and open enough in his opinion to belong to a blameless Christian, he began to hesitate; and breathing over her as he handed food, and noting how waxen her cheeks were beneath the dark sweep of eyelashes—just what sad cheeks should be, in his opinion, after the death of a husband—he hesitated even more, for upon his word, thought the butler, she could have been transplanted then and there, and not

a thing altered, straight to the luncheon-table at the
bishop's palace, and been nothing but a credit to it.

Mabel too, furtively watching her, couldn't help
thinking that she looked very good. How deceitful of
her, thought Mabel; however had she the face to? It
was better, of course, for everybody that she should, but
how ever had she the face to? They knew all about
her, and she knew they knew all about her. She knew
they knew she was a firebrand, and it was sheer shame-
lessness to behave like one's idea of a damp squib.
Exposed as a serpent, really it was horribly deceitful to
seem to be a dove—of all animals, thought Mabel, in her
agitation not sure whether doves were mammals or not.
What mixture could be more dreadful than an adulterous dove? Mabel asked herself; and immediately was
much shocked by her own expression.

Adulterous dove. What a sentence. Where had it
come from? From what unexplored and ugly part of her
mind? Words like that had never entered her head
before. Were they, perhaps, an emanation from the
figure quietly eating mutton? Goodness, what an upsetting idea; how horrid if Milly were one of those car-
rier people, and even if she were good herself—which she
wasn't, interpolated Mabel, determined not to be fooled
ever again—managed to put bad thoughts into blameless brains. Nice, very nice, with her innocent boys within daily range for a whole month, and even Fred—she
could imagine nothing more hateful than having to
look on while Fred was gradually being polluted.

Much worried, Mabel furtively watched Milly. She
oughtn't, she thought, to be eating mutton. It didn't
seem right, somehow, to Mabel—obscurely unsuitable,
she felt, though she couldn't have said why. True she
was eating it half-heartedly; but still,—mutton. Toast
for widows, Mabel felt vaguely; dry toast for widows,

and certainly dry toast for found-out sinners. Besides, if Milly had refused the mutton she could have said, "You are eating nothing," and Milly could have answered, "I'm not very hungry," and Mabel could have said, "You really ought to *try*, you know"—which would not only have been hospitable, but conversation.

As it was, what did one talk about to Milly? Sitting all anyhow on her chair, too nervous to bother, as she usually bothered when the butler was present, about deportment, Mabel tried vainly to think of things to say which wouldn't be tactless. Everything seemed tactless, and dangerous as well. Ordinary subjects, such as weather, sounded heartless when one was talking to a woman with a husband only three days in his grave. Gossip as to the family's doings was impossible, not only because gossip sounded heartless too, but because the family's doings lately had consisted entirely of horrified discussions of Milly herself. Ernest couldn't be mentioned; even if they were alone, without the butler, he couldn't be mentioned, now that he was a wronged husband as well as being dead—one couldn't, that is, comfort Milly any more about him. The Will was taboo. So were clothes, because there she was in weeds. So, even, were things like gardens, because they naturally led to flowers, and flowers—well, wreaths were made of flowers, and there you were, at once landed in cemeteries. Oh, it was difficult. And all the time, all through each long silence, one could hear the butler breathing.

Mabel, damp and flushed, thought with dismay of having to have a solid month of these sorts of luncheons —or nearly a month, till Rosemary came home, and then they would only be worse. Useless, too, to invite any of the relations to join her and help her out, for they would say they were going to have quite enough of Milly when their turn came round, and would refuse. If only one knew *really* what she had done, thought Mabel—who she had done it with, she meant, for they knew only too well which commandment she had broken,—it would be such a help. One would know better where one was, then. Ruth, the evening before, had whispered that Milly had arrived home in George's car; she didn't want to suggest anything, Ruth whispered, but the fact remained that it *was* George's car. Probably there was nothing in that, thought Mabel; but it just showed how awkward it was for everybody to be in the dark, and how easily it made one think things. George? Her own brother-in-law? Oh, no—too shocking. Besides, George always wore enormous spectacles, and Mabel did think it must be impossible to commit—well, what Milly had committed, with somebody who wore enormous spectacles. Of course, hesitated Mabel towards the end of the meal, if poor Milly hadn't done anything, and they were all, beginning with Ernest, accusing her wrongfully, she must say it would have been rather a shame. . . .

§

When, after what seemed centuries of time, the butler, performing his final rites, had breathed his last, and they could get away from the dining-room, she asked her waxen guest if she didn't think she ought to rest up in her room till tea, while one of the maids unpacked for her and put her things away. It would be such a good thing, thought Mabel, for everybody, if Milly rested quite a lot; safe in her bedroom; out of the way.

"Do you want me to?" asked Milly, turning her heavy eyes to her.

Now if that wasn't tactless, thought Mabel, reddening.

"No—of course I don't *want* you to," she said, vexed. "I was thinking of you."

Milly went and rested; and Mabel, having given orders tea was to be sent up to her at five o'clock, escaped in the car, going for a long drive away from everybody, right into the depths of Kent, and not coming back till it was time to dress for dinner, so as to shake herself down inside a little, and recover, before having to face the evening. And pausing a moment outside Milly's door on her way upstairs when she got back, she heard a man's voice talking, and it was Percy's.

Percy. In there.

Well, why shouldn't he be? How natural to go in on getting home from his office, and greet his aunt. Funny that it should stab her. Percy knew nothing—could know nothing, for everyone had been most careful to keep that sentence in the Will, and their aunt's disappearance, from the younger generation; yet stabbed she was. She didn't want him to be in there, talking to Milly—not alone, she discovered; violently she didn't want him to. It had come so suddenly upon her, this having to have Milly in her home, that she hadn't got the details at all clear of what it would be really like with the boys about, and all made so extra difficult because of her being their aunt. *They* didn't know she was an adulterous aunt—and, "Oh, dear," thought Mabel, "there I am thinking awful words again!" But now she saw the bigness of the sacrifice Fred was asking of her. Rot about the family, she said to herself indignantly; who cared for its silly old honour, and not being touched by scandal and all that stuff, when it came to the protection of one's own children?

"I'm sure it's time to dress, Percy," she said, opening the door and speaking in an unusually sharp voice.

There he was, sitting on the rug in front of the fire,

and Milly was lying on the sofa, and it all looked so pretty and cosy, what with the flowers and things Mabel herself had put in.

"Is it, mother?" said Percy, not moving. "But I am dressed. I got back earlier, so as to see Aunt Milly."

"Oh," said Mabel; and shut the door again, and went on to her own bedroom, and stood in front of her looking-glass passionately sticking more hairpins into a head already full of them, which was what she called doing her hair, and asked herself whether the sanctity of the home wasn't to be considered, then, and if it wasn't more important by long chalks—Mabel's thoughts, when she was really roused, easily clothed themselves in expressions which were not refined—than whitewashing Milly. Why should she help to whitewash Milly? Because the Botts would say—oh, she was fed up with the Botts!—that only by doing so scandal could be kept at bay. That was the answer, she knew, and she didn't care a fig for it—not a *fig*, she told herself, indignantly.

§

But at dinner, with Fred and Dick there too, as well as Percy, and Milly so quiet and passive and looking as if she were half asleep, she was ashamed of her sudden flare-up of suspiciousness. It really was rather ugly of her; very ugly, to be quite honest. Repentant, she renewed her attentions to her guest, eagerly backing Fred up in his hospitable speeches, pressing food and drink on her, doing her utmost.

Fred rewarded her with an approving glance, and she redoubled her efforts. It wasn't anyhow half as difficult as lunch had been, she felt, with her three men to support her, and Percy no different to his aunt than he had always been. They really got through dinner very well, thought Mabel thankfully, and Fred helped nobly, talking about business every now and then to the boys, and thus easing the strain of general conversation.

But what she had felt outside Milly's door was the sort of thing she was going to feel, she was sure, on the slightest occasion. Unfair and unfounded or not, she was bound to feel it. It was an impossible position Fred had put her in. Sooner or later——

Afterwards they sat in the Winter Garden for coffee, with the fountain turned on so as to show the butler that Milly was a particularly honoured guest, because only for the best guests did they turn the fountain on; and then they went into the billiard-room while the boys played billiards, taking Milly with them, and sitting watching the game on the raised dais through a cloud of cigar smoke; and when they had done that for some time, not having to talk because of watching, they took her back to the principal drawing-room—it made the time go more quickly, changing rooms—and had some gramophone music on their super-gramophone, their so to speak eight-cylinder sixty horse-power gramophone, being careful, Mabel was, anxious to play her part as well as possible till the moment when it left off being possible, that Dick only put on sacred records like *Oh for the Wings of a Dove*, and not having to talk, because of listening.

Such a blessing, not having to talk, Mabel felt. As long as they could avoid doing that, things might jog along. It was talking which upset everybody. No wonder royalties and restaurants had bands.

The evening wound up with soda-water. There was whiskey as well, but soda-water was what Fred gave, a glass each, to Mabel and Milly. At ten o'clock punctually it appeared, and at five minutes past ten Milly was being said good-night to, and taken up to bed.

Mabel went with her, turning on the lights in the mahogany spare room, feeling for the hot-water bottle between the sheets, plumping up the pillows, being solicitous.

At last came the moment when she was forced to leave off fussing, and turn round. Would there have to be kissing? Yes; no getting out of that, she was afraid.

"Well—good-night, Milly."

"Good-night, Mabel."

"I wonder if you've got everything?"

"I'm sure I have."

"Well, then——"

Bracing herself, Mabel advanced to kiss. It was slightly less of a peck than the kiss on the door-step, though still of a darting, beaky nature.

Milly received it passively.

"I believe she's asleep," said Mabel to Fred, when, thankfully, she rejoined him.

"Already?" asked Fred, surprised, looking at his watch.

"Oh, I don't mean *really*," hesitated Mabel, trying to catch what she did mean into words.

§

Left alone, Milly stood in the luxurious room without moving, her eyes fixed on the door through which Mabel had departed with such evident relief.

So this was it, she thought; this was what it was going to be. The music she had braced herself to face was to be all sweet. She was to be taken to the Botts' bosom, and however much it hurt them, clasped close. Coals of fire were to be heaped on her head. Fatted calves slaughtered. And, sure she was guilty, they had made up their minds to behave as though they were sure she wasn't.

Titford . . . family honour. . . .

Slowly she began drawing the hairpins out of her hair; mechanically dropping them from her fingers one by one on the carpet, not aware of what she was doing, only knowing that her head felt heavy and she must lighten it. Strange and unexpected development, she thought, staring at nothing; but she had no doubt at all that here at last she was in the very arms of expiation,— and none the less expiation that it came to her so disconcertingly, with a smile on its face.

That smile. It paralyzed her. She knew she mustn't pick and choose among punishments, but how much rather would she have had to meet abuse. At least abuse would have been genuine, and though terrifying at the moment presently over, and she allowed to go her way. This embarrassed kindness, this pretence of affection, wouldn't ever be over: it would go on. Having started on these lines, unless she did something more that was wicked, the Botts wouldn't be able to leave off again. She and they, for the rest of their lives as far as she could see, would be stuck together in their own terrible honey.

A round of visits. She had entered on a round of visits. It seemed incredible. Slowly, having dropped all her hairpins on the floor, she began plaiting her hair in its customary bedtime plaits. At the end of the visits, would she be let go? Or was it to be a round and round of them, and when she had worked through the whole family would she have to begin again at Fred's, and so on, over and over, till death released everybody? Unhappy Botts. They too, then, were expiating. And unhappy Mabel, with her flushed, worried face, forcing herself to kiss, to be hospitable, heroically trying to carry out what had evidently been strict instructions —wasn't it hard that she too, without ever having set eyes on him, should have to suffer because of Arthur?

It was very hard; and Milly, mechanically plaiting her hair, could see no way out of it. What could she do except pretend, except play up to the family, except make it easier for them by behaving as if she were really as innocent as they apparently were going desperately to insist? And what, in that case, became of her resolve to have done with lying?

"I can't—I *can't*," she suddenly said out loud, her hands dropping at her sides; but even as she said it she knew she must and would. Hadn't she sworn to herself to make amends to the Botts, to do in all things what they wished? And if this were what they had decided was the best way for them out of the situation she had put them in, then mustn't she help in whatever way she could? But what a punishment, she whispered under her breath; for everybody, what a punishment. Ah, if it had been real, the welcome, the kindness, in spite of what she had done—why, then, with what flooding gratitude, with what quick response of love, she would have applied herself for the rest of her days to goodness. . . .

That, however, was nonsense. She resumed the plaiting of her hair. How could it be real? What right had she to real affection from the family she had disgraced? The Botts weren't saints; and only saints didn't mind sinners. Also—she, at least, would face the truth—if she had been going to marry Arthur, if that had been settled and happy, would she have minded much about the Botts?

"Oh, I'm contemptible," said Milly, again aloud, her hands dropping once more at her sides, staring wide-eyed at nothing.

⁜(XIII)*⁜*

THE next day was Saturday, and when the gong went for breakfast no Milly appeared.

Mabel, always the first in the dining-room because of prayers, fidgeted about nervously among the coffee-cups, glancing frequently at the door; but minutes passed, and first Percy, and then Fred, and then Dick, came down one after the other, and ate their porridge and proceeded to their sausages, and still there was no sign of Milly.

Late; she was going to be late. Slowly relief began creeping round the table. "She's late," Mabel half whispered once, and the heads bent more assiduously over their plates in a kind of hush of suspense, lest this remark should be overheard by Fate, and immediately produce her.

But more minutes passed, and nothing happened. The relief increased. No one wanted Milly at breakfast, not even the boys, who felt that their white-faced, black-garbed aunt wouldn't mix at all well, somehow, with sausages; and Fred, as he ate his, found they tasted better and better the longer she delayed, and Mabel became gradually almost sprightly.

Mabel, indeed, all through prayers had kept an anxious eye on the door, in case Milly should come in before they were over. She was, Mabel had already discovered, a painstaking guest, and on her first day had been where she ought to be each time not merely on the tick but a minute or two ahead of it; so that Mabel had

greatly feared she might, on the first morning, in the
excess of her zeal to give no trouble in small things
because she was giving so much in big ones, be over-
punctual at breakfast, and thus tumble into the middle
of prayers.

Passionately Mabel didn't want Milly at prayers.
She positively raced through them, and only dared
breathe again when the Bible was going out and the
porridge coming in. How could she have prayed with
Milly present? It was bad enough doing it with the
butler present, but he at least was known for a moral
man. Milly's presence, among the stonily hostile servants, would have dried up the collects on Mabel's very
lips. She had tried to get her to stay in bed for breakfast,
asking her the night before, when she accompanied her
upstairs, whether she wouldn't like it in her room,
but she seemed to have lost her tact as well as her virtue
—that famous tact they used to hear so much about—
and said she would rather come down. Some idea, Mabel
supposed, of not giving trouble; as though the worst
trouble of all wasn't having her wandering round in
contact with the boys, and everybody having to pretend!

Bed, of course, was the best place for Milly, Mabel
thought as she poured out coffee, one ear cocked, listening for footsteps approaching across the hall; anyhow
for a bit. A slight illness was really what she ought to
develop, Mabel felt—naturally nothing much, but
enough to keep her upstairs during the next week or so.
It was almost her duty, in the first stage of a widowhood
caused by violence, to have some sort of breakdown.
People would expect it; everybody would think it
natural; and if it could be spread over the whole month
of her stay, then Mabel, instead of being the worst off
of the family for having to be the first to welcome her,

would think herself the luckiest of the lot. What could be an easier way of getting through the visit—*any* visit, thought Mabel, at all times an awkward and reluctant hostess—than for the guest to stay in bed? In this way no one would see her except the maids and Mabel herself, Percy would be preserved from harmful contact, Fred would be spared irksome efforts to talk, and the butler wouldn't have to wait on sin.

And, as though in answer to these unspoken wishes, the butler, who at breakfast only hovered occasionally and didn't stick, came in with a message the head housemaid had just given him from Mrs. Ernest, saying she was very sorry but she had rather a headache, and might she be excused from coming down.

Might she? Oh, hallelujah! sang Mabel to herself.

Fred was all heartiness. "Certainly, certainly," he cried, reaching across the dishes in front of him and spiking a pat of butter on his knife. "No place like bed when one is—when one isn't—Send word, Smith, we're all deligh—we're all very gl— I mean, we're sorry to hear it. No—hold on a minute. You go, Mabel, and see if she's got everything. Tuck her up, and tell her to take care of herself. That's all right, Smith," he nodded dismissal to the butler. "And you might ask her," he continued to Mabel, whose hallelujah had already died down at the prospect of having to go and tuck up Milly, "where she has put that thousand pounds."

"What thousand pounds?" instantly asked Percy, jerking his head up from his plate.

"Your aunt's legacy," said Fred shortly, regretting he had mentioned it before the boys. One thing leads to another, and in what concerned Milly all the things were damned unpleasant.

"I thought there wasn't a legacy. You said last night——"

"Pass the marmalade," commanded his father.

"How did she manage to get hold of it so soon?" persisted Percy. "I thought——"

"Daresay you did," interrupted his father; and waving him aside with a gesture of the marmalade spoon, he continued his address to Mabel, who was reluctantly preparing to obey him and had pulled the cloth askew, and spilled some coffee, in the process. "It's somewhere up in her room," he said. "It mustn't lie about loose, tell her, over the week-end. I'm going to invest it for her on Monday, and meanwhile it mustn't lie about loose. Ask her to let me have it to put in my safe."

"But, Fred—do you think I ought to? If she's got a headache?" hesitated Mabel. It was Fred's job, surely, she thought, to do any talking to Milly which approached business; she had more than her share of her as it was. "I don't see how I can bother her if she isn't well," she said, doubtfully.

"Then go and have a look round the room, and see for yourself where it is."

"Oh, Fred——" Mabel feebly protested.

"It's not fair to the servants to have a sum like that lying in a woman's bedroom," said Fred. "It's putting temptation in their way. Besides, they'll talk, and we shall be burgled sure as Fate."

"Good gracious!" exclaimed Mabel at that, who lived in dread of burglars; and she went away rather quickly to the mahogany bedroom.

But when she got there, and after knocking and getting no answer opened the door, she found Milly was asleep—or seemed to be. Her eyes were shut, anyhow, and stayed shut in spite of the noise the door made.

"Milly——" began Mabel, tentatively.

No answer.

"Asleep," she decided; and stood hesitating, wondering whether she had better go in and wait till she woke up, or go down and finish her breakfast. She decided to finish her breakfast, and she shut the door softly and went back to the dining-room.

"She's asleep," she said.

"Then go and wake her," said Fred. "I've got to catch the 10.15, and must lock up that money before I go."

"But how can I wake her if she's got a headache?" Mabel again protested; and the boys too seemed to think it rather a shame.

Fred, however, had made up his mind, and was adamant. Looking round the table he requested his family to allow him to be the judge of what was the proper course to pursue; he wasn't going to risk the loss in his house of a thousand pounds merely because a woman was having forty winks and they thought it a shame to disturb her; also he had to catch his train. Mabel must go up again at once, he ordered. And Mabel, bound to obey when Fred spoke in that voice, went.

But when, on opening the door a second time, she found the same picture on the bed of closed eyes and apparent sleep, opposition, away from Fred's eye and voice, became more active, and instead of waking Milly according to orders, or even looking round among her helpless things according to orders, she softly tiptoed across the room to a chair by the fire, and sat down and waited.

It was quiet there, and safe—the one place in the house Fred couldn't come into without permission. Plenty of time, thought Mabel, noiselessly sitting down, to find out about the money when he came back to lunch—to luncheon, she corrected herself. Being Saturday, he would be back almost as soon as he had started, and Milly would be awake by then, and perhaps up and dressed, and he could talk to her himself. There wasn't any hurry. Burglars wouldn't come before dark; maids wouldn't be tempted while there was someone in the room. Ridiculous of Fred suddenly to fuss, thought Mabel, becoming more courageous every minute in that safe place. He hadn't said a word about the wretched money the day before—all night long it had been lying somewhere in Milly's room, and he hadn't even mentioned it. He had just simply forgotten it yesterday; and if he could forget it, it couldn't be so terribly dangerous and risky for it to remain wherever it was a little longer.

Mabel settled herself more comfortably in the chair. She would stay where she was till after Fred's train had gone. There wasn't another door in the house she could shut against him, but she could shut this door, and it was so much easier not to obey him when she knew he couldn't get at her. Afterwards, if he was very angry, she could say she had had to do things for Milly.

Poor Milly. Let her sleep. There could be little fun for her, these days, in being awake, thought Mabel, so much obliged to her for being in bed that she felt quite softened. Whether she had done whatever she had done or hadn't done it, she must know they all thought she had, which must be horrible for her. Why had she come back? Mabel in her place would never, she was sure, have had the face to come back, especially not if she had a thousand pounds in her pocket. She ought to have gone to that sister of hers. Birds of a feather. . . .

But were they birds of a feather? Watching her from her chair by the fire, Mabel thought she might quite well at that moment be taken for a good school-girl, her figure hidden under the bedclothes, and her fair hair in two thick plaits down each side of her smooth face. Mabel's own face was all crumpled up into creases, though she was only two years older than Milly—but how much better to be creased than wicked, she thought. Perhaps creases had something to do with virtue, and one either had both or neither, she said to herself, gazing at Milly, ready to turn away quickly at the first quiver of those quiet eyelashes. Since Ernest's accident she hadn't had such an opportunity of studying her, and really and truly, Mabel said to herself, almost as if she were reasoning aloud with Milly, she had no right to look good like that if she wasn't. It made it so difficult to be *sure*; and it was so worrying not to be *sure*. Because, suppose——?

Well, they couldn't all be wrong, the whole family, and Ernest at the head of them, she told herself. Still —again she hesitated—suppose they were?

And then she started, for Milly, unexpectedly opening her eyes, caught her, after all, staring at her.

"Oh—you're awake," said Mabel, embarrassed, getting up and going over to the bed.

Milly put out a languid hand. "Do you mind my not coming down?" she murmured, raising her heavy eyes to the face above her.

Mabel took the hand. What can one do but take a hand put out?

"No, of course not," she said. "We like it. I mean," she hastily corrected, "we like you to do what you like to do."

"You're so kind," said Milly in a low voice. "So terribly, terribly kind——" and added, her eyelids drooping as if too heavy to stay open, and her hand sliding from Mabel's loose grasp back on to the quilt, "I've got such a headache."

"I'm *sure* you have," said Mabel fervently, almost as one who congratulates on a propriety. "I mean," she went on in some confusion, herself noticing this tone, "it's natural you should have one, isn't it, after—after all."

To this Milly said nothing, but lay, lax and motionless, her eyes shut, her mouth slightly open, overcome by a hopeless fatigue.

Mabel stood staring at her. Was she going to be really ill? Ought one to send for her doctor? It would look well, of course, for Milly to need a doctor, but suppose she developed a temperature, and talked before him, as people with temperatures do sometimes talk, and let out what was, what must be, so heavy on her conscience? That would be awful. No, she mustn't be allowed to be as ill as all that. She must just lie there quietly and rest, and Mabel would look after her herself—indeed, Mabel felt she would nurse Milly with real enthusiasm if only she would stay in bed quietly, out of everyone's way, and not get worse, and not get better, but just simmer along till it was time to get up and go on her next visit.

"You'll be all right if you stay in bed," she said, trying not to sound too eager.

"May I?" asked Milly, without opening her eyes. Her headache was so enormous—as big, it seemed, as the whole world.

"Of course. It's *much* the best place for you," said Mabel, with such conviction in her voice that Milly opened her eyes and looked at her languidly a moment.

Then she shut them again, and turned her face to the wall, muttering something Mabel couldn't catch.

"What did you say?" asked Mabel, bending over her.

But Milly seemed to have once more dropped off to sleep; and after waiting a minute, Mabel, knowing that by now Fred must have gone to catch his train, tiptoed away to give orders for an immediate and lavish preparation of beef tea, jelly, and barley-water.

§

For ten days Milly was really ill; but, fortunately,
so reliably ill—by which Mabel meant she was comatose
rather than excited, and didn't wander in her head and
let out secrets—that a doctor could safely be sent for.
Not a nurse. This, Mabel felt sure, would be dangerous,
because one becomes so familiar with one's nurse, and
easily tells her things. Mabel remembered how she herself, in her confinements, had told her nurse all sorts
of intimate and not at all proper things about Fred,
which still made her hot to think of. No; Mabel would
do the nursing, and was very glad to, for Milly wasn't in
the least alarming in her apathetic, drowsy state, and it
relieved Mabel of all anxiety about Fred and the boys to
know her safely in bed and nobody, except the doctor
and Mabel herself, able to get at her.

The doctor was most sympathetic. He said it was
what he had been afraid of, but expected, after such a
shock, and prescribed quiet and tonics. Really it was
all exactly what Mabel would have wished. She went
about full of thankfulness; and Fred was so nice and
kind, and several times called her old girl, which was his
highest form of praise, though he did rather worry about
not being able to get hold of the thousand pounds.

"You must wait," Mabel told him—quite important
these days, a real somebody, she felt, at last; and since
it seems to be difficult to wash and feed people for any
length of time without becoming fond of them, by the
end of a week of plying the unresisting Milly with beef-
tea she began to soften towards her, to believe she had
been wronged, and found herself developing a tendency
to allude to Fred's deceased brother as "that Ernest."

Once she spoke of him in this way, before she knew
what she was saying—which was indeed her usual

method of conversation—in the presence of her sisters-in-law Edith and Maud, who, with the rest of the female portion of the family, now that they were sure they wouldn't meet Milly, frequently dropped in to hear how things were going. It slipped out, somehow, as the things in Mabel's head did slip out, and they stared at her in shocked surprise.

"Mabel, I can't let you speak in such a way of my poor brother," said Maud, *née* Bott, after a scandalized pause.

"Milly's getting round you," declared Edith, her thin lips drawn down at the corners.

Getting round her? Mabel felt all the customary indignation at the suggestion, but could think of nothing to say back, she being of those who can't when most they need to, except, "I like that."

Yet Edith turned out to have been right. Mabel, at the end of another week, had bitter occasion to admit it. How *could* Milly, Mabel asked herself, after the way she had nursed her, the really devoted way—she had seemed like a baby, a grateful baby, in Mabel's hands—oh, never, never again would Mabel believe in man, woman or child—and as for poor Ernest. . . .

What happened was that, at the end of a fortnight, Milly had so much benefited by the quiet and the beef-tea—in fact, by Mabel's kindness, Mabel reminded herself—and was, though apathetic, so evidently better, that the doctor said she might get up and lie on the sofa for a few hours every day so as to begin to get her strength up; and directly he heard this, Fred insisted on paying her a visit. Mabel's instinct warned her, she afterwards remembered, that it was funny of Fred not to be able to wait till Milly came downstairs, but he was so positive it was most important he should see her and have a business talk, that Mabel gave way. Business!

How many wives, thought Mabel afterwards, must have heard that word applied to the sort of conduct she caught Fred indulging in? And she remembered afterwards, too, how restless he had been, how more and more fidgety every day, always asking when Milly would be up again, always pretending he wanted to see her on business. Business! Mabel felt she would never believe him again, when he talked to her of business.

"You can't," she said at first, when he wanted to go up, still feeling authoritative and important after being in sole command of Milly so long. "What an idea."

"Why not? She's dressed, isn't she?"

"You can't go into Milly's bedroom, Fred. It wouldn't be proper."

"Not proper? What, when she's dressed and up, and I'm her brother-in-law? Don't be silly, Mabel."

Then Mabel began to falter, in spite of her instinct. Perhaps he was right, and she was silly. After all, sofas weren't beds, and Milly had all her clothes on, except her crape and hairpins. She couldn't really object to Fred's going up, any more than that first night she had been able really to object to Percy's visit to his aunt's room. Still, she didn't like it. Fred knew Milly was different from an ordinary sister-in-law, or believed he knew she was. Mabel herself no longer believed it, because she had been nursing her, but she was conscious this wasn't a good reason and that the family would make short work of it. Fred, though, did believe it, and accordingly oughtn't to wish to go into such a room.

"Why do you want to?" she asked, uncertainly; for though her word had been law with Milly for a fortnight it hadn't been law with Fred, who was just as masterly and headstrong as ever.

"I want to talk business," he said. "You know I do.

You know I've been worrying about that money. I want to talk over investments. I want to find out where it is."

"Can't I find out just as well as you?"

"You wouldn't before, when I wanted you to, so now I'm going to myself. I'm responsible to the family for its safety. You don't seem to understand the value of money. Tell her I'm coming up after tea."

"Oh, Fred—you can't after tea. She goes back to bed then."

"Well, to-morrow. First thing after breakfast."

"Oh, but you can't after breakfast, Fred—she isn't up then."

Mabel, however, had now over-reached herself, for after staring at her a moment from under his heavy eyebrows, Fred said, "Then I'll go now."

And he went.

§

It was Saturday again—the day fortnight from Milly's first being ill. Fred had arranged to play a round of golf with George on the West Titford links after lunch, but George would have to wait, he said to himself, for he was damned if he'd be put off any longer by Mabel and her Oh but you can'ts. During this fortnight he had seen a good deal of his brothers and brothers-in-law, who all thought it very risky that Milly's money should be somewhere in a bedroom for so long, and told Fred so, and seemed to think it strange that he hadn't placed it in safety the very first day Milly arrived at his house —which added to his own uneasiness and annoyance with himself. Still, he couldn't very well raid a sick woman's bedroom, could he? he asked them. And they admitted he couldn't; especially not this particular bedroom.

"You may take it from me," Fred assured them, "that I'll seize the first opportunity"; and this was the first opportunity, and he seized it.

Mabel had been a brick and all that, he knew—indeed, she had rather overdone the brick business, he had been thinking lately—but he wasn't going to let her come between him and his duty to that thousand pounds. Latterly he had hardly been able to sleep, knowing such a sum was lying about in his house just because he had so unaccountably forgotten to ask for it the first day. It had been worrying him more and more; and Milly's being confined to her bed, which otherwise would have been a reason for congratulation, became, as the days passed, an increasing exasperation. Besides, if anything happened to the money while under his roof the family would probably regard him as responsible, and expect him to make the loss good, and he saw no fun at all in that.

The thought made him go upstairs two steps at a time and knock very loudly on Milly's door, and when he didn't get an immediate answer he opened it a slit, and said, automatically becoming hearty, "Any admittance?"

There was a pause inside the room of evident surprise. Then Milly's voice, small and slow after all the days of being in bed, said, hesitatingly, "Is it you, Fred? Oh, yes—come in."

She was on a sofa drawn up to the fire, and the room was bright with flowers and early afternoon sunshine. The windows were open, and it smelt sweet. Books, barley-water, grapes, violets—all the accompaniments of well cared-for convalescence, were on a little table by her side. Clean and attentively nursed she looked in her rose-coloured wrapper, her hair plaited in two long plaits. Mabel certainly had done her duty by her. But the minute he saw her Fred felt as much embarrassed as he did the last time he was alone with her, when he fetched her from Mandeville Park Road—more embarrassed, in fact. Perhaps Mabel was right, and he oughtn't to have come up. He hadn't seen Milly in plaits before, and they somehow produced an atmosphere of intimacy which was the last thing he wanted. So he began to be boisterous, trying to appear genial and at his ease.

"Hello, Milly," he said, striding across to the sofa and speaking very loud, "how are you? Feeling pretty fit again? Sorry you've been seedy, but you'll be all right now. Keeping your pecker up, eh?" he added, noticing a tray with food on it. "That's right. Splendid."

And checking a desire to rub his hands, so as to give himself countenance, he drew up the chair Mabel usually sat in, and settled himself in it for, he informed her, a talk.

The quick flush of the weak flew into Milly's face, and as quickly flew out again.

"I've been worrying ever since you've been ill," he said, settling himself in the chair; and there was such unmistakable sincerity in his voice that Milly looked at him, startled and touched.

"You needn't have," she murmured, flushing again. "Mabel has been an angel to me."

"I've been worrying," Fred, doggedly stalking his subject, persisted, "about that money."

"Which money?" asked Milly, who for the moment had quite forgotten it. There had been so many things to think of, a whole existence to rearrange, while she lay in bed slowly coming back to life, and the thousand pounds, belonging to the wretched past and gone anyhow, had drifted during her illness out of her mind.

"Which money?" repeated Fred, pulling a grape off the bunch on a plate beside her, and putting it in his mouth so as to give himself something to do, for he couldn't very well smoke in a sick room. "Have you got any more, then?"

"Oh, you mean——"

She made an effort to concentrate, and little beads came out on her upper lip because of her having been in bed so long, and this being her first day up. "You mean what Ernest left me. No, I haven't got any more."

She hesitated.

"Not yet, that is," she went on in her slow, weak voice. "Not till I've sold my jewellery. I hope—perhaps I'll be able—to do that soon."

"A good idea," approved Fred, nodding. "But George told me you got your legacy, and you'd better let me have it to invest for you. I think I can get you a safe five per cent. I wouldn't advise more, though of course I could——" he turned over in his mind, his mouth, with the grape in it, screwed up, a few of the slightly less sound and slightly more profitable investments he knew of, and dismissed them. "No," he said, shaking his head, "I wouldn't advise it. Best be on the safe side. Of course I ought to have asked for the money at once, directly you arrived, and not wasted a fortnight's interest."

"But," said Milly, confused, "I haven't got it."

"Haven't you?" said Fred, so much surprised at this that he found himself looking straight at her. "Why, George told us you'd been to Jenkyns, and he——"

"Yes," said Milly as he paused, "but——"

The flush was fixed now on her face. It hadn't occurred to her that her not having the thousand pounds would surprise the Botts unpleasantly. She hadn't thought about it at all from their point of view, not foreseeing, not dreaming, that she was to be on their hands as their permanent guest. During those three days before she collapsed into bed, what time had she to think? Engaged as she had been in perpetual flight from one dreadful situation to another, what time had she had to do anything but feel? Now, however, it occurred to her; very clearly it occurred to her. And her eyes, fixed on Fred, were startled.

"But—I did," she faltered.

"Did what?" Fred asked.

"I did get it."

He stared. 'Then where——" he began, his mouth working because of the grape in it, which was big.

Before saying any more he had to swallow it. Having done so, he began again: "Then where is it? Excuse my asking, won't you. But as I explained the day I brought you here, we're taking you on now, the family is—a pleasure, I'm sure—and we must get the financial side straight."

"I thought," said Milly, the beads on her upper lip spreading to her temples, "it was mine"—a remark which sounded ominous to Fred.

"Certainly it is yours," he said; but he didn't go on because he had an unpleasant feeling that he was getting near something very objectionable, something which might land him, if he questioned further, right up against—well, the wretched fellow Milly had obviously been in London with. *He* had got the money, Fred suddenly felt terribly sure. Bad enough that, in all conscience; but worse if he questioned Milly till she admitted it, for then good-bye to ignoring him, good-bye to ignoring her adultery, good-bye to saving the family's good name.

Frowning, he pulled off another grape, with movements so significant of mental disturbance that Milly's eyes became more startled and afraid than ever.

"Of course," he went on, not looking at her as he ate

it, "it isn't really my or anyone else's business. If you haven't got it you haven't got it. But if you've deposited it in a bank"—his voice lightened at the possibility—"you might just tell me. It'll help, you know—the interest will."

"It isn't in a bank," said Milly.

There was a tiny pause, and Fred gulped down his grape.

"I've—given it away," she said.

"Ah," said Fred.

So that was it. The fellow had got it. Just as he suspected. Perfectly revolting. And now was she going to make it worse, make the whole position impossible for everybody, by telling him who she had given it to? It looked like it. She was beginning to speak——

"For God's sake, Milly," he said sharply, suddenly glaring across at her from under his shaggy eyebrows, "let's leave it at that. I don't wish to——"

"But, Fred—I want to tell you. I gave it to my sister."

"To your sister?"

He stared at her. "What," he said, "the one who——?"

"I've only got one," said Milly.

"But—doesn't she live in Switzerland? I seem to remember she——"

"Yes. But when she saw Ernest's death in the paper—" Milly stopped a moment to wipe the beads off her upper lip—"she came over to—to see me."

"And did you see her?"

"Yes, I saw her in London. I gave her the money."

Fred was silent, staring at her. Then he said, on a sudden impulse, his voice quite different, "I beg your pardon, Milly."

"Oh, Fred—what for?" she asked; adding, before he could say anything, for she didn't want an answer to that ill-advised question, "I couldn't not have given it

to her. Anybody would have, in my place——" and
speaking slowly, pausing and going on again, the hair
round her ears quite wet now with effort, she told him
of Agatha's situation, of how desperate it had been for
years, and of how she had come over to live, as she
thought, with Milly in Mandeville Park Road, knowing
nothing, naturally, of Ernest's Will.

"You wouldn't have liked," she ended, lying back on
her cushions with the glimmer of a smile, for somehow
the atmosphere had lightened, "having two of us on
your hands, would you?"

"But did she know it was all you had?" Fred asked.

"Well, she knew I'd got——" Milly's eyelids quivered
and drooped—"all of you," she finished.

"Yes," Fred reflected. "Yes. Still, you know, to take
every penny a woman possesses——"

"But she didn't. I've got my jewellery," said Milly,
raising her eyes again and looking at him. "I told you
I want to try and sell it soon. I think it's quite valuable
—don't you?"

"Still, you know," persisted Fred, not to be deflected
from his consideration of Agatha's conduct, "to take
every penny a woman possesses——"

Milly was a fool to have given it to her, of course, but
what sort of a creature could she be to take it? Well,
he knew the sort of creature she was; out of the distant
past the old scandal came back quite clearly to him
again, and his mouth took on an expression of distaste.

Milly guessed what he was thinking. "I made her
take it," she said. "And naturally she thought it didn't
matter, because I was going to be m——"

She stopped with a small gasp. Had he noticed?
If this talk went on long enough she would be sure to
let out what at all costs the Botts didn't want definitely
to know. Oh, she was too weak for an interview like this.

She ought to have been given a lot of meat, or something, before Fred came up, to put some strength into her. Just then, in her anxiety to protect poor Aggie, and having nothing but beef-tea and milk puddings inside her to steady her, she had been on the very verge . . .

Fred, however, hadn't noticed. He was still deep in unflattering consideration of that sister.

"You hadn't heard anything of each other for years, had you?" he asked after a moment. "Never since she——"

"Ran away," Milly finished for him; and saying to herself that here at least was something she could talk openly about, that she could confess, now that it was all over and didn't matter to anybody, she told Fred how they had written to each other during the whole time. She knew it was a deceitful thing to have done, she said, but she had loved her sister, and couldn't endure, she anxiously explained, her eyes on his face, to be cut off from her for good and all.

And again she had that feeling that if only she had had a tonic, or some meat or something, before this interview, she would have managed it better.

"He forbade you to write, didn't he? Ernest, I mean," said Fred, who had listened intently. "I fancy remembering his telling us he had."

"Yes. And I disobeyed. Wouldn't you have, Fred?"

He grinned a little. "I don't know," he said. "I don't quite see Mabel forbidding——"

A tone of friendliness, as distinguished from his first awkward heartiness, was warming his voice, crept into it at the point where Agatha had entered the conversation, and increasing as he talked. Great was his relief that at least it wasn't that fellow who had got the money, and that it was her sister she had been with in

London. One blot at least, and a nasty one too, had been
removed from Milly's character. Also, it now seemed
possible that the secrecy of her journey might be explained by a desire to evade the certain hostile criticism
of the family if they had known what she intended doing. They would have been mightily and properly
shocked to think of Milly's meagre inheritance going to
that sister. She well knew how much they had all objected to the sister, and how painful the whole story had
been to them. Natural that, determined to see her sister
and help her, she should have run off without a word.
And he had always liked poor little Milly, and it was
exceedingly difficult for Fred, sitting with her and
talking, and seeing her looking so good and sweet in her
plaits, and hearing her sounding so much too weak to be
able to tell anything but the truth, either to remember
or believe that she was a deceiver and a bad lot—in fact
it was getting more difficult every minute. While as for
the money, what was the loss of fifty pounds or so a year,
compared to the comfort, the relief, of knowing Milly
wasn't quite so wicked after all?

Then a thought struck him. He leaned forward.
"Did he ever find out?" he asked quickly. "Ernest, I
mean. About the letters," he added, for Milly was
looking frightened, and as though she didn't understand.

"I—don't think so. Why?"

"But he may have without your knowing, mightn't
he?"

She hesitated. "Yes—he *may* have," she said slowly,
remembering that which he had indeed found out.
Since Ernest was such an expert at finding out, why
should he not also have known all about the letters?

"And he never would forgive you if he had, would
he?" asked Fred, with curious and unusual eagerness.

"Oh, *never*. I can't imagine Ernest ever——"

"Nor can I," Fred agreed. "No, I'm certain he wouldn't have."

He was leaning forward, staring at her with an odd expression in his eyes, and his sallow face was red.

"My dear Milly," he said after a moment, stretching out his hand across the dish of grapes, and closing it tightly over hers.

She shrank back, but he held it fast.

"My dear Milly," he said again, his eyes fixed on her face, "anything we any of us can do to make up——"

A hot flood of still brighter colour rushed into her already flushed cheeks. She knew what conclusion he had jumped to. She tried feebly to pull her hand away.

"But, Fred," she began in consternation, for here she was being whitewashed with a vengeance, being forced to take in poor, kind Fred really, not just playing her part in a game of pretence they were all joining in. "But, Fred," she began, trying to draw her hand away— and who knows what she wouldn't have said next, if at that moment the door hadn't opened, and Mabel, who had been fuming and fretting downstairs, and at last couldn't endure the idea of Fred being alone up there any longer, hadn't appeared.

She stopped when she saw them, and stood rooted. Even a person who wasn't a wife would have had the feeling of intruding on something very like a love-scene, they were both so red and obviously agitated, and he leaning over the grapes and the violets and everything, so as to hold her hand.

Mabel's puckered face was a study in amazed, indignant misery. Edith's words came crashing into her mind. Taken in indeed she was; taken in all round.

She stared at them, rooted. She couldn't have believed it of Fred—the very first moment he was left alone with her. And Milly—Milly, of whose innocence she had been so sure, whom she had nursed so devotedly, who had seemed like a grateful baby.

"I suppose you know," she said slowly, trying to keep her voice from going up and down in squeaks, "George is waiting for you all this time on the links?"

§

Fred was now to discover what Mabel could be like when roused.

He hadn't had an idea of her possibilities; nor had he dreamed how small a part reason played in her make-up. He now was to find out. For, as he hurried downstairs to get his clubs and be off to old George, who must have been cooling his heels for the best part of an hour—"By Jove, yes," he exclaimed, looking at his watch—she caught him up, and said in a voice he didn't know, "I wish to speak to you. Please come into the study."

"Not now—after tea," said Fred, seizing his cap.

He did, however, go into the study; he found himself in it, apparently of his own free will, and the door shut; and there he became, for the first time in his married life, really acquainted with Mabel.

Just as she, upstairs, had had difficulty in believing that that was Fred, so he, in his study, had difficulty in believing that this was Mabel. Yet she looked like Mabel; she had on her clothes. And also she looked like an ordinary, reasonable human being—with a face, that is, and a forehead, and all that. How could he answer her? What could he say to someone who consisted entirely—he had never suspected it—of violent possessive emotions, uncontrolled by any, or the very smallest amount of, intelligence?

He looked, and listened, dumbfounded. They had jogged along the years together, no demands made on her mind beyond housekeeping, and he had done the thinking, and she had done the rest, and done it quite nicely; and if, sometimes, he had thought her a little silly, he had supposed that all women were, sometimes, a little silly, and it hadn't disturbed him.

Now he discovered that silliness, an inability to understand, even to listen and try to, was her usual condition, had always been her usual condition, hidden only by the want of occasion for exercising sense.

"If what I've just seen," said she, her voice trembling with fury, her whole body shaking, "is your idea of talking business with Milly, let me tell you I won't have it. Do you hear, Fred? I simply won't have it."

And, as he stared at her, really at first not understanding, she flung up at him, "What were you doing, holding Milly's hand, and your face all red, and you pretending to me it was business? Business! A nice sort of business. I shall know what you're up to next time you tell me you must do business."

Mabel speaking to him like that. Mabel.

Calm in the face of such monstrous excitement, Fred tried to explain what he had discovered—that they had all been wrong about the unfortunate Milly, that there wasn't a man in it at all, and Ernest had cut her out of his Will for nothing whatever except disobeying his order not to write to that sister of hers; and Mabel, she just laughed at him—loudly, strangely, derisively, her hands pressed against her sides.

Such sounds as these he had never before heard proceeding from her whose mirth, when there was any, expressed itself in small titters; and, still not understanding, his blood a little chilled by the unaccustomed noises she was making, on his asking, "What on earth's the matter? What has happened to you?" her amazing answer, jerked out on a shriek of laughter, was, "You're a fool."

A fool. He. Mabel telling him so.

Then Fred settled down to it; settled down to his melancholy realizations. He tried, before quite giving up hope, to regain some control over her, to sober her by calling her My dear—"Don't call me names, my dear," said Fred, who had only addressed her as his dear once before in their life—years ago, when in spite of having been told she wasn't to, she drove his favourite mare and let her down and broke both her knees, and the effect of this endearment, used in the particular tone he was again using, had been devastating. But now it passed over her like water, because Mabel, born all heart and no head—she began, he slowly realized, from the chest downwards, and above her chest, though she appeared to have a head, there seemed to be nothing really but a strange little box, full of a litter of disconnected flimsy odds and ends—Mabel, having been born like this, couldn't concentrate, didn't listen, intent only on what her injured heart felt, which was that she had been made a fool of, and shamefully taken in.

Slowly Fred, as he listened to her, realized this—that he was, in fact, talking to a person with the mind of a child and the enormous heart of a woman. What a combination, he thought; perhaps more frequent than he knew. He had only not found it out sooner because of the uneventfulness, the plain sailing, of their life. And it considerably depressed him, for a man, he thought, likes his wife to have a head as well.

It did, however, this realization, keep him from getting angry and saying things no Bott husband had yet said, and he was very sorry for his poor distracted little wife, making herself so miserable about something which hadn't happened, when, her sense of injury, of having been taken in by the husband to whom she had devoted her life, and by Milly in whom she had come to believe, overwhelming her, she burst into a wild flood of tears.

Then he took her on his knee. She was a child; a kind, unreasoning child, he said to himself, feeling suddenly lonely, as if something he had supposed was there had gone out of his life, and she would never be anything else. And because he hadn't sat her on his knee since the early part of the first year of their marriage, Mabel was so much overcome by this action that her fury melted, and with her arms round his neck, her wet cheek ruining his tie, she asked him, sobbing, why he had been like that with Milly—why, why—so dreadful of him when she had been such a good wife to him—and loved him, loved him——

"Why?" said Fred. "Because I was so ashamed of myself, and ashamed of all of us, for having at once believed what we have believed about her."

"But Ernest—" sobbed Mabel—"he wouldn't have —not for nothing—just for letters—oh, Fred—as if he would!"

"Wouldn't he?" And Fred, remembering Ernest, repeated with conviction, "*Wouldn't* he."

"You'd rather believe your d-dead brother has——"

"Much rather. What do you think?"

"I think," said Mabel, dropping from sobs into plain despair, "you're very fond of Milly. Fonder of her than you ought to be."

And Fred couldn't go and take counsel of old George, he couldn't tell anyone his troubles, because she was his wife, and the Bott tradition shut his mouth.

*⁑(*XIV*)⁑*

WHILE this was happening, the Alec Botts, at Brighton, were enjoying sea breezes, mild sunshine, and complete immunity from worries. They had been doing this for over a fortnight, their time filled up by morning strolls on the front, afternoon drives along country roads, evening repose in a corner of the lounge watching the other sojourners in the hotel but not speaking to them, and regular and excessive meals.

The family didn't write to them; the family was annoyed with them; and accordingly they were steeped in peace. Alec stroked his beard, and congratulated himself. Ruth, thankful to have escaped Milly, couldn't do enough for him who had saved her, and, happy to have her husband exclusively to herself, said at frequent intervals that it was like a honeymoon, with which Alec, though his idea of a honeymoon was different, politely agreed.

At first he felt peaceful and pleased, not only because he was clear of Milly but because of the comfort of having a virtuous and devoted wife; but, as early as the second week of peace and comfort, he began to notice a good deal of sameness about Ruth when one was with her without stopping, and by the third week he was wondering, as he stared out the window at the illimitable sea, whether being alone with virtue and devotion couldn't be overdone. That his wife was delighted to be alone with him was evident; and this, to which he was indulgent at first, being rather pleased by it in fact, presently cloyed him. Never since their honeymoon had they gone off by themselves and not a soul to speak to, she reminded him, with a kind of meek exulting which he bore in silence. She asked nothing better, she assured him, than not to have a soul to speak to except him, unless—but this she didn't say aloud—it was that he shouldn't have a soul to speak to except her; and she inquired—foolishly, it seemed to Alec staring out of the window, for she well knew it was impossible, even if they had really wanted to—"Why can't we always live like this—just you and me?" And he, avoiding a direct answer, confined himself to correcting her grammar and telling her she shouldn't say me, but I; which she accepted with meekness, submitting herself in all things to her husband, according to the directions of St. Paul.

Meekness, devotion, virtue, accompanying his every step—what could a man want more? He didn't want more, he wanted less, Alec said to himself, after being shut up with these attributes for a fortnight. And by the end of another week he became aware that he was secretly glutted with Ruth.

Shocked at this, he grew very quiet; and the quieter he grew the more she plied him with devotion, and he was more glutted than ever. In fact, at last he could hardly bear it. Then one evening, when their tête-à-tête had gone on for nearly three mortal weeks, and Alec in his dinner jacket, the garment Ruth admired most, and said he looked such a gentleman in—didn't he look like a gentleman in the mornings, then, and wasn't he anyhow a gentleman? he asked himself, glutted—was thinking, as he settled down opposite Ruth in her black beads to his nightly struggle to keep his beard out of the soup, or, alternatively, the soup out of his beard, that there were worse things in the world than the worries he had dodged, and was wishing, though he knew vainly, that

Ruth were somebody else, anybody else, really anybody else at all, if only for a few hours, one hour, half an hour, five minutes—who should walk into the dining-room but Fred.

"Fred! Old *man!*"

In his pleasure, in his relief, Alec didn't at first grasp the significance of such an arrival, but Ruth did; Ruth was good at grasping unpleasant significances, and knew at once that it could bode, as she put it to herself, nothing but evil, and her heart, after a most uncomfortable stoppage, sank like lead. What was he doing there by himself, and why had he left Mabel alone with his disgraceful guest?

Strange as his appearing like that was, and ominous, and agitating, Ruth was yet able to find room in her sinking heart for surprise that Alec should seem so much pleased to see him. After having been out of sorts the last week, with a touch of liver he said, and not wanting to talk, here he was suddenly quite bright and perked up because Fred, of all people, had arrived. Had they not come to Brighton on purpose to get away from Fred, and his distressing plans? You would have supposed, thought Ruth, darkly watching the brothers thumping each other's backs, that they hadn't met for years. And she felt Alec slipping away from her, away from the closeness, the almost sacred intimacy, there had been between them during their blissful little holiday.

She felt it still more, this slipping away, when Fred, apparently in high spirits but with harassed eyes—oh, she noticed them at once—ordered a bottle of champagne, and Alec, who had been having only barley-water lately because Ruth, who lost her meekness when it came to his bodily welfare, wouldn't let him have anything else while his liver was upset, and told him lovingly and earnestly and before the waiter (making him look like a fool, thought Alec, glutted) that he knew it was poison for him, when he didn't know anything of the sort, was obviously delighted. Slipping away from her; at once; after all they had been and meant to each other for three blissful weeks. . . .

"I'm with you, old man," cried Alec. "Let's have a drink. Waiter!"

"But, Alec——" began Ruth, her heart like lead.

"Waiter! Bring the wine list," cried Alec, out of hand.

Withdrawn into her jet beads, Ruth sat stricken. Why were men so different, such changed creatures, when they got together? And why had Fred come? What could be the object of so sinister an interruption to her and Alec's quiet happiness?

She soon got an answer to the second question, for, studying the wine list, the waiter bending over him and Alec making expert suggestions, Fred said casually, as though it were the most natural thing in the world, "Milly's here."

Milly?

Ruth sat back in her chair, stunned. Before the waiter—on purpose before the waiter, Fred had sprung it on them, so that they should be gagged, and couldn't do anything.

Alec, one would have supposed, would be stunned too, but, strangely, he wasn't. On the contrary, he looked round quite vivaciously, and said, "Here? Where?" as though expecting to find the dreadful woman at his elbow.

Perhaps, however, it was a good thing he could conceal his real feelings so completely, Ruth was able after tremblingly sipping a little champagne to reflect, for the waiters were listening, and the people at the next table, to whom they had lately begun bowing, could hear every word; perhaps he was only being very wise and diplomatic, hiding the extent of his anger, hiding what he thought of Fred for playing such a disgraceful trick on them, till they should be by themselves. It would be just like him if he were, Ruth said to herself, recovering her trust and pride in Alec. But what of his brother? What was she to think of his brother, foisting Milly on them by a trick? Not as an honourable man, certainly, could she ever, she feared, think of him again; and, about to sip more champagne in search of strength, she remembered it was he who was paying for it, and pushed away her glass.

"She's gone straight up to her room. Number nineteen. On your floor. I asked which floor you were on, and got her put near you," Fred was saying very loud in answer to Alec's question, and everyone could hear him.

Of course. That was his intention, that everyone should hear him, Ruth was sure. She and Alec were being exploited. Her blood boiled.

"She's been ill, you know," Fred went on, turning to Ruth.

She couldn't speak. She couldn't even look at him. How completely she had been mistaken in Fred. And there were the waiters listening, and there were the people at the next table, to whom they had lately begun bowing, able to hear every word.

"Indeed? I'm sorry," said Alec, concealing his real feelings.

"Yes. She's had a breakdown. And old Wilson said Brighton was the place for her to pick up in. So I brought her along. She isn't quite herself yet," he explained to Alec. "Needs a little cosseting still," he explained to Ruth. "But a few days here with you will soon set her up," he explained to them both.

Cosseting? And the waiters listening, and the people at the next table able to hear every word, so that they were committed, positively committed, to—dreadful word—cosseting. That, of course, was Fred's intention. How would she ever be able to think of him as decent again?

But Alec, wiser and more self-controlled than she was, bless him, said, "Of course we'll do what we can——" and Fred, talking very loud and fast, explained that he wasn't staying that night himself, but was going back by the ten-fifteen—"Just time to have a bit of a chat with you both," he said, spuriously cheerful, Ruth was convinced, "and then back to home and bairns."

"Why didn't you bring Mabel along too?" Alec asked; how well he kept it up, Ruth thought, through all her consternation and anger admiring him.

"I did think of it," said Fred, tossing off another glass of champagne, and having tossed it calling to the waiter to take up half a pint of the same brand and a grilled sole to number nineteen—"Must feed her well, you know," he said to Ruth, who gazed at the table-cloth, noting how he slid off the subject of Mabel. "You'll see to that, won't you."

And again he told them that she needed cosseting, and again Ruth doubted whether she would be able in the future to think of Fred as honourable.

Afterwards, seeking out the most private corner of the lounge—"You should have had a sitting-room," Fred said. "We don't throw money away," said Ruth— and drawing his chair as close to them as it would go, before Alec could begin, as Ruth was sure he was about to, to express his indignation and disgust at Fred's behaviour, Fred, in hurried undertones, hurried because he hadn't much time, and undertones because of the people sprinkled near, told them of his discovery of Milly's innocence, gave them the real explanation of Ernest's Will, and informed them how, in his opinion, she had been used more badly than any woman he had ever heard of.

Alec leaned forward surprised and flushed, his hand buried in his beard. Ruth listened in silence, her head bowed, nervously playing with her coffee-spoon. Again, she thought, this terrible topic. The mere mention of it made her feel quite ill. Innocent or not innocent, Milly hadn't *seemed* innocent. St. Paul said, *Avoid the very appearance of evil.* Milly certainly hadn't done that. It behoved everybody, especially women, most carefully to obey this injunction. And what proof had Fred that what she said was true, and that she had really run away only to her sister? Besides, that awful sister . . .

Ruth shuddered; and however ready and anxious she was to see good in everybody, the case against Milly didn't seem one less whit black than before.

"I tell you," said Fred, "I'm more pleased about this than I've been about anything for a long while."

"So am I," said Alec, taking a long sip of brandy— sheer poison, Ruth's eyes told him, but he didn't look at Ruth's eyes. And he repeated, with increased conviction as he put down his glass, "So am I."

"I'm sure *you* must be, Ruth," said Fred, determined to get some sign of gratification out of the silent figure in the beads. She of all people, being so pious, ought to be glad there should be one sin less in the world. And he remembered, much ashamed, the way he had abused poor little Milly to Ruth that day he went to quell the rebellion of the servants at Ernest's house. "It just shows," he went on, "how careful one ought to be before deciding people are guilty."

"And perhaps," said Ruth, "before deciding that they are innocent."

Fred looked at her. He wondered what Alec made of a wife like that.

"What does Mabel say?" asked Ruth.

Fred was taken aback. Commend him to women, he thought, for putting their finger on one's raw place. Mabel at that moment was his raw place. It had been like ploughing the sands, trying to get her to be reasonable, like beating off flies—such unending, such useless effort. He had had to take her on his knee so often that his very trousers were losing their shape, and it hadn't helped a bit either, because the minute he put her down, thinking he had brought her round to being sensible, she began at exactly the same point where she had been when he took her up, and she had refused to go on looking after Milly, turning her over to the housemaids, and discomfort had settled on his house like a pall, and the butler and the cook had both given notice, scenting, with the infernal flair of servants, that there was a row and that Milly was in it, and at meals it was most awkward, with the boys pretending they didn't notice anything, and, in short, it was because of Mabel and her folly that he was there. The *power* of wives, he had often thought these days, astonished; the wearing-down power of wives. . . .

"Mabel?" he repeated, trying to look at Ruth with the care-free face of the contented husband. "What should she say? She's delighted, of course—I mean, she's been devoting herself to Milly and has tired herself out, so she's gone off for a rest to the old lady."

"Really," said Ruth, manifestly considering this from every angle. And she added, having done considering it, "That'll be very nice for her."

Clear it was to Ruth that Mabel had been having a bad time; but her conjectures as to what she had prob-

ably been going through at once gave place to conjectures as to what she herself was about to go through
—highly unpleasant conjectures, painful ones. For
Mabel and Fred evidently had quarrelled because of
Milly; was it possible that she and Alec, her own Alec,
her husband whom she so much loved and in all things
till now had submitted to, might be brought to such a
state of difference of opinion about her that they quarrelled too? Oh, not quarrel—never quarrel; but be
separated by an inability to agree. Sad days, she
feared, were ahead for her; difficult days. For why,
exactly, had Mabel and Fred quarrelled? Was it because Mabel, like herself, was unable to accept without
proper proofs Fred's story of Milly's blamelessness?
Or was there—she shivered—some other reason?

"Cheer up, Ruth," Fred said, startling her out of
these dark thoughts. He was getting up. He was going.

"It's natural," he said, holding out his hand in fare-
well, "that you should feel down in the mouth, like the
rest of us. One feels a bit ashamed, having judged poor
little Milly as we did. But you'll have lots of opportunities now for making it up to her. Taking it to heart, she
is," he said, turning to Alec and jerking his head towards
Ruth—she was very certain now she could never think
of him as decent, as even possible, again—"but you'll
find it quite easy," he continued to her. "Milly doesn't
bear us any ill will. There's no grudge about her, I'm
thankful to say. Good-bye. Look after her well. Coming
with me to the station, old man?"

Yes—Alec was coming with him to the station, was
coming with alacrity to the station.

"Your overcoat, Alec," Ruth moaned after him.
"Your *overcoat*, dear——"

§

They walked, so as to talk more comfortably. Directly they got away from Ruth, everything seemed simple and natural. Fred had noticed that before—how, directly one got away from women, difficulties disappeared, and it was quite easy to discuss and arrange calmly. A silent wave of understanding, of sympathy, washed between them, very soothing, very lulling, and both felt how real, after all, and in spite of sometimes being forgotten, was the bond of brotherhood, and neither mentioned their wives. Alec was sorry, for more reasons than one, and much ashamed, that he should have come away to Brighton so as to shirk his share of Milly, and being an excellent man he not only rejoiced that the family had after all escaped dishonour, but was heartily glad he could now once more think of his sister-in-law as good. Of Ernest's conduct they didn't speak, the subject being all too painful, but Fred had a suggestion to make, and Alec at once fell in with it, that they should ask George and Bertie to join them in paying back the thousand pounds that fellow Jenkyns had advanced to Milly. Fred said it was a slur on the family that Jenkyns should be allowed to help her when there they all were. The money had already gone, Alec heard with concern, to her sister, but this didn't alter the fact that Jenkyns must have advanced it, and would be out of pocket till the Will had been proved unless they paid him. Why, asked Fred, should the fellow be out of pocket on their behalf? Why should he lend money to their family—which was what it amounted to? Why indeed, echoed Alec, briskly stepping out; confounded impertinence, it was. They would only have to put up two hundred and fifty pounds apiece, the four of them; George and Bertie would be certain to agree, said Fred; it wouldn't hurt any of them much; and it would just show Jenkyns.

Alec was entirely with him. After his three weeks of cut-offness, he was ready to coöperate in almost anything. He had a natural reluctance, concealed from Fred, who had it too and in his turn concealed it, to part with two hundred and fifty pounds, and much disliked the idea that it was really Milly's shady sister who was getting it; but greater than this reluctance and this dislike was his objection to that fellow Jenkyns's insolent assumption that if he didn't help Milly nobody would. Fred felt precisely the same; they didn't need words, they were brothers. And Alec went back to Ruth so much cheered by Fred's visit, and his news, and his unspoken understanding, and his not being a wife, that he felt quite reconciled to her company again, and was sorry, now that the time in Brighton alone with her was over, and in another week they would be going home to their customary occupations and salutary separations, that his thoughts hadn't been more kind.

"Are you awake, dear?" he asked, putting on the pyjamas she had hung by the fire to warm.

Yes, Ruth was awake; Ruth was always anything Alec wanted her to be.

"It's good news about poor Milly, isn't it," said Alec.

Yes, it was very good news; wonderful news.

"Been in to kiss her good-night?"

No, Ruth hadn't been in to kiss her good-night, because she thought she might be asleep.

Contentedly, as he got into bed, Alec felt there would be no trouble with Ruth. She would eat out of his hand; always had, and always would. A little stand-offish, perhaps, to old Fred she had been, but that was natural seeing how suddenly the whole thing was sprung on her.

Ruth took time to get going, but once under way there was no one to equal her for obedience and devotion. Didn't he know it? After all, it was a great blessing to have an obedient and devoted wife, and he was sorry he had had bad thoughts about her.

"Good-night, dear," he said kindly, that ungrateful word, glutted, on his conscience.

"Good-night, dear. Have you found the hot-water bottle? I put it your side. I do hope you haven't caught a chill."

§

But no wife who is good can look on placidly at her husband lavishing expensive attentions on another woman. To be able to do that she must be bad, with her own particular and regrettable irons in the fire. Ruth was the best of wives, and therefore when Alec, moved by a creditable desire to make up for the family's unjust judgments of poor Milly, liberally interpreted Fred's injunction to cosset, though she looked on, being obliged to, she didn't do it placidly. If he had cosseted —the word afflicted her—with effort, as a duty which went against the grain yet must be honourably discharged, she wouldn't so much have minded, though still deploring his excess of zeal; but there was no evidence at all that it went against Alec's grain—on the contrary, there was every evidence that he liked it. And indeed Alec, after the extreme boredom and idleness of his time alone with Ruth, would have flung himself on a far less important opportunity for activity.

Nothing was too good for Milly. Inclined to parsimony where his wife was concerned, on behalf of Milly he spent his money—surely Ruth's money too, the marriage service said so—like water. Pints of champagne appeared as the usual accompaniments of both

lunch and dinner, and since Milly didn't drink them—
Ruth would have disliked it excessively if she had, yet
thought it ungrateful of her not to—Alec did, paying
no penalty proper to having taken poison, as she for-
lornly expected, seeming on the contrary in better
spirits after every pint. Special dishes were ordered
daily. Oysters became commonplaces. A private sitting-
room was engaged, and in it the fire, as also in Milly's
bedroom, blazed from before breakfast till bedtime.
And he went out each morning and bought her papers,
and magazines, and even flowers; and he insisted on her
having a bathchair, walking himself beside it as if he
were her husband.

Nothing, in fact, was good enough for Milly. Yet,
thought Ruth, secretly thought Ruth in her outraged
heart, was not everything really too good for her? That
story of Fred's, unauthenticated by any proof—how
could Alec so easily believe it? Mabel was the person
Ruth at that moment most wanted to see; she could tell
her much. The first thing she would do when she got
home would be to go over to Denmark Hill and have a
talk with her, somewhere away from the old lady, whose
ways of approaching serious matters, almost of pooh-
poohing them, was so very trying, as well as being sad.
But it would be a week before she could hope to meet
her—an endless week, she feared it was going to be, and
all she could do, while it dragged along, was to watch
and pray.

But she found they excluded each other—watching
she couldn't pray, nor praying could she properly watch.
So she reserved her prayers for the night hours, concentrating in the daytime on attentiveness, and withdrawing into a silence which at last became so complete that
Alec noticed it, and injudiciously asked her before
Milly—everything now was said and done before Milly,

there was no more privacy, no more intimacy, except at night in their bedroom, and even then there wasn't any, because he was either asleep or not being intimate —what was the matter.

The moment the question was out he recognized its injudiciousness. A man, he had long known, should never ask his wife what the matter is, in case she tells him. But Ruth only said she thought she had a touch of liver—at which Alec began to draw his fingers through his beard, looking at her sideways. However, it was easiest, he decided, to accept this explanation as true, for he wanted no trouble with Ruth, being determined that nothing and nobody should stop him, during the one week at his disposal, from doing all he could for Milly.

He needn't have been so determined. Nobody tried to stop him. Ruth didn't attempt to, and Milly seemed dazed. Between these two almost speechless women he went through the week in an orgy of spending—at last, it seemed to him, all by himself. Since he couldn't do it in words, material luxury was the only way he had of apologizing for the atrocious conclusions his family had jumped to, and of which, thank God, owing to Fred's insisting they should all behave to their unhappy sister-in-law as though nothing had happened, she wasn't aware. Gladly did he lavish; but he did think there might have been some response. Well, not response, perhaps, but some sign that what he was doing was being appreciated. Well, not appreciated, perhaps, but noticed.

Nothing seemed to be noticed by anybody except the waiters, who certainly leaped about him in a furious zeal. Ruth, he soon suspected, was ignoring on purpose, and Milly continued dazed. He kept it up, however, his voice, as he made determined cheerful remarks at meals,

but only with her own intolerable behaviour. "I'm perfectly well, thank you, and perfectly in possession of my faculties," he loudly and angrily informed her from the bed.

"That's what people always think, dear," Ruth said soothingly, "when their systems are a little poisoned. You'll be better in the morning. You must try and get some sleep."

Sleep? Alec didn't want sleep. What he wanted was a wife who behaved herself; a decent helpmeet was what he wanted. Sleep? Was that the way to talk to a man with a legitimate grievance? As if he were a fool? Or a child?

Violently he asked her which of these did she take him for; and pale, but obstinately soothing, Ruth said, finishing plaiting her meagre hair, "Hush, dear—don't try to talk. Just get off to sleep, and I'm sure you'll be quite yourself in the morning."

"If you think you're going to muzzle me——" began Alec furiously.

"Hush, dear—I want to say my prayers now," interrupted Ruth, kneeling down meekly on her side of the bed.

"Well, whatever you do don't pray for *me*," cried Alec.

"Ah, dear," said Ruth, shaking her head, level with the bed, sadly at him across the counterpane, "you can't prevent my doing that."

And closing her eyes, and folding her hands, she withdrew out of his reach; for he couldn't pursue with argument a woman praying. And he was left to solitude, impotently tugging at his beard.

✲✲(XV)✲✲

IT WAS Nora's—George's wife's—habit, when in more than usually high spirits, to tell such of her sisters-in-law as happened to be present that she had no time for stick-in-the-muds. The implication estranged them. Much about Nora estranged them. She was, they considered, remarkably unlike a lady. She enjoyed, for instance, food and drink, and said she did; her observations on the subject of love-making, when, in spite of watching, it somehow got into the conversation, had to be interrupted at once; and her whole attitude towards the physical and material sides of life was unpleasantly suggestive—they hated saying it—of one who is smacking her lips. Vulgar, undoubtedly, Nora was; very. Some of the ladies of the family went further, and called her gross. And they all invariably spoke of her husband as poor George.

Milly too, in Nora's view, had been a stick-in-the-mud, and, though they had been perfectly friendly, the friendliness Nora felt for her was not much different from that which she felt for a tame mouse or a pet rabbit if and when she came across one. Just about the same, Nora thought; there was just about as much go in Milly as that, just that sort of pleasant, unenterprising softness; and it had been the great thrill of her life to know that she was wrong. What a triumph, thought Nora, dazzled, what an *artistic* triumph, to behave like a mouse, a rabbit, and a stick-in-the-mud, and all the time be leading a secret life of ardours and ecstasies!

Fred's ridiculous story that there was no man in it at
all, and only her sister, Nora impatiently brushed aside.
Too burning was her faith in the existence somewhere,
if one could get away from rabbits and mice, of warmly
throbbing human beings engaged in happy amorous
activities, to believe that such skill in deceiving everybody for years on end should have been practised only
on behalf of a sister. Enthusiastically she was sure it
wasn't with a sister Milly had hidden herself in London,
nor was it because of a sister that Ernest had cut her
out of his Will, nor had a sister got her thousand pounds.
The facts were far too divinely fishy for so silly a theory
to hold water. Sister, indeed! How well she could imagine giving the man one loved all one's money with a
great, splendid gesture, and all one's everything else, if
he wanted it. Stuff to pretend, as Fred pretended, that
no man would take money from a woman. A man would
take anything—at least, she fervently hoped so. She
hadn't proved it herself, not being the sort of woman
men had ever wanted to take things from, but for the
honour of vitality, of full-bloodedness, of all the jolly
things which were the opposite of death, she fervently
hoped so.

In this spirit of tiptoe excitement she prepared for
Milly's visit, which was due the day after Alec tried in
vain to quarrel with Ruth in the Brighton bedroom;
and she welcomed her on her arrival so enthusiastically,
with so much of the clamour, as well as of the gesticu-
lations, of delight, that Ruth, who witnessed the meeting from the window of her car, her painful task having
been to motor down from Victoria alone with Milly, and
hand her over to Nora on her way home, was much
shocked. She could only suppose Nora gave credence to
Fred's story of Milly's innocence, though even before
that absurd story had been put about, she remembered,

she had been ready to gush over her. Why? No doubt
because she was coarse-grained, and didn't mind what
form excitement took so long as she got it. Shivering,
Ruth refused all offers of hospitality and caused herself
to be driven away as quickly as possible, shutting her
eyes and trying to forget the scene on the door-step—and
trying, too, to forget Milly altogether, and Brighton,
and the swift descent from peaceful happiness to wrongs
and injuries, and Alec not speaking a word to her since
the night before, and the hotel bill being simply appalling.

"Well, Milly, you *do* look peaky!" cried Nora, left
alone with her guest and twisting her round by the
shoulders to the light—wonderful to Nora, thrilling in
the highest degree was it, that, known to be inwardly
a raging fire, Milly should look so exactly like a rabbit
that has been out in the rain. Nora's eyes danced over
her. Vitality streamed out of them. "What has Ruth
been doing to you?" she asked. "Giving you a rotten
time, I bet. I can see she has. Well, what can you expect? I always say that in spite of her children and
grandchildren, Ruth's nothing but an old virgin. Let's
go upstairs, shall we? Come up and take off your things.
Would you like anything before lunch? Milk, or something? It's at one. Sure you can hold out? Oh, I'm so
thrilled at getting you here! Your trunks came this
morning. Fred sent them. You know Mabel's gone to
stay with the old lady? Funny of her, isn't it, to go off
like that and leave Fred. Here's your room—near mine,
you see. If you want anything you've only got to shout.
Look—we've put your things through here, in the
dressing-room. I'll unpack them for you—yes, I will,
I'd love to. And then we can talk. I'm *dying* to talk—
have been, ever since everything happened. You *will*
talk, won't you—you're not going to stay all corked up?

Oh, but don't you look *ill*, Milly!" she broke off with
sudden compunction. "I believe you ought really to go
to bed at once, and not bother to come down to lunch.
Wouldn't you like to? Oh, do—and I'll ring for a hot-
water bottle."

Kindness; warmth; every appearance of affection.
The change of temperature was so abrupt that it took
Milly's breath away. Only that morning she was still,
as it were, being whistled through by an icy north-
easter, and now at lunch-time the atmosphere was hot
enough for alligators. Here was high summer; here,
for the moment at least, was a life-giving, tropical sun.

She blinked a little, blinded. The free and copious
chatter, after Ruth's frozen silence, poured over her
numbed spirit like warm oil. Wasn't this too good to
be true? Could it possibly last? Then into her dulled
mind came the recognition that it is the women of a
family who make the temperatures, and that in this
house she need fear no sudden drops. Slowly she began
to relax, to thaw, to give herself up to the atmosphere,
to have a feeling as if, after being interminably on her
feet, she now for a while might sit down by a fire, and
rub her stiffened joints, and rest.

Without more ado Nora undressed her and put her
to bed; and when, having fed her, she bent down and
gave her a hearty kiss and told her she was to go to
sleep till tea-time—sleep off Ruth, Nora said, with one
of those loud laughs which made the ladies of the family
wince—Milly with a deep sigh of thankfulness for this
interval of comfort, this blessed respite before proceeding to what she dimly felt would be the rigours of Edith's
hospitality, murmured gratefully, her eyes shut, her
body relaxed, snuggling down in the pillows, with Nora's
kiss warm on her cheek, "Angel."

"Who—me?" exclaimed Nora, with another of the

laughs. "Ask George. But I tell you what *you* are, Milly—you're the one real live woman I've ever met."

"Who—me?" said Milly in her turn, opening her eyes, and looking up at the face bending over her, in wonder. "Me, Nora?" And she added, with a small, tired gesture of the hand lying on the quilt, raising it a moment and dropping it again, "Why, I'm dead. I think you must know I'm dead."

"That's where you're so wonderful," cried Nora, red with enthusiasm for so admirable a piece of acting. "You manage to look dead, and are really the only woman in the family who isn't. You'll never believe it, but for years I've been putting you down in my mind as a sort of rabbit. Really I have. Doesn't that just show? Fancy *you* a rabbit!"

And on Milly's staring up at her in silence, she went on, "Do you know, I'm simply bursting with admiration for you? Yes, I am—you're so talented, Milly, you've got such complete mastery over yourself. And I dare say you'll laugh, but I'm bursting with respect into the bargain. There," she finished, stooping down quickly and tucking her up, "now you're to go to sleep. I'm off till tea."

And blowing her a kiss, with vigorous movements, Nora hurried out of the room.

§

Milly lay in the bed dumbfounded. Admiration? Respect? What words were these? After the iciness of Ruth at Brighton, after the bewildering last days at Mabel's, when, suddenly handed over to the care of obviously unwilling servants, she had been left to guess at the reason as best she could—and she had guessed it very soon, but it had taken a long while before she could believe it—they sounded strange indeed.

What could Nora mean?

Milly's mind groped about. It hadn't been much use to her lately, her mind hadn't, having fallen, before leaving Mabel's, into a condition of blank bewilderment, but it was beginning to work a little now, warmed by the brightness of her welcome. What could she mean except that, passionately believing her innocent, she passionately admired and respected her for—Milly turned a dull red with shame—her patience in bearing such grievous wrongs?

This must be stopped, she thought, sitting up in the bed. It would be the last straw that she should be looked up to as a saint. That was what Nora would be doing next—reverencing her. She stared at the grotesque picture of herself on a pedestal, being reverenced by Nora. Down what gulfs of hypocrisy was she being forced? It was hardly decent of Fate to be so vindictive. That Nora should love her—and she had every appearance of loving her warmly—was an unexpected development in her wretched situation, and to go on deceiving in her own house someone who loved her as well as believed in her, to accept her admiration and respect and not say a word, would surely be as base as anything she had done. Oh, she didn't want to be base any more —she didn't, didn't want to be base any more, Milly cried to herself, twisting the sheet in her fingers. Yet how stop it, except by telling the truth? Nora would be terribly upset by the truth. For all her way of talking, of saying things the rest of them never dreamed of saying, she hadn't in her life *done* anything that wasn't strictly proper, and at heart was every bit as conventional, Milly was sure, as the others. Besides, the truth couldn't be confined to Nora. It would spread. Nora would have to tell George, and George the others, and the family's peace and honour be after all destroyed.

"No, no," thought Milly, "they couldn't bear it. They mustn't ever know. It's got all, all to wash over me——"

And looking round the gay bedroom without seeing a thing in it, not a single one of those bright-coloured objects in which Nora expressed her flamboyant personality, not even noticing that the sheet she was twisting in her fingers was, like the rest of the bed, orange-colour, she said to herself, "I do think I'm being punished very *much....*"

§

The maid appeared, and asked if she should bring tea, or wait any longer for her mistress's return.

Tea? Milly gazed at her, hardly taking this in. It seemed only ten minutes since Nora had left her. How deeply lost one could become in the agonizing puzzles of which life for her now consisted.

"It's past five, m'm," said the maid, who looked pleasantly at her—not like the maid at Mabel's, who wouldn't look at her at all, nor like the butler at Mabel's, of whom her last glimpse, as Fred took her away, had been a nose held high at an angle of sternest disapproval.

"Mrs. George said she would be back to tea," hesitated Milly.

"Yes, m'm—at half-past four. But it's nearly a quarter past five now. Hadn't I better bring it up?"

Milly was doubtful. Nora had made a point of having tea with her. Where could she be so long?

It was brought up, and when it had stood till it was cold, and there was still no Nora, she got out of bed and began to dress, and by the time she was dressed it was half-past six, and there was still no Nora.

What could have happened? She went downstairs, wondering; and going into the drawing-room found

George there, standing in front of the fire looking worried, and the moment she spoke to him she knew that George, whatever Nora might do, didn't respect her.

His manner was most chilly. He was quite different from what he had been the last time she saw him, that afternoon he had come across her at Victoria, and brought her home. Then he had been agitated, and embarrassed, and human; now he was as heavily cold as lead. And when she said, "Oh, are you home, George?" —somehow expecting he would be like Fred and Alec, and welcome her as Alec had welcomed her at Brighton, naturally expecting it, seeing the extreme warmth of his wife, he said, his face like an empty church, "How do you do. Where's Nora?"

That was all. Just, How do you do, and then at once, Where's Nora? and no attempt to shake hands.

She stood uncertain of everything except that George didn't respect her—did, apparently, the exact opposite, in spite of being Nora's husband. Well, that oughtn't to surprise her, she told herself; look at Fred and Mabel, and look at Alec and Ruth. Still, in this house, full of Nora's personality, she had somehow been sure. . . .

"Yes—where is Nora?" said Milly, confused and timid.

George, however, seemed to disrespect her so much that he couldn't bring himself to say anything more. Looking at his hands, turning them over and examining them on both sides, he appeared to decide that they needed immediate washing, and without more words he walked heavily past her and through the door.

Milly stood looking after him, feeling as she had felt when Jenkyns suddenly turned from ingratiatingness to ice—as if she had been whipped. Could she stay in a house where the host wouldn't speak to her? And what was the matter with George? He was the last person she would have imagined taking a line different from his brothers and his wife. Why had he let her come there, come to stay a whole month, if he was only going to be rude? It was his house. He could have refused to have her. Better, surely, to refuse to have her than to let her come, loathing her so much that he couldn't even speak to her?

She sat down miserably by the fire. Wherever she went, was she to be raked on one side by cutting blasts while on the other she was being basted? And she had been so thankful, so grateful, to have got into what she had thought was going to be a shelter.

She sat, her spirit blown out again, staring into the fire. Where was Nora? Why didn't she come home?

But listen as she might for sounds of arrival there was nothing but silence in the house, and the clock on the mantel-piece ticking away the empty minutes, and outside the window a loose bit of leafless creeper ceaselessly banging against the pane.

§

George stayed up in his dressing-room. It was safer than his study. Milly wouldn't be able to walk in on him there, and nothing would have induced him to come home so early if he had known Nora was going to be out. But he had caught an earlier train on purpose to be alone with her a little, before dinner forced him to meet his guest, for he was worried; much worried; worried out of his life; and wanted the comfort of Nora's irresponsible cheerfulness. He wouldn't tell her, he couldn't tell her, what was worrying him; he simply had a great wish, strange and unusual in him, to feel her propping him up with her jolly optimism.

Just his luck, considered George, that they should find out the true story of the thousand pounds on the

very day he was to start having Milly in his house; and
his opinion of his luck in everything that concerned the
woman became even poorer when he got home to find
himself facing her alone. He needn't have gone into
the drawing-room at all; he could have gone straight
to his study, and sent a servant after Nora. But he was
so much distracted by the need to be with her at once
that he went to where she always was at that hour, and
for the second time, without anybody to help or advise
him, ran into Milly.

He found he couldn't speak to her, in spite of knowing
he ought to. Perhaps he would be able to by and by,
helped by Nora; but for the life of him, he being a plain
man not used to hiding his feelings, he couldn't do it
at that moment. What was he to think of this latest
development in her wretched affairs? Alec and Fred
didn't know what to think either. In Fred's office that
morning—Fred had rung up and asked them to come
round—they had sat nonplussed. Bertie? It wasn't
that he should have advanced the money; that, they
agreed, was a decent, praiseworthy action, which they
regretted not having thought of themselves; but that
he should have done it secretly, have kept quiet about
it that night at George's when they were all so much
surprised, and have told Jenkyns, they were now aware,
not to let any of them know. This was it, this evident
fear of being found out, which worried the brothers.
They didn't say so, but that they were much worried
was implicit in their silence, in their avoidance of each
other's eyes, in the way Alec held on to his beard.

Fred hadn't been able to get into touch with Bertie,
who was in Birmingham on business, so as to ask him
to contribute his share towards the paying off of Jenkyns,
and unwilling to wait longer, and sure he would agree,
as Alec and George had agreed, had that morning rung

up the fellow to say he was sending him a cheque for the amount he had advanced to his sister-in-law, Mrs. Ernest Bott—kindly advanced, Fred amended, cold and polite. And then Jenkyns cold and polite at the other end, who had been in a state of fuming fury with all Botts and their connections and transactions since Bertie's and Milly's and Agatha's visits to his office, said he had not had the privilege of advancing the money himself, and the cheque should be sent—kindly sent, he amended—to Mr. Herbert Bott, who had merely made use of the firm of Jenkyns and Rowe as the instrument of his thoughtful generosity.

Mr. Herbert Bott. That was Bertie. Fred was so much surprised that he lowered the receiver in order to think.

The voice at the other end, however, went on speaking. What was the fellow saying? Fred picked up the receiver again, and attended.

The fellow was saying that he hoped, on second thoughts, he had not been guilty of an indiscretion, for he now remembered what had momentarily escaped him—the particular request of Mr. Herbert Bott that the matter should be kept private. No doubt, however, he could rely on Mr. Frederick Bott—it was Mr. Frederick himself speaking, was it not? Yes, quite—to do so.

"Private from Mrs. Ernest, I suppose?" said Fred into the telephone.

"I gathered," said the smooth professional voice at the other end, "Mr. Herbert was also anxious it should not be mentioned to his brothers. Nor, presumably—" there was a pause, and a clearing of the throat—"to his wife."

Fred had told Alec and George all that Jenkyns had said—no use not to, no use trying to keep it to himself— and they sat silent, worried, not quite knowing what to think. It was plain enough what Jenkyns believed, but then a scoundrel like that would believe anything. Dead against them, he was; dead against the whole of Ernest's family—they saw that the day he read the Will. Still, dead against them or not, in the minds of all three insisted on creeping a paralyzing thought: Jenkyns would have first-hand information from Ernest, and didn't need even to believe, because he knew.

Each in turn carefully stamped out his thought. Nothing at all had happened, they said to themselves, except that Bertie had been secretly generous and they had found it out; and it was mere accident that before Fred's eyes should pass irrelevant visions of himself, ashamed of his foul suspicions, anxiously begging Milly's pardon that day in her room, of himself going round to the others trying to make them be sorry and ashamed too, of being forced into repeated scenes with poor old Mabel, of being at last so angry that he couldn't any longer keep his anger in, and she, scared and weeping, departing to seek sanctuary with his mother. Mere accident, too, that Alec should suddenly remember Brighton, and all he had done there, his efforts to proclaim his belief in Milly's wrongs and innocence in terms of expense, his quarrel with poor old Ruth, to whom he hadn't said a single word since, and the staggering nature of the bill he had had to pay that morning. What had this to do, each asked himself, trying to put these visions and memories aside, with their present discovery? But, chancing to glance at Fred, Alec found Fred was glancing at him, and both their glances were rueful.

Only George was spared irrelevant visions, not having yet begun with Milly. He, however, though he was accordingly unable to look backwards ruefully, could and did look forwards ruefully, and sat outwardly stolid, and inwardly dejected. Milly would be at his house

when he got home; what was he to do about it? No one
had been more glad to hear from Fred than George that
she was after all virtuous, but now he was hanged if he
knew what to think. These things keeping on happening
upset a man. A thousand pounds from Bertie? And not
a word said about it by either of them? George was much
worried. That it should chance to be his turn to have
her for a month just at such an unexpected crisis, appeared to him downright cruel. Fred or Alec would, he
hoped, soon say something suggesting the line for him
to take. He was blest if he knew one himself. He would
far rather, far and away rather, neither see nor speak
to the woman ever again, and here he was going to be
her host that very day. Somebody certainly ought to
give him a lead. He supposed they would all have to go
on behaving as though nothing had happened. He didn't
see what else they could do, now that Bertie was mixed
up in it. Poor old Bertie—she had got round him, thought
George, having successfully stamped out that first
paralyzing thought. He was such a good-natured chap
that he would fall an easy prey, thought George. "Don't
let her try any of her tricks on *me*, though," thought
George, squaring his shoulders.

Then at last Fred did give him a lead. He suddenly
pushed back his chair, got up, looked at his watch, said,
"Well, I'm for lunch," and while he fussed round locking
up things, declared that he thought it jolly decent of
old Bertie to have done what he did, and if he didn't
want it mentioned why should it be? Humour him, they
ought to; back him up in his idea of not wanting his
left hand to know what his right hand was up to—doing,
Fred meant to say. "It has cost him a thousand pounds,
anyway, poor old chap," said Fred, taking down his
hat. "All gone to that sister. And what I say is," he
finished, turning and looking them in the face, his hat

crushed well down over his eyes, and speaking slowly and emphatically, "what I say is that it would be a shame to rub it in. Least said, best for everybody. And for heaven's sake don't tell the women."

With anxious, with almost servile unanimity, Alec and George agreed. And tell the women they didn't; but by that same evening the women were telling them.

§

Nora heard about it at Denmark Hill, at the old lady's, whither she hurried on leaving Milly so as to get exercise, so as to blow off some of the steam she was so uncomfortably full of, and at the same time have another look at Mabel, at whom she had already had several since she so mysteriously left Fred, without yet having made out why she had done it. Her chief reason, however, for choosing this particular walk was because there was a nice long stretch of uphill at the end of it on which she could let herself go; and though it had often struck her as a poor fate for a woman only to be able to let herself go on a hill, on this occasion she blessed the hill, for it was really the cause of her happening to be present at the best family crisis anybody could possibly wish for. She hadn't been in the house ten minutes before it began to develop and to it she remained glued, absorbed, with time become as nothing to her; so that she not only wasn't back to tea, but hardly was she back to dinner.

To begin with things went, as Ruth would have said, their usual gait, the old lady quietly shaking in her chair by the fire, a mauve woollen shawl round her, her small feet on a footstool—"Ah, my dears," she would sometimes say, drawing attention to them, "they don't make feet like these nowadays"—just as she had been ever since Nora could remember, placidly glad to hear about Milly, as glad as Mabel obviously wasn't, who sat not saying a word, and looking like a sick monkey, and as if her fur were coming off in patches, thought Nora, eyeing her eagerly and wishing to goodness she would up and tell them what the row with Fred had been about. And Ruth presently came in and joined them—part, too, of the usual gait, for the women of the family were always coming in and joining each other at this hour of the day, especially when they were, as now, in mourning, and unable to join anyone else. And there was no indication that there was going to be a crisis anywhere visible.

Ruth seemed taken aback at seeing Nora—this too was quite usual—who concluded that she seemed so because she was, and cheerily called out from the hearth rug, where she was standing with her legs not at all nicely together, observed Ruth, and also observed the old lady, who, however, condoned what legs did so long as hearts were kind, though of course she would rather they behaved like the legs of ladies, "Hullo, Ruth, here we are again——" just as if, thought Ruth, ignoring her, they were a pair of rough and tumbles in a pantomime.

"I thought," said Ruth, looking away from her to the old lady, "I would like to have a little talk with Mabel, mother."

"Oh, *do*," encouraged Nora, in a most uncalled-for manner, Ruth considered, ignoring her. "By all means, if you can. She hasn't uttered a single word since I've been here, but you may have more luck."

Poor George, thought Ruth, ignoring her; and Nora, her bold bright eyes dancing over Ruth's dim respectability, thought, Poor Alec. For the Bott wives readily pitied each other's husbands.

"Do you mean somewhere by yourselves, my dear?" asked the old lady. "Well, there's a nice fire in the dining-room—would you like to go in there together, and have a cosy chat?"

"*That's* put the wind up Mabel!" cried Nora; and indeed Mabel's expression was that of one averse from chats.

Before Ruth had had time to do more than ignore this remark, the door opened and Edith came in.

"Oh, Lord—I'm off," said Nora when she saw who it was, hastily picking up her gloves from the sofa where she had flung them; and even the old lady found Nora's implications trying.

"Not just yet, my dear," she quavered. "Sit down, won't you? And rest yourself a little. Such a long walk. And wouldn't you like a nice cup of tea before——"

"No, thanks, mother—I must get back to Milly. I promised——"

"Perhaps you'll take your guest a message from me," Edith cut in like an icy knife.

"Yes—do, Edith, my dear," quavered the old lady. "Do send poor Milly a nice message. And come and sit by the fire, won't you? It's quite chilly again to-day, I think, in spite of all the pretty spring flowers everywhere."

"Tell her," said Edith, addressing Nora, "to drop me out of the list."

"What list, my dear?" inquired the old lady.

"I think it's time," said Edith, looking round at them, "that we took the gloves off about Milly."

"What gloves, my dear?" inquired the old lady. "Mabel my dear, will you ring the bell and tell Jenny we would soon all like our tea? There's a fresh cake been made to-day that you girls will enjoy, I'm sure."

"I may stay, I suppose, mother?" said Edith, advancing into the room. "My things are in the hall."

"Stay, my dear? Do you mean for the night?"

"Nights," said Edith shortly; and it was at this point that Nora drew up a chair, sat down, and prepared to enjoy herself.

"Nights, my dear?" repeated the old lady. "Well, of course if you want to. That makes two of my sons' wives here staying nights, what with Mabel as well. Still, you'll be pleasant company for each other. And there's a roast chicken for dinner, and I daresay a nice cauliflower. I fancy I smelt it just now. Mabel my dear, will you tell Jenny?"

Edith walked to the fire, and stood waiting till the elderly servant had been in, received her orders, and gone out again, before saying anything more. Her nose was pinched and sharp, the nostrils drawn flat, and her mouth seemed to have gone into a single thin line. Nora was a little subdued by the unusual look of her, and Ruth, her legs beginning, she was sure prophetically, to give way beneath her, sank on to the end of the sofa, and bowed her head to receive whatever new unpleasantness should be poured over it, while Mabel, huddled by herself in a corner, looked drearily out of the window.

"What I always think," said the old lady, directly the door was shut behind the servant and before Edith could open her mouth, "is that there's a great deal more fuss made over everything than there need be, my dears —a very great deal more."

"You don't think anything matters very much, do you, mother," said Edith, hardly unlocking her mouth to let the words out; upon which Ruth, bowed on the sofa, thought, "I'm glad Edith said that. Very glad——" for it had often seemed to her tragic that anyone so old, so inevitably near eternity, as her mother-in-law, should still apparently not have made up her mind on the great simple questions of right and wrong, good and evil. Indeed, sometimes it actually almost looked as if the head of the family didn't—only of course this couldn't be possible—believe in sin, or, believing, didn't—this of course couldn't be possible either—mind it. Therefore Ruth was glad of Edith's words.

The old lady, however, said nothing in answer to them, and merely sat shaking her head, which with her, naturally, didn't necessarily mean disagreement, and looking all-embracingly benevolent.

"Perhaps, though," Edith went on, "you'll think what I've come to tell you this afternoon is important, mother."

"Yes, my dear, I daresay I shall. Especially if it isn't about somebody's wrongs. We all have our wrongs, and I find the only ones I can enjoy now are my own. Won't you sit down, Edith my dear? It's nicer sitting down, I always think."

There; that was mother all over, thought Ruth with a sad movement of her bowed head. And one couldn't do anything with her because she was so old, as well as so obstinate. But—what was Edith saying?

Ruth became suddenly prickly with attention, though still apparently lost in a detached contemplation of the carpet, and Mabel at the window gave a convulsive start, while Nora's eyes came farther out of her head.

Edith was saying, holding on to the mantelpiece with one hand to steady herself, that she knew who the man was.

"The man, my dear? What man?" asked the old lady. "There are so many men, I find."

"Oh—*mother!* " exclaimed Nora, in an agony of impatience. "Milly's man, of course. Yes, Edith? Yes?" she cried, leaning forward eagerly, trying to drag the words out quicker.

But Edith was having difficulties. She seemed for a moment unable to go on.

"Milly's man?" repeated the old lady. "Has poor Milly got a man after all? I thought you all decided she hadn't. Dear, dear—poor little Milly. They're such a worry. But I daresay he won't last."

"Mother——" began Ruth, raising a shocked head. But what was the use? She bowed it again. Everything slid off the old lady like water.

"I didn't mean to tell you—not to-day," said Edith, the words seeming to force themselves out. "I only came to say I'll have nothing to do with Milly. I won't, I can't. But you'll know soon enough—oh, you'll all know anyhow, and the whole place will know, and all the children and servants——"

Rage and shame choked her.

"Dear, dear," said the old lady. "Dear, dear, dear. We'll have to be extra kind to poor Milly, then. Nothing but trouble, one has with men. Still, they pass."

This on the brink of eternity. Ruth could only shiver.

"I hope you'll find it easy to be kind to her, mother," said Edith, "considering he's one of your own sons."

"Oh, my goodness! Oh, my goodness!" burst out Nora, starting up. Remembering herself, she put her hand to her mouth. "I mean, how too awful," she finished, sitting down again quickly. Then, struck by a tremendous, a breath-robbing possibility, she leaned forward and said awestruck, "It's not George?"

"George!" Edith glanced at her contemptuously. George? That slug?

"*In all time of our tribulation*"—Ruth began murmuring, taking hasty cover in prayer, fleeing away from this room, away from the dreadful words being said in it, and those still more dreadful ones that were coming next. Which son? Which? Not George—then which? Was it possible—no, it wasn't possible—*In all time of our*—still, the champagne, the fuss, the wild extravagance, the things he said to her in the bedroom because she too hadn't made a fuss, because she had remained dignified and aloof—"*Good Lord deliver us, deliver us, deliver us,*" murmured Ruth feverishly, over and over, so as not to hear, so as not to remember and think, so as to fend off. . . .

Mabel, in the window, had begun to cry.

"It's Fred," flashed into Nora's mind. "Of course. That row they've had. Oh, my goodness—and I who've been thinking the lot of them stick-in-the-muds!"

"Don't cry, Mabel my dear," soothed the old lady. "Mabel's a good girl, and very kind—there's nothing for her to cry about, is there, Edith my dear?"

"Mabel!" said Edith, in scornful wonder. "I should think not. You don't imagine it's *Fred?*"

And there followed that which had never yet happened in the whole annals of the family—the open denouncing of a Bott husband by his wife.

The words, once loosened, flowed in torrents. The room seemed instantly to become awash with them, and the listeners to bob up and down helplessly. All Edith's bitter wrongs swirled round them, and they were so much tossed about that they weren't able to see looming ahead the rock the family was being driven towards. Even old Mrs. Bott didn't see it, and sitting shaking in her corner only thought pityingly of these poor distracted children, and of how sad it was for women that their wrongs should have the effect of setting one against them. The more wrongs they had the less, somehow, one liked them. Look at poor Edith now, for instance—full of wrongs, and only put at a disadvantage by them. She didn't remember ever having seen poor Edith to less advantage. And it really was hard, because it was bad enough having wrongs, without becoming less likeable than usual at the same moment.

Edith did seem to the old lady ever so much less likeable than usual. Was it her way of saying things? Was it the way she put her story? Or was it the story itself? The old lady, shaking her head, and nobody could know if it was in disapproval or sympathy, listened attentively to poor Edith's story—how she went up to town that morning, and before coming home thought she would look in at Bertie's office—

"Why, my dear? Bertie is still away, isn't he?"

That was just why, said Edith—because she knew he wasn't there, and she had been uneasy about him for some time—oh, she had had good reason, she could assure them—and wanted to have a look round and see what she could see——

(Well, well, poor children; they got suspicious of their husbands occasionally, and so, the old lady supposed, they couldn't help trying to find out things. But finding out things never made anybody happy yet.)

—and there, on the table, was a letter sent by hand, and marked private, so of course she opened it, and it was from that solicitor of Ernest's——

(Not a very nice man, the old lady was afraid.)

—apologizing for having forgotten till too late Bertie's having asked him to keep it from the family that he had given Milly a thousand pounds—"Why, only the other day," cried Edith, white with her wrongs, "he told me he couldn't afford something I, his wife, particularly wanted!"—but assuring him there would be no unpleasant consequences, as he had carefully impressed on Fred that it was to go no further, and especially that it was on no account—Edith choked—to reach the ears of his wife. So of course she went round at once to the solicitor himself, and questioned him, and though he had been guarded and reserved, he had said quite enough

to convince her that it was because of Bertie Milly had
been disinherited by Ernest.

That, as far as the old lady could make out through
the torrent of words, was Edith's story, interrupted once
by the arrival and arranging of tea, which nobody
touched except herself—such a pity, and that beautiful
fresh cake, too—and resumed and continued with ever-
increasing volume—poor Edith, making her seem so
unattractive—for a very long time afterwards. But
once a poor girl gets really started on her wrongs, who
shall stop her? thought the old lady. There isn't much
reason in a poor girl with wrongs—not much reason,
and not much idea of consequences. All very well being
angry, but after all one's husband existed, and one had
got to live with him, and it didn't make it any easier
being angry. Well, well—poor children. Edith would
have finished some time, was bound to be quiet presently. What a good thing it was that everyone was
bound to leave off talking sooner or later. And it just
showed how one oughtn't to open somebody else's
letters. The whole trouble came from that—opening
poor Bertie's letter. Once, she remembered, her attention straying a moment, and wandering off down
the years, she had done that herself to one of poor Alexander's; not opened it, because it was open already, but
she had read it as it lay overlooked on his desk, and it
hadn't been meant for her to see, of course, and it had
made a good deal of trouble between them at the time,
because in those days she didn't yet know how all such
things pass.

"Such a pity you opened the letter, my dear," she
remarked, when at last Edith's story reached the state
of quivering off into a panting pause. And when they
all looked at her open-mouthed, even Edith dumb be-

fore this failure to grasp essentials, this failure once more
—or was it unwillingness? lamented Ruth—to dis-
tinguish, she went on, "And perhaps, my dear, it isn't
nearly as bad as you think."

"What? Not so bad that he has committed——"

"Oh, hush—oh, hush!" gasped Ruth in agony.

"And it was only very nice and kind of Bertie to
help poor Milly," continued the old lady, determined to
have her say.

"What? Nice and kind to give our money, mine and
the children's, to his——"

"Oh, hush—oh, hush!" gasped Ruth, wringing her
hands.

"And anyhow, Edith my dear, it will soon pass."

Then Edith was beside herself. "Soon pass?" she
cried, loosened once more into fury. "Soon pass, mother?
Yes—it soon will. I'll see it does that. I'm going to
divorce him."

§

Divorce.

The word fell on them like a stone. Even Nora was
stunned by it. This, she thought, was going too far.
Having fun, having secrets, blowing off one's steam,
wasn't after all very thrilling if it ended in atrocious
scandal. Besides—a brother-in-law. Better be good,
thought Nora, much subdued; far better, really, just
be good, and put up with being bottled up and bored.
Divorce? No one in Titford, she said to herself, ever was
divorced. It simply was unheard of. One wouldn't get a
servant to stay with one. And fancy the leading family,
the very top of the Titford tree, being the one to start
it, and getting cut in the streets!

"But, Edith——" gasped Ruth. This was too much,
too awful. They would all be in the papers. Edith must

be stopped. It meant black ruin for everybody. Didn't she see?

"Why, my dear—why, my dear," quavered the old lady, "what grounds have you? Why, you have no grounds at all."

But Edith, deaf to reason, indifferent to consequences, out only to smash—smash everybody, herself too, if at the same time she could smash Bertie, assured the stricken assembly that she would soon find all the grounds she wanted; and the old lady trembled into silence, for she remembered how much struck she had been on the afternoon of Ernest's funeral by the skilful noiselessness of the way Bertie had opened and shut the bedroom door. It had occurred to her then that he must be practised in such entries and exits. Indeed she feared Edith might find grounds if she set to work, and perhaps more than, and different from, what she had bargained for.

Ah, let be, leave it alone, she almost begged—and would have begged if poor Edith had been in a condition to listen. What would the unhappy child get out of it but misery? Such a mistake, such a mistake, thought the old lady, to start digging about in what one's husband did in his private moments, behaving as if they were the most important things in life, those stray and fleeting moments of foolishness. It seemed as if these poor children had no sense whatever of proportion. They wasted their short time in making much of what was little, and little of what was much. Well, they must settle their own affairs.

And looking at Edith, distorted by her emotions, convulsed, blinded, she found she couldn't wonder much at poor Bertie. Only—was one woman better than another, in the long run, to get mixed up with? Didn't they all, however different they seemed at the begin-

ning, during the course of the affair become alike, and
end by going equally curdled? Well, there was nothing
to be done.

"You don't think Milly will have waited for her tea,
and be waiting now for her dinner, do you, Nora, my
dear?" she asked with a sigh, for she was tired, and the
clock on the mantelpiece said half-past seven.

An astounded silence fell on the room. Milly's tea;
Milly's dinner. Was it possible to think of such things,
after hearing what Edith had been telling her?

"George will be getting hungry," continued the old
lady. "And there's Alec, too—won't he be wondering
where you are, Ruth, my dear?"

That was it: second childhood; complete inability to
grasp. They oughtn't really to mind anything she said.
Entirely negligible she was, really. George getting
hungry and Alec wondering, when life, as they had
known it, threatened to be shivered to atoms at their
feet!

The old lady held up her withered little cheek to be
kissed. "Good-night, my dears," she said, waiting. "I'm
tired." And negligible or not, in her second childhood
or not, Ruth and Nora found themselves taking their
dismissal, and getting up and crossing to her chair and
kissing her.

"You too, Mabel my dear," she said, when they had
done, still holding up her cheek. "You'll be wanting to
go home now, won't you, to Fred?"

"If you don't mind, mother," said Mabel, shame-
facedly coming out of her corner, her one longing being
to fling herself into Fred's arms and beg him to forgive
her. Awful, of course, about Bertie, but how thankful,
how thankful . . .

"Mind, my dear? I like it. I always think it's nice
when people go home. Edith won't, of course, because

she's angry, poor child, so she and I will have a quiet little dinner by ourselves. There's a rhubarb tart for dinner, Edith my dear. You'll enjoy that. So nice, I always think, the first young rhubarb."

The door was shut behind the departing two before Edith recovered her speech. Then, she said, very bitterly, "Rhubarb!"

"Yes. And cream," nodded the old lady.

There was a silence. Then Edith, looking down at the figure in the chair, said with icy scorn, "You haven't much sense of proportion, have you, mother?"

And the old lady said, "Well, my dear, perhaps I haven't." And asked, after a moment, "Have you?"

⁂(XVI)⁂

No Bott went to bed that night till the small hours, nor did anyone who was married to a Bott. Disaster, staved off so carefully, lately indeed regarded as out of the question, was at last full upon the unhappy family; and much worse disaster, of course, than that which they had been staving off.

Laden with their dreadful news, Ruth and Mabel and Nora hurried home, and in each of those three homes, where there had been merely a worried man before, there was now an overwhelmed one. Bertie? Their own brother? The whole thing going to be dragged into the courts by Edith? In that case the family was ruined. Socially, if this happened, it would certainly be ruined. In Titford it could never hold up its head again, and there would be nothing for it but wholesale migration, and scattering.

Unless Edith could be stopped, that is—but who can stop a wronged woman, maddened not only by the discovery that somebody else has got her husband, but has also got a substantial slice of his money? The wrongs of such a wife go up with a shout to heaven, and she doesn't care a straw who hears them; as if the life of a whole family, its diligently built-up position, its reputation and honour and all its happiness, were as nothing compared to the avenging of what one member of it had done in his odd moments.

The brothers were overwhelmed; and Ruth was so deeply horrified by the idea of a divorce in the family, with all its accompaniments of scandal and publicity, that she didn't even wish to remind Alec how sure her instinct had been about Milly, while Mabel was much too thankful it wasn't Fred to think of anything but craving his forgiveness.

Mad of Edith, of course, Fred at first blustered to the abjectly agreeing Mabel, trying to reassure himself, to suppose she could do anything with that letter of Jenkyns's; the only proof to be got out of it was that Bertie had been kind. But the letter, he knew beneath his bluster, was fatal, because it set Edith off on a track at the end of which, he now was quite sure, would be Milly. Jenkyns knew. Ernest, obviously, had told Jenkyns all about it. The whole of Jenkyns's behaviour had been that of one who knows. And Fred was so much submerged in consternation that he hadn't even the breath to say what he thought of that tight-jawed scoundrel.

In each of these three homes that night was consternation; and by the time the small hours had been reached, five more homes had become filled with it—the ones, that is, inhabited by those who had married Botts. For presently, coming a little to the surface of the tumultuous waters, Fred began telephoning, and his voice was so anxious, as he asked the still unconscious members of the family if they wouldn't come round and have a talk, that in spite of its being very late for Titford, and most of them beginning to think of bed, they did go, the brothers-in-law dutifully accompanying their wives. Milly, of course; Milly again. They were only too sadly sure that this invitation of Fred's meant more Milly.

The one thing to be done, they agreed with him when they had got over their first incredulity, was to go and see Edith as soon as possible—proceed *en masse* to Denmark Hill, and by the pressure of their united weight try, at least, to stop her further explorations. She must be brought to reason. She must be made to see the frightful, the fatal results for the family if, having got her proofs, she persisted in divorcing Bertie. How easy, how almost pleasant, they now realized, had their dealings with Milly been, compared to what it was going to be like trying to restrain Edith. These virtuous women, the brothers-in-law silently felt, were the very devil once they got on the warpath.

It was too late to do anything that night, but they arranged to meet at the old lady's house next morning directly after breakfast, and there talk the whole thing over with Edith as calmly as possible—point out, impress, enlarge. By that time she would have had leisure to think, and might be more open to argument than, they understood, she had been in the afternoon. They ought all to go, the husbands said—their wives as well, because not only was it now impossible, they realized, not to acknowledge the flair, insight, intuition, or whatever the unpleasant thing women had was called which enabled them to be right when decency and charity would prefer that they should be wrong, but the wives, every one of them, would be dead against any divorcing, and their pressure should also be brought to bear on Edith.

Then there was the pressure of her grown-up children. She must have forgotten them. She couldn't possibly have thought of them. For surely no woman could be so blinded by fury and the desire for revenge that she didn't care what her children would suffer by her satisfying it? They would remind her of her children; they would talk much to her of them; they would do everything in their power to get at her softer side. But had Edith a softer side? Doubt lay leaden on the husbands' minds. If it had been Milly now . . . Milly, they were

each privately sure, was made up entirely of softer sides
—things you could appeal to, things you could get
round, things, in short, no woman should be without.

In the small hours each went home to bed, but not
to sleep; and through Fred's mind, as he got into his
comforted, to some slight extent, by the fact that
Mabel, restored to him and penitent, was in it too—except that she kept on being penitent, just as she had
kept on being foolish, and he had to spend a good deal
of the time needed for collecting his wits in keeping on
forgiving her—passed Milly's image, with, beside it,
Edith's as Mabel had described her that afternoon.

He stared at the two in the darkness, comparing
them; and he wondered for a moment, being worn out
with worry and fear, and accordingly not quite himself,
whether perhaps sinning made a woman soft and kind,
educated her, helped her to wisdom and understanding,
—the sort of sinning, he meant, in which, in some form
or another, as there must have been in Milly's and
Bertie's, there was love.

But when he realized what he was thinking he was
much shocked, and dismissed it sternly from his mind.
Was he, in his anxiety, losing his sense of moral values?

"Yes, yes, old girl—that's all right. Of course I
know you didn't mean it. . . ."

§

In those same small hours Nora, walking home with
George and holding him affectionately and encourag-
ingly by the arm, gave it a little squeeze every now
and then, and said, "You've always got your Nora,
Porge——" to which he made no reply.

He made no replies to anything she said; not even
when, having got home and both gone upstairs, she informed him, just to test him, for his silence was rather

frightening, that she was going into Milly's room to wish her good-night. Good-night at three in the morning? And to the person who ought, in George's view, never to be wished anything good again? Nora did think this would bring him back to life. But it didn't. He remained dumb. And she began to be afraid that what had happened had broken poor Porge's spring—such spring as he had ever had.

This sobered her still further. The consequences of vivid and daring living, what with George gone speechless and Milly found out, seemed pretty poor fun. She supposed the great thing, in the interests of everybody, not only of oneself, was never to be found out; and Milly, in spite of her startling cleverness and amazing histrionic talent, hadn't been able to avoid that.

Poor old Milly. Nora wanted badly to go in and kiss her—just give her one little kiss before the next day should be upon her, and all its trials and distresses.

She stood hesitating in the passage, sorely tempted. It wouldn't do anybody any harm, she thought, and there would be one more kiss in the world. If the world were fuller of kisses there'd be less room in it for such a lot of quarrels, thought Nora, hesitating in the passage. Edith, for instance, would probably be quite quiet and contented if some vigorous philanthropist, intent only on helping, started really kissing her. Let one kiss while one could, thought Nora, not at all sure how long she was going to have Milly in her house. They had been saying things to George about it at Fred's, and though George hadn't answered, because of his spring having broken, she was afraid he might get mended enough in a day or two to start turning Milly out—or else the others would come and do it for him.

Besides, she had rushed away and left her without a word directly after dinner, being obliged at once to take

George into his study and tell him about Edith, and
dinner had been awful, having to sit down to it the
minute she got home, with George looking as though he
had swallowed a broomstick, she supposed because she
had kept him waiting, and little knowing what tremendous reason he really had to look like that, and
Milly being the most marvellous impersonator of still
life—a perfect masterpiece, positively behaving as if she
were nothing more alive than a bunch of grapes and an
apple on a plate, instead of being a force so violent that
she was blowing the family to atoms, and she herself,
agonizingly bottled up and bursting, trying to hide from
them both, by chatting as usual, that the heavens were
falling about their ears, and then, when Fred telephoned, leaving the house with George at once, quite
forgetting in the excitement to go and say good-night or
anything to Milly, who had been left alone in the drawing-room—just disappearing.

So that, apart from everything else and whatever the
time was, oughtn't she, as a duty, to go in now and give
her a kiss?

She was sorely tempted, but she resisted. Better resist, thought Nora. Better go to bed, and let poor Milly
sleep. If she went in, she might be led to blurt out something best not blurted, and the poor soul ought at least
to be allowed to sleep on this night before catastrophe
was upon her.

So she went into her room, softly shutting the door,
and undressed and lay down by the side of the inani-
mate George, where she tossed for the rest of the night,
with him taking no more notice than if he had been a
corpse.

§

In those same small hours Milly, sometimes in bed,
sometimes walking about the room, sometimes sitting

by the remains of the fire, was telling herself that she couldn't stay in that house, that it was the worst of any, and that George was the last straw.

She was nearer indignation than she had yet been in her life. Really there were things a woman oughtn't to be required to bear, whatever she had done, she thought. George's hostility was far more difficult to endure than Mabel's or Ruth's had been, because it was so entirely unlike him. Flat, downright, shrivelling contempt in one who had always been the least important of the family, the slow good-natured one, the one who didn't matter, who was to be relied on to follow suit and do what his brothers did—why, it was as unexpected and as humiliating as if a dog should suddenly begin openly and utterly to despise one. And he was her host. Much worse, she now knew, when a host was hostile than when a hostess was. He paid. It was his food, his house, his everything. George's food choked her. His very fires— this one, this one in the bedroom—she hadn't even been able to bring herself to poke, though she was growing colder and colder.

Ridiculous position. And so sinister, because one couldn't in the least understand it. While as for Nora— what was she to think of Nora? Her behaviour was even more incomprehensible, the way she had gone off promising to be back to tea, and then staying away till dinner, and going out again without a word of explanation, not only for the evening but for nearly all the night. Soon it would be quite all the night. What did it mean? What was she to think of the gulf of difference between the Nora who left after lunch, and the Nora who came back, flustered and unnatural, to dinner? And where had she gone afterwards with George, where was she during these endless hours, each added one of which

made her absence more mysterious? Nora, so frank
and open, beginning to hide, to disappear—who could
stay in a house where the hostess took to disappearing?

Oh, impossible, impossible, thought Milly, to endure
these visits. Each seemed worse than the last. They
were torments to everybody. There was only one house
where . . .

Suddenly she was quiet. She was in bed at that moment, got back into it again driven by the cold, and she
lay motionless, her hands, which had been nervously
pulling at the frills of the sheet, quite still, wondering
why no one had thought of it before. The house on
Denmark Hill. The one place in the family where she
might yet find comfort. Mother's house—mother's, who
didn't seem to mind things as other people minded
them, who had always been uncritical, incurious, kind.

But—would mother be kind now?

Milly didn't know. She began turning her head from
side to side on the pillow and pulling at the frills again,
because she didn't know, and it was so important.

Perhaps, she said to herself, her restless fingers twisting and pulling, when one was so old, so old, it was more
difficult not to be kind. She had finished, mother had,
with the heat and burden of life. She had withdrawn
from the clamour, she could take a bird's-eye view of the
fighting going on down where people still tormented
each other, and be pitiful, and be patient. If mother
were able to be kind to her now, or even if she simply
took her in without being either kind or unkind, what a
refuge it would be, her house! In that one house she
would be safe from crushing aversions and reluctances
and equally crushing efforts to make much of her. There
she would stay quietly, if mother would let her—oh, but

wouldn't she let her? Wouldn't she? If she knew it was her last hope?—till the family decided the time had come when she might go away for ever.

Each minute she saw clearer: each minute what she saw seemed more desirable. Really astonishing that nobody had thought of it. With mother she would be out of everybody's way, yet still visible to Titford, and able to be produced at a moment's notice if necessary. George would be relieved of her, Nora wouldn't have to disappear, the looming visit to Edith, which made her go cold to think of, would be avoided. How could anyone possibly object? The most it would do would be to upset the family's plans—and not even upset, merely defer; for always later on, when the Botts were more unanimous as to what they really wished, she could resume the rounds. . . .

She threw back the bedclothes, and got up again. Now she was in a tumult of impatience for the morning, for the moment when she would see Nora, and explain and insist that it was the only thing to be done.

As she got out of bed a distant church clock struck three. That was St. Timothy's; and there, a second after it, so solemn, so slow, booming across the sleeping fields, was St. Jude's at West Titford. She knew them both. She had heard them for years. All the hours of all her grown-up life they had solemnly, the pair of them, tolled off one by one.

She pulled on a dressing-gown, and went to the window. Starlight and quiet. The night seemed deep in thought. Where was Nora, in this huge silence?

She turned her head, listening. At last there were sounds in the dead house—the front door being opened, and then carefully shut; footsteps on the stairs; cautious footsteps in the passage, hesitating, stopping. . . .

She padded across the room on her bare feet, and

stood with her ear to the crack of the door. Was someone
standing just outside it? Didn't she hear heart-beats?
Or were they only her own?

"Is that you, Nora?" she whispered; and after a
pause, anxiously, "Nora—is that you?"

No answer. Nobody was there. A distant door shut
softly.

§

And the same thing happened next morning—no
answers; nobody there; Nora not coming near her.

When, having waited with what patience she could
for George to have had time to eat his breakfast and be
seen off by Nora to the City, she still didn't come up,
Milly, trying to be reasonable and allow wide margins,
told herself that now she was probably with the cook,
ordering the day's meals, and would be with her in a few
minutes. But she wasn't. Minutes passed, and still
Nora wasn't with her. They stretched into half an hour,
into an hour, and still she wasn't—the reason being
that she and George were in one of a procession of cars,
all full of heavy-eyed Botts, proceeding in the direction
of Denmark Hill.

For Fred, afraid of Nora's careless and indiscreet
tongue, had telephoned before she had finished feeding
the passive George, telling her to hurry up and bring
him along, that he himself and Mabel were just starting,
and nobody must on any account be late and give Edith
time to do something irreparable.

"You'd better not go near that guest of yours," he
said, "till we've met and decided what we intend doing.
It's important we should act absolutely together."

"She won't be awake yet," Nora answered, thankful
now that she had resisted the temptation in the early
hours to go in and kiss her; and Fred at the other end

of the telephone, for the first and only time in his life
lashed by his bitter cares into epigram, said, "Let lying
Millies sleep——" immediately hanging up the receiver, and leaving Nora open-mouthed.

So that by the time Milly's patience came to an end
and she started out of her bedroom in search of Nora,
both she and George were well on their way to Denmark
Hill.

§

She went along the passage, and leaned over the
banisters and called.

As in the night, no answer. The house seemed
deserted; empty of everything, except sunshine and the
April wind. Windows and doors stood wide open.
Nora's bed was airing, the mattress turned back.
George's Jaeger pyjamas hung over a chair in his
dressing-room, their limp legs flapping in the draught.
Everywhere a smell of soap and toothpowders struggled
with the smell of the wallflowers blowing in through
the open front door. The only sound, apart from
garden sounds, was a noise of plates and knives from
somewhere where the servants were having breakfast.

She went downstairs, looking into all the rooms, even,
cautiously, into George's bleak study.

Nobody.

She went back to the drawing-room, and rang the
bell.

The maid said her mistress had gone out. No, she
had left no message. And this was so queer of Nora,
such a culmination of queerness, that Milly had all the
sensations of a worm turning, and made up her mind
then and there to go at once—not wait to explain and
suggest and if needs be insist, as she had meant to, but
just go.

She had had enough. Not an hour longer would she stay in George's house. Straight would she go to Denmark Hill, leaving her trunks to be fetched when she knew whether the old lady would take her in. And, if she refused to, she felt she would do almost anything—sleep on mother's doorstep, sit up all night on a seat in the playing-grounds, or on a straw-bottomed chair in St. Timothy's, rather than come back to George and Nora. Who could have believed Nora would behave like this? Who could have imagined her capable of such swift changes, of such unfairness, and unkindness?

Her eyes full of indignant tears, she went upstairs and once more packed the little bag she had had with her at Brighton; and arriving by means of two omnibuses and a tram at Denmark Hill soon after eleven, she went straight to the old lady's bedroom, where she knew she would find her still in bed, went straight to it unhindered by Jenny, who was too much startled on seeing her to utter a word, and opening the door, after knocking and hearing the old voice quaver "Come in," found herself staring into the faces of the assembled family.

§

The room was black with Botts. In astonishment she gazed at them. Crowded into the not very big space were sixteen of them—seventeen with the old lady, whose voice she had heard, but who was invisible in the bed behind the clustering figures; and every face was turned to her as she stood motionless on the threshold.

What were they all doing there? And so quiet, as she came up the stairs, that she hadn't heard a sound. Nora—that's where she was, then. George too—not gone to his office. And Alec, and Mabel, and—but everyone of the generation she belonged to except—no, she couldn't see Bertie.

She gazed round in such surprise that for a moment she forgot she was the family outcast.

Haggard, from the depths of the exhausted silence that had fallen on them, they gazed back at her.

Milly.

After their prolonged struggle with Edith, trying to bring her to what they called reason and she called their cowardly desire to save the family at the price of her humiliation, after the exasperations of the last hour, the anxiety, the efforts to propitiate, the constant being driven back by her flinty determination to be avenged, it was, the husbands felt, curiously refreshing to see Milly. So easy to manage, so pliable and ready to be convinced. Every one of the baffled brothers-in-law felt this secret, and they feared reprehensible, relief when they turned from Edith's destructive virtue, and beheld the soft sinner in the doorway.

Milly; the cause of all their troubles. Yet at that moment they had it in their hearts to forgive her, simply because, the exhausted Botts felt, she was the opposite of Edith. Wrong, wrong, all wrong, they knew, some of them, wiping their foreheads, said to themselves; but it was Edith's personality driving them. Virtue shouldn't be so violent. It shouldn't scold. It shouldn't force one to dislike it. Above all, it shouldn't ruin a whole family. And even into the women's hearts, friable now from fear, even into Maud's, even into Ruth's, trickled the confusing feeling that if Edith had been a little more like Milly everything might have been avoided.

There she stood, blankly staring. They, in silence, stared at her. And the invisible old lady in the bed, who for once had been finding her knowledge that these troubles would soon be over, soon be fallen into dust and forgetfulness, not enough to keep her calm, unable to see who it was that had come in because of the crowd around her, immediately felt a different quality in the silence, and asked, a little petulantly because of being so much hemmed in, "Who is there?"

No one answered her. The eyes of the absorbed assembly were watching Milly as her glance, after travelling round the room, reached Edith and stayed fixed.

Now was the moment when they expected her guiltily to shrink back and disappear again; but she didn't. Her face, on which had been nothing but wonder, when she saw Edith took on an expression of surprised concern. That was all—just surprised concern.

Edith was standing at the foot of the bed, in the middle of everybody, but not much crowded upon, and she looked so extraordinarily unhappy, so desperately tormented, that anybody who hadn't been alienated, as they had all been alienated for the last hour, by her vindictive unreason, would have shown concern—anybody, that is, one might have thought, except Milly. Milly oughtn't to. Her showing it, felt the Botts, was hardly in the best of taste.

But they were not given time to consider questions of taste. Edith, her blazing eyes on Milly, was saying so evenly, so quietly, that it seemed impossible she should be using the words, "I wonder you dare show your face here——" and there wasn't a man in the room who didn't wish on this, wish with all his heart, that he were somewhere else. Two women, one injured and the other injuring, meeting and going to have it out—what man wouldn't, if he could, from such an occasion slink away?

"It's Bertie," thought the old lady when she heard Edith's remark—poor Bertie, being spoken to like that by his wife. "Come in, Bertie my dear, and shut the door," she called out, unheeded. "No use making draughts."

"But I'll do you this justice," went on Edith. "You didn't bargain to run into *me*. Even you aren't as shameless as that."

Dear, dear—talking like that to her husband. Annoyed, of course, at seeing him, when she had been making up her poor mind never to see him again except in the divorce court, as she had kept on telling them all —such an unpleasant place to see one's husband again in, the old lady tried to point out, but no one had listened. Still, annoyed or not, it was a pity to talk in such a way to poor Bertie.

"Bertie my dear," she quavered from the invisible bed, "don't mind her. Mother's here."

Milly, her eyes on Edith, groped for comprehension. What was the matter with Edith? What had happened to make her look so ill, and let loose such—wasn't it hate?

"I—don't understand," she faltered.

"Why, it's Milly!" shrilled the voice from the bed. "Well now isn't that a pleas—— a surprise. Come in, my dear, and shut the door. Some of you get upset by husbands, but what upsets me is draughts."

"If she comes in," said Edith, "I go out."

"She's feeling a little sore about Bertie, my dear," explained the old lady, in so loud and hurried a quaver that they were bound to attend. "It'll pass, though. If you dear children could make a little room now, so that I can see poor Milly—yes, that's better. Thank you, my dears."

"About Bertie?" repeated Milly, her eyes and lips showing such complete surprise that into the dark hearts of the Botts straggled the faintest ray of hope. "Why? What has happened?"

"Oh" said Edith, at that, through her closed teeth. "Oh, you accomplished liar."

The room winced.

"Now, now, Edith," expostulated Fred.

"No use calling names, Edith my dear," expostulated the old lady, visible at last between the pressed-back figures, and apparently as complete in her cap and shawl and ribbons as if she were dressed all over, instead of only down to where the counterpane began. "I should have thought anybody could see poor Milly doesn't know what you are talking about."

"Oh," said Edith, looking at her scornfully, "you poor, deluded old woman."

The room started. Talking to mother like that? Calling her an old woman?

A storm of protest rose from every corner. The sons made angry movements towards the defiant figure.

"Look here, Edith—you keep a civil tongue in your head to mother," said Alec in high indignation.

"How dare you talk to mother like that?" threatened Fred.

"A brawl, a brawl, a public brawl," Ruth was heard to gasp over by the window.

"Poor child—so unhappy," explained the old lady indulgently.

"Absurd you are," was all Edith said to the menacing faces, waving them aside, and striding towards the door, against which Milly stood frozen.

"Let me pass, please," she ordered.

"No, no, my dear—you're not to go away," cried the old lady. "Fred, find Edith a chair—on her feet, poor child, so long, and being annoyed and all——"

"Let me pass," repeated Edith, directly addressing the frozen Milly.

"You can't disobey mother, Edith," remonstrated Fred angrily, laying a detaining hand on her arm.

"Can't I? Can't I?" she answered, turning on him; and suddenly burst into wild, violent weeping.

The room was appalled. Nobody had ever seen Edith cry before. The effect was overwhelming. The old lady's head wagged faster, and Milly's eyes, dark in her white face, were fixed on Edith's, so close to hers, as she shrank back against the door in horror.

"Oh, Edith—what is it?" she stammered. "What's the matter?"

"She thinks you've taken her husband from her, Milly my dear," explained the old lady hurriedly. "Such a pity, I always think, to think a thing like that, because if it's true it only leads to trouble, and if it isn't it's not a very nice thought to have had. Much better," she went on as nobody spoke, and Edith's bitter weeping was the only sound, "not worry, and just wait. They always come back, husbands do, if one just waits—and sometimes that isn't very nice either. Mabel my dear, give poor Edith the smelling-salts. You'll find them in the cupboard behind you."

"But——" said Milly, her astonished eyes on the convulsed Edith, "taken her husband? Do you mean Bertie?" And with a helpless glance round the room she asked, idiotically, "Where to?"

"Yes, my dear—that's what poor Edith believes, and whether she's right or wrong it's very sad for all of us, because she's going to try to divorce him. And that, you know, will disgrace us all a good deal, I'm afraid— especially as it's because of you, his sister-in-law. Nora my dear, just come and tie this ribbon better. No use not looking one's best, I always think."

Milly's bewildered eyes appealed to the nodding figure on the bed. "I don't understand, mother," she said.

"Why should Edith—what has her divorcing Bertie to do with *me*?"

"You see, my dears?" quavered the old lady. "The poor girl doesn't know anything at all about it. Edith thinks, Milly my dear, that you've—well, it's no use not saying it, is it, when you dear children are all thinking it—she thinks that you've committed adultery with poor Bertie."

The room held its breath to hear her answer.

It was merely to repeat, in a whisper, the terrible word, "Adultery"?

"Yes, my dear—adultery. What people commit," explained the old lady a little irritably, as Milly's face continued blank. "Some, that is. Such a pity, I always think, for it only seems to lead to worry. But fortunately it doesn't last."

Milly looked round at them in amazement, her hands spread out behind her against the door.

"With—*Bertie?*" she whispered.

"Yes, my dear—Bertie. My son, and your brother-in-law. Not a very nice thought for Edith to have, is it? However, she insists that it's true, and the family will be a good deal dragged down, I'm afraid."

"But——" began Milly, staring round.

"Do you dare," burst in Edith, pushing aside the smelling-salts Mabel tremblingly offered, and trying to control her twitching face, trying to stop the humiliating tears at least while she asked this one question, "do you *dare* stand there, Milly, and say you haven't committed adultery?"

"Oh, how terrible—oh, I can't bear this!" gasped Ruth.

"Answer the question, Milly my dear," quavered the old lady. "Answer it like a good girl, and set all our poor minds at rest."

And Milly, looking round at the crowding faces, her

hands spread out behind her against the door, her face frozen into a mask, said slowly, as if each word were a drop of her blood, "But it wasn't—with Bertie."

§

Faces, faces, faces; crowding so close to see her shame. Or was it—she caught her breath—her release?

It was her release. Suddenly she knew it. Here, in this room, she had reached freedom; here she had got to the end of all her torment.

An extraordinary sensation of being healed came over her; and something in a poem Arthur used to read aloud stirred in her memory as she stood, still pressed against the door, her eyes on the faces but no longer seeing them, and the room and everybody in it gone hazy—*Then clear, unburdened, careless, cool*, it went; and it was about what it was like after one had died.

That was what one felt, that was what one was, when one had finished with being afraid. Clear; unburdened. How lovely. What depths of—peace.

"Give her the smelling-salts," said somebody.

"No, no, my dear—Milly doesn't want smelling-salts," said the voice from the bed.

Slowly she became aware of the faces again, the crowding faces—Edith's with red eyes, incredulous, as if she weren't going to believe.

But she must believe. This one service Milly could do the Botts before she passed out of their lives for ever— she could force them to believe, save them from tragedy by telling the whole truth.

"No," she said, leaving off pressing back against the door and taking a step forward—towards them now, instead of shrinking away, wonder on her face that she should no longer be afraid, "it isn't smelling-salts I want. It's to tell you everything."

And then and there she was going to—going to strip herself naked before them, pick off all her lying shred by shred, tell them everything except only Arthur's name, give them such details that they couldn't but be convinced, when a loud quaver arose from the bed.

"My dear, I shouldn't do that," vehemently protested the old lady.

They all turned to her. They hadn't ever heard mother speak so loud before. Supported by the heaped-up pillows, sitting in the bed as on a throne, she was wagging her head with awe-inspiring violence. Her cap, its mauve ribbons shaking with the rest of her, had gone a little crooked, and the crookedness only made her the more impressive. She had raised a trembling hand. She was imposing silence. Her old face was flushed with determination.

"We don't want to hear anything more, Milly my dear," she announced authoritatively. "You've told us what we wished to know, and taken a great load off our minds, and I'm sure we're all very thankful and glad, especially poor Edith. But I always think long stories should be kept for winter evenings and rainy days and when we're old, my dear—no, no, don't speak—that's the time for telling everything, not now when it's spring, and we're none of us nearly as old, I'm sure, as we're going to be. Besides, it's getting on for lunch-time. We don't want to stay all boxed up here together on a nice bright morning when it's getting on for lunch-time talking about what's finished and done with, and the boys anxious to be off, I'll be bound, to their offices, and the girls worried, I'm sure, about not having ordered dinner yet."

She paused; but her eye was on Milly. If Milly had so much as begun opening her mouth, the old lady would instantly have interrupted. No more of that, she was

determined; no more nonsense from anybody. They
didn't know how to manage their lives, didn't they?
Well, she would manage them for them. They had
talked quite enough, the poor sillies, about what the
others had done or not done, and what they were going
to do next, or not do, and she wasn't going to have Milly
making a fool of herself too.

But Milly stood quite quiet, not attempting to do
anything, and the old lady, seeing this, ceased to hold
her with her eye and looked away at the others. Considering that her head was shaking, it was remarkable
how pointedly she managed to look at them.

"I'm tired," she announced briefly.

There was a movement, notably among the sons-in-
law squeezed together over by the windows.

"I'm tired, my dears," she repeated, encouraging the
movement. "I always think," she went on, as it showed
signs of subsiding, "that offices in the City are such a
comfort, because then people go to them."

The movement became more pronounced. With
curiously abashed faces, on which was yet relief, the
sons-in-law began disentangling themselves one by one.

"Are you going, Walter Walker my dear?" asked the
old lady approvingly, as her eldest son-in-law appeared
from behind the dressing-table, edging his way carefully
to the door. "That's right. And my Noakes son-in-law
too. Katie, of course you'll want to go with your husband. My dears, I'm tired," she said again, looking at
her own sons, who stood jammed together with their
wives, not quite sure what they ought to do.

The movement became general. Waistcoats were
straightened, and bags picked up. The old lady, her
eye on them, checked any tendency she observed to
linger by saying with increasing insistence, "I'm tired,
my dears——" and when Maud, her eldest daughter, a

woman not easily removed from such places as she wished
to stay in, began to protest, she was cut as short as if
she were still in the nursery, and briefly told to hold her
tongue.

After that the daughters went very quietly, cowed by
hearing one of themselves, a woman of sixty-two, bid-
den hold her tongue and seeing her obediently holding it.
Besides, mother's face was dangerously red. Suppose
she had a fit, and died then and there? What would
their consciences feel like then?

"I'm *tired*, my dears," repeated the old lady, annoyed by
their slowness, the red of her face deepening alarmingly.

They began to move more quickly. The sons, intensely relieved at being let off, anyhow for the present,
further scenes and explanations, grabbed at their wives
and drew them along with them towards the door.
Mother was quite right. Much best stop Milly getting
things off her chest. They had had enough, first and
last, of Milly's chest. Besides, what did it matter now,
her exact form of sinning? The great thing was that
old Bertie wasn't in it, and that they were all saved from
any beastly divorcing. One or two of them would have
liked to have shaken hands or something with the poor
creature, who stood at the foot of the bed as if she didn't
know whether she too was expected to sheer off or not,
for after all she had got them out of no end of a hole, and
Nora and Mabel both wanted to kiss her; but every time
anybody showed signs of lingering, the old lady repeated
commandingly, "I'm *tired*, my dears."

Edith got away one of the first. Her departure was
watched from the bed with approval.

"Edith's gone," the old lady remarked, encouraging
the others to follow so excellent an example. "Sensible
of her. She'll be better next time we see her. We'll all
be better, my dears—and rested."

The room grew lighter. Presently Milly, still uncertain, her hands on the rail of the bed, had quite a large empty space round her.

Lighter and lighter grew the room, larger and larger the empty space round Milly. At last there was nothing but space, and light, and herself, and the old lady.

Except for the birds in the garden, very busy that fine morning, and the rumble of traffic on the road beyond, the room was quite silent.

They looked at each other—Milly, at the foot of the bed, her white face framed in the thrown-back crape veil against the bright window behind her, the old lady in her quivering mauve ribbons, propped up on the pillows at the other end.

"Then," said Milly at last, her eyes on the flushed old face, her voice very low, "then—I may go?"

"Yes, my dear. Upstairs, to take off your bonnet."

Silence; except for those birds, and the distant banging of the doors of cars as Botts departed.

"You can't keep on your bonnet for the rest of your life, can you?" the old lady, after a moment, pointed out.

Cleared of blocking black figures, the windows were streamed through by warm sunshine. Light washed round the room, flooding the face on the pillows.

"Do you mean——" began Milly.

"Come here, my dear," interrupted the old lady in a commanding quaver, "and kiss me good-morning. You haven't yet, you know, and we must keep up our manners, mustn't we, as we're going to live together. Besides, Milly my dear"—she held out both her unsteady hands—"I want to bless you."

THE END

Introduction

But yield who will to their separation,
My object in living is to unite
My avocation and my vocation
As my two eyes make one in sight.

From *Two Tramps in Mud Time* by Robert Frost

Home-based businesses are one of the fastest growing areas of the U.S. economy. One study estimated there were over eighteen million home-based businesses in this country as of early 1997. Of these, about one-fourth of them focus on personal services or creative design, such as sewing.

Perhaps you already belong to or are tempted to join this growing army of the self-employed. It's only natural to want to use your talents and favorite activities to make money. Sewing skills were once a part of life in nearly every home but are now much less common and becoming increasingly marketable. Many sewing enterprises have begun with a talented seamstress helping nonsewing friends and relatives. By identifying the need for such skills in your community, you have taken the first step toward creating a successful sewing business.

However, a sewing-business owner has an awful lot of hats to wear: contractor, financier, designer, accountant, buyer, marketer and tax specialist—to name just a few. How does a person who loves to sew keep the business productive and profitable—goods flowing out, money coming in—without losing the artistic, creative flair that inspired the business in the first place?

To fulfill your dreams you need to have more than just a good idea and a desire to create. You also need the skills to market your service or product, the ability to develop your particular market niche, and the flexibility to change your business to fit both your needs and the needs of the market.

This book is a compilation of the combined business experience of several successful sewing entrepreneurs, plus all new information on the latest in machines, computers and pricing. I hope to help you smoothly conquer the learning curve of a fledgling sewing business so that you can successfully unite *your* vocation and avocation!

CHAPTER 1

How to Know if It's Time to Turn Your Hobby Into a Business

Everyone knows how well you sew. People ask you how much you would charge to make that dress for them. Or that crib blanket. Or that window treatment. Or one of your unique craft items. Is this the time to begin that sewing business you've had in the back of your mind for awhile? Maybe it is. Let's examine all the possibilities.

Questions to ask yourself

- Are your sewing skills up-to-date?
- What sewing specialty interests you?
- Is there a strong market for this specialty?
- What kind of local competition exists?
- Are you confident of your ability to own a business?
- Are you confident of the concept you've designed?
- Can you sustain your interest in the business long enough to succeed?
- Are you ready to lose your hobby?

Are your sewing skills up-to-date?

Perhaps you have sewn all your life. You're fairly confident of your ability to sew for yourself, but what about sewing for others? Before you take on the responsibility of starting a sewing business, you must first carefully evaluate your skills and knowledge in the field.

Are you up-to-date in the latest methods and fabrics? What are the latest trends in your area of expertise? If you have a desire to do dressmaking, are you able to fit any type of body style? And what about your knowledge of patterns? Are you willing to learn to create your own patterns, or can you change existing patterns to suit your customers' needs? If you've chosen to create custom window treatments, are you current with the latest styles in this ever-changing field? If you wish to make quilts, how is your spatial ability? Can you determine which colors are most pleasing with one another?

These are important considerations. If you feel unsure about your sewing skills, this is the time to update your training. Taking some refresher classes at consumer shows may help, or perhaps more comprehensive training in your field is in order. Many professional organizations offer classes, seminars and other training resources to keep you current with the latest techniques and trends in your field.

Joining a professional sewing group is another way to develop your sewing skills and meet like-minded professionals. Being able to discuss difficult situations and share common experiences helps everyone—you, the others in the group and eventually your clients. If there isn't such a group in your area, you might want to start one. See the appendix for more information on sewing groups and other valuable training resources.

If you aren't confident of how well you can sew, your customer won't be either. A quiet assurance that you know what you're doing will go a long way toward easing many customer objections.

What sewing specialty interests you?

Are you turned off by the idea of sewing window treatments but fascinated by the intricacies of lovely beaded wedding creations? Or does the thought of creating a custom-designed dress for someone appeal to you? If you are drawn to one kind of sewing, think of how you can develop this into a business. Is there a market for your wonderfully original, hand-sewn teddy bears? Has the experience of moving frequently given you excellent skills in dressing windows? Or has your frugal practice of re-covering your furniture given you an interest in doing slipcovers?

Think about what type of sewing particularly appeals to you. Having a specialty area, or two or three, helps your business succeed where others may fail. There are many reasons for specializing, which will be discussed in chapter two.

James Powell

Powell Manufacturing Industries, Inc.
Washington, DC

"It all began with a string. Someone had given me a string of cotton fiber and told me that I should try to figure out a way to make a business out of it. It was a challenge that kept my mind going for months," says James Powell. He had been downsized from his government job, and for several months he researched possible business ideas he could implement himself. One aspect of his severance package included the accrued value of his retirement program; James planned to use this money to start his business.

After more than two months of pondering what to do with that string, James saw someone using a mop to clean the lobby of a nearby office building. He suddenly realized how he could use that string to create a business—he would manufacture and sell cotton fiber mops.

First, James did a market study. He wanted to know how many cleaning companies there were in the Washington, DC, area. Another important statistic was the number of public buildings, apartment buildings and private homes in the vicinity. Once he had determined that a market existed for his cotton fiber mops, James put together a business plan. After discussing the plan with his wife, Rebecca, he took a deep breath and withdrew his retirement money.

Because mops need to be sewn to their bases, James bought an industrial-strength sewing machine and taught himself to sew. But it was a frustrating experience. "I broke about 1,500 needles—the repairman became my best friend," James remembers. "He finally asked me to sew while he was watching, and he realized he needed to explain to me that the feed dogs pull the fabric past the needle. I was pushing it along, which is why the needles kept breaking." This didn't slow James down, though—he practiced twenty to thirty minutes a night to get the rhythm of sewing down pat.

In addition to training, James found that starting a sewing business required ingenuity and problem-solving skills. Because mops are sold by weight rather than by size, he designed a machine to "manicure" the mops—to trim them so each conformed to the specified weight. Along with this machine and the sewing stations, James worked out an assembly line, moving from the raw materials to shipping the finished goods out the door.

After he had his product design and the operations all figured out, James had to find a larger market. His first attempt was to make a bid on a contract for the DC public schools. Winning the bid proved to be a Catch-22—he needed the lucrative account but couldn't produce the necessary two thousand mops by himself. Because he was still working alone, James had to buy the mops from another company in Georgia. By the time he'd been in business eight or nine months, he was ready to hire his first employee.

One of the lessons James has learned from his business is that persistence pays off. When he contacted Joan Henderson, a buyer for the local grocery chain Giant Foods, she invited James to meet her. Though she said Giant had no business for his company at that time, she told him to stay in touch. James took her literally.

Every Wednesday at 10:00 A.M. he called her. "After about three months, she knew it would be my call at that time," he says. "I would say 'Good morning, Ms. Henderson,' and she would answer, 'Good morning, Mr. Powell,' every week." Finally Ms. Henderson made an initial order, for ten dozen mops a month. This business has grown to an average order of forty dozen mops a week. "Giant Foods nurtured my business; when I could produce more,

they ordered more, " says Powell of this business partnership. Currently his company has eight full-time employees and four to five seasonal hires.

James Powell has this advice for businesspeople: "The margins are better in manufacturing than in custom work, so look into that aspect of your business. Be relentless in your pursuit of whatever you want to do; you have to be obsessed by a dream. Work hard, but smart. Be willing to deny yourself; I worked seven days a week for four years before I could relax a little. Never give up. Rest—you *need* to rest—but don't quit. I want to inspire people to be producers instead of consumers."

Is there a strong market for this specialty?

This is a key consideration, and one on which your success will depend heavily. One frustrated seamstress told me she had a fantasy of owning a dressmaking business. But her small town just didn't have the clients to support such a specialized enterprise. A more realistic approach is to make a match between your interests and skills, and the needs of your community.

For example, you may find there is a strong market for altering ready-to-wear clothing in your town, but little call for custom work. On the other hand, perhaps your city is experiencing a surge in new home construction; this could create a great demand for window treatments and other home decor items. Because many industries are calling for more casual work clothing, only bigger cities are good markets for career wear right now.

Perhaps your specialty isn't dependent on the local market. Some of the entrepreneurs profiled in this book are creating goods for the national or international market. Even if you live in a remote or rural area, you can have a successful business if you choose your specialty wisely.

What local competition exists?

If you live in a small town that already has three bridal shops, this obviously wouldn't be the wisest choice for your specialty. But maybe there's a need for alterations on ready-to-wear gowns, or perhaps you would prefer to cater to the needs of the family after the wedding. Are children's clothes readily available? Is anyone else making slipcovers? Is there a product that is popular locally (garden flags, cement goose clothing, mailbox covers, horse blankets) that isn't being made by anyone else?

The key is to identify where you can compete in your local market. If the dry cleaner down the street charges so little for its customers' alterations that you just can't compete, a better choice might be to change your specialty to something else. Another example of this problem is the production of bridesmaids' gowns—an area where many beginning sewing businesses cut their prices substantially in an attempt to undercut prices at local shops. It's almost impossible to compete in this business atmosphere, and my advice is not to even try. Let others lose money doing such work for little pay; it simply isn't worth the aggravation to make $75 (or less) a dress. In most communities this price would cause the dressmaker to lose money. If you can't make a profit in a particular segment of the market, choose another specialty.

Are you confident of your ability to own a business?

As I said in the introduction to this book, there are more considerations to having a successful sewing business than knowing how to sew well. If you feel you have a need for more knowledge in general business subjects, there are some great resources available. Your local Extension Agency may have classes specific to a sewing business. Service Corps of Retired

Executives (SCORE), a volunteer offshoot of the Small Business Administration (SBA), may have a volunteer on staff who can help you. If none is available at the moment, don't hesitate to check again later. The service is free and can be invaluable in helping you identify the strengths and weaknesses of your business ideas.

Are you confident of the concept you've designed?

One pitfall in starting a new business is that others around you will test your resolve; they may even try to put obstacles in your path to success. If you have firm assurance and confidence in your plan, these obstacles will melt away, along with the objections family members or friends might have to your ambitions and dreams.

Again, here is where some expert advice can help. If you plan to offer concierge service alterations to office buildings but are too shy to present the program to concierge managers, it probably won't work very well. And if you don't think it will actually be to their benefit, you're sure to fail. There are some terrific motivational tapes and books that can help you overcome your own fears. Any library or bookstore will have such resources; avail yourself of all the help you can get.

If you sense there might be objections to your new business, keep your plans to yourself for awhile, at least until they have enough strength to sustain themselves in your mind. There's no substitute for a burning desire or ambition! If you are driven to accomplish a goal or to create a plan for yourself, you can't help but succeed.

Can you sustain your interest in the business long enough to succeed?

Consider this scenario: You decide to make three hundred teddy bears to sell at shows. By the time you have finished them, you're so tired of seeing fur all over the place you never want to even hear the words *teddy bear* again! Can you make a business of this, or would it be better for you to make more of a variety of products to sell?

Likewise, do you enjoy doing alterations enough to make a business of them? Can you stand being around interior designers who want you to change designs all the time? Or do you want to voluntarily place yourself in the way of a bride whose weight is fluctuating wildly the last few weeks before her wedding, or whose mother may be forcing the daughter to accept a wedding that fulfills *her* desires?

Look ahead to see how you feel about recreating any one activity for an extended period of time.

Are you ready to lose your hobby?

A "hobby" is fun; "work" isn't. It's as simple as that. If you turn your hobby into a moneymaking enterprise, will it still be fun for you? For some people it is a dream come true to do something they love all day long. For others, it's a nightmare. Why? Because they no longer have the time or the inclination to enjoy the activity just for fun. Before you spend any more time on planning a business, this is something to consider carefully.

For Karen Howland, a couture bridal designer in Chillicothe, Illinois, her once-favorite hobby is still a wonderful, enjoyable business pursuit. However, she has changed her attitude toward sewing considerably in the fifteen years or so she has sewn for the public. When she wants to relax now, she switches to knitting, also a longtime hobby. Knitting is a pleasure because it's totally for herself; there's no client input as to design, color or style, and Karen can create to her heart's content.

Before you decide to commit yourself to weekly work activity that you used to enjoy for fun, decide how you feel about this. Are you willing to relegate your own projects to the back burner, or do you hope to fit them in during your workday? Any time you aren't sewing for others you aren't making money; is this OK with you?

Deborah Jackson

Sewing Services
Fairfield, Ohio

Debby Jackson loves to make the same thing over and over, the more the better. She likes the "mindless" repetition of not having to think about what comes next. Her business, Sewing Services, specializes in contract and production sewing. She and her employees make thousands of the same item for each of their customers, which means creativity is almost nonexistent in their work life.

Sewing Services makes uniform shirts and aprons for grocery store chains and restaurants. One of Debby's specialties is maternity uniform pants; her company inserts the stretchy panels into hundreds of pre-made slacks. Because of the limited need for this item, the large uniform companies don't want to retool their entire line for this small segment of their customers. Instead, they subcontract the work to someone like Debby, who can more easily handle these "smaller" quantities.

While this type of work suits Deborah Jackson just fine, for some it wouldn't be any fun at all. By identifying her own personal strengths and preferences, she has built a successful business with the sewing she enjoys.

9

CHAPTER 2

Specialize!

In my book *Sew up a Storm: All the Way to the Bank!*, I identified seventy different sewing specialties, and there are many more ways to make money with sewing. Already in this book, I have referred to several ideas, but there are almost limitless opportunities.

Look around you; notice what the sewn products are everywhere. In a catalog of novelty goods, you'll find stuffed toys, home decor items, specialty clothing, garden items, all manner of giftware, household helpers, table decorations and so much more. Driving down a city street, you'll observe awnings, streetlight banners, flags, display props, even the "headlight bra" on the front of that foreign car! Further investigation will reveal boat covers, sails, motorcycle packs, bicycle flags, kites, hot-air balloons, backpacks and on and on. Ideas abound.

Why should you specialize?

There are lots of good reasons to specialize. The first, and best, one is that there are vast pricing differences between various sewing disciplines. For instance, custom dressmaking is not necessarily your route to sure success, unless you are able to target an affluent customer base to which you provide select service and quality garments. It is possible to make a modest income with custom dressmaking, but you need to be vigilant about pricing and spending and be careful not to allow your customer to dictate your price point. There are always customers who will pay; sometimes you just have to search for them.

Compared to dressmaking, drapery and window treatments command a higher per-hour fee. There's a perception that sewn clothing should be cheaper than ready-to-wear but that anything for the home should (and does) cost more.

Why is this? In the past, people sewed for economy, and many can still recall their grandmothers, mothers, aunts and neighbors sewing clothing for them as a money-saving measure. But custom-made draperies, avail-

10

able at most department stores, were fairly expensive. The cheaper alternative was to purchase factory-made curtains at discount stores. In recent years many finer retail stores have closed these departments, and now the customer must have window treatments made in drapery workrooms or purchase them from decorators (who have them made in drapery workrooms). The result is that draperies and top treatments are now even pricier than they once were. In addition, newer homes with volume space and high windows have rendered the once "standard" window sizing useless. Nearly every window in the average new home is custom sized, making nearly every window treatment custom sized also.

Because of customer perceptions and the fact that there are fewer sources for specially made draperies, it's possible to gross three to six times as much per hour to sew custom window treatments as it is to make custom clothing. Also, the skill level is different; creating well-fitting clothing for the human form is among the most complicated of tasks. Window treatments utilize nearly all straight seams, thereby making them simpler to sew.

When you are known for doing one thing well, you receive better public awareness of your business. Word-of-mouth advertising is the cheapest but most effective of all ways to let the public know about your business. If your customers tell one another and potential new customers about your terrific way with a round window, or a bridal train, or altering a jacket sleeve vent, you are miles ahead of the game.

When you specialize, you eventually streamline your focus and, consequently, all your operations. You don't waste energy refocusing several times a day; you know what you're going to do each day, and each task becomes routine. Also, when you have a tough problem, it is more likely to be a repeat of a problem; eventually, less time is wasted in problem solving. This makes you more efficient and ultimately brings you more money per hour. It even streamlines your supply closet: If you only need tailoring interfacing, you won't waste the time or the money to purchase, or the space to store, bridal interfacing, for instance. If you're a bridal designer, you can concentrate your thread and lining investment in colors of white, off-white and ivory.

If you're known as a specialist, you will experience a faster track to success. Only those people who want your specific service will come to you, and you can focus on honing your craft in that one area. You may even consider centering your energy on two or three specialties as this can help even out seasonal swings in income.

By honing in on one or two markets, you can create more income for yourself also. When you have that market in focus, it enables you to pinpoint the marketing ideas that will work best. You won't waste time, and money, trying to sell air conditioners to Alaskans!

Here's a suggestion for defining your services for your customers: Practice presenting a thirty-second synopsis of your business that defines exactly what you want to be known for. For instance, if you are a childrenswear manufacturer, say so. Don't just say, "I make children's clothing." That's an invitation to the customer to take advantage of you and call upon you to do other sewing jobs. This wastes your time and energy and antagonizes prospective customers. Don't allow this to happen; describe your business specifically and in easy-to-understand terminology.

The worst thing you can say is, "I sew." That opens you up to any and all who want sewing done for them. Be specific, and help your potential customer make you successful.

How to choose your niche

Evaluate your skill level

Be brutally honest with yourself. Determine whether you have the fine skills to be successful. Are you truly ready to bill yourself as a couturier? Would you be intimidated working with interior designers with the slipcover-making skills you have now? Are you confident your production work is up to snuff? Would you pay the prices you'll set for the items you make for craft shows? In what skills do you excel?

Evaluate your tolerance for people

Are you a people person, or would you rather work alone and just sew things? If you hate working with the public, choose a specialty that doesn't require direct contact with customers. Some crafts, production sewing, and some manufacturing, for instance, are specialties that can offer such seclusion.

Pinpoint your own areas of interest

Can you dedicate yourself to making crib quilts for five years, or would you rather create lovely heirloom christening gowns? If you can sustain

Chris Wilson

Mystiques
Harker Heights, Texas

Unable to find G-string lingerie in department stores, Chris Wilson began making it for her own personal use, then for a non-sewing friend. Although neither are strippers, her friend said Chris should sell to local clubs. Chris resisted the idea for awhile, but when she was laid off her job, she decided to try to make a business out of making dance costumes.

Harker Heights is situated about sixty miles from Austin, but it boasts the largest Army military base in the world. Nearby Fort Hood brings lots of young men to the area, and topless dance clubs abound. Chris started knocking on the doors of clubs to see if the dancers would be interested in buying her garments.

Chris and her husband, Jimmy, who acts as her bodyguard, usually began their "workday" at 7:30 P.M. They made the rounds of about four clubs, once or twice a week, selling a variety of clothing to the dancers, usually getting home shortly after closing time at 2:00 A.M. In the beginning, Chris says she only visited clubs that didn't charge her for admittance, but the better clubs charged her about 10 percent of her total sales for access to the girls' dressing rooms each evening. Now Chris makes the clothing for just one club, which has about 140 dancers.

"There's a lot of competition," says Chris. "There are four or five other people making costumes around here, so I have to be sure my things are different from theirs.

To keep up, I was making, then ordering, more elaborate pieces for awhile, but it didn't pay to do that, so I'm not anymore. Now I do more basic pieces: T-backs (thongs), hot pants, tube skirts (cut to a *V* in front), triangle tops and pareaus (wrap skirts)." Most of the garments Chris makes are made of Lycra fabric in prints and solids, and the dancers can request fancier treatments, or fabrics such as Lycra foils, for a glittery look under the lights.

"My prices are lower than some," she points out, "mostly because I stay with the basic styles. For a T-back, for instance, I charge about $25, but to add rhinestones, I double the price. Underwire tops with rhinestones go for about $200." Chris herself can make about $700 a night in sales, mostly to regular customers. Occasionally, a big tipper adds to her profit margin.

Chris also makes a $20 basic dress that she can't keep in stock—most places charge $40 for the same thing—and a longer gown of the same pattern for $100. The basic dress is made from Chris's own pattern and from inexpensive fabrics. This item takes her a mere fifteen minutes to make, using a home serger and a tabletop coverstitch hemmer.

When we talked, Chris was planning to buy industrial machines soon and to start a catalog service for clients outside her own community. She plans to start simply, doing all the sewing herself, then eventually to hire employees. A web page was already in the works at the time of our interview.

interest in your chosen field for twenty to fifty hours a week, you will be much more successful than if you force yourself to slave away in an area that doesn't appeal to you much. Go for the specialty you like best, as long as a market exists somewhere.

Determine whether you have superior knowledge in a particular specialty. As an example, people who ride and own horses have a wide variety of needs for sewn products, and each discipline has a different set of garments and accessories. Western saddle clothing differs greatly from hunter jumper gear. The various competitive riding areas sometimes require costumes for even the horses. If you or a family member rides and you have special insight into the kinds of merchandise preferred by the other riders in your circle, this could be your niche in the marketplace. The horse industry pumps over $3 billion into the U.S. economy per year. As a specialty, it offers rich possibilities.

Determine your local market interests

Survey local interests before you invest anything in your business. If you buy a $3,000 sewing machine with the intent to embroider towels and baby items, you may be in for a rude shock to find that no one in your local area is interested in purchasing such services. Do your market research first, then make your decisions and purchases.

If you don't find a local market for your work, you may be tempted to respond to ads about doing piecework for money. Be careful about these companies. If the job hinges on you paying for kits, I advise against getting involved. There have been reports of earnest sewists working hard to comply with a company's supposed skill level only to have their work rejected. Legitimate offers will not require a monetary outlay on your part.

Tap into a wider market

Would those same baby items sell at craft shows? Or could you offer your sewing services to a specialty group over the Internet? Kateri Ellison, a dressmaker in Washington, DC, has sewn for clients in other states. She requests that her clients send their measurements via E-mail. Patterns are made by computer so they can be easily adjusted. Garment designs are approved by mail, and the finished garments are sent via FedEx. She has had a wonderful response to this service from her satisfied customers, some of whom she has never met.

Chris Llewellyn

Custom Sport
Bainbridge Island, Washington

With many years' experience in pattern drafting and designing for outerwear manufacturers in the Seattle area, Chris Llewellyn decided to use her knowledge to start her own business making sports outerwear. Because Chris and her family are all active in sports, this line of work comes naturally to her. Everyone skis, sails and rides. Each of them teaches at different ski schools, which brings them a lot of business. Students ask where she gets her pants and jackets, and they often end up buying some. She offers a group discount to some classes.

Chris and her two employees' sports outerwear includes ski school uniforms and other skiwear. One specialty is skiwear for children. One-piece suits for kids, hats and other outerwear articles fill one wall of Chris's light-filled second-story workroom. Custom Sport also makes uniforms for rowing teams across the country, cycling wear and lift operator clothing. Other products include riding school jackets, helmet covers with matching vests and saddle pads for riders, and more equestrian wear, mostly for cross-country jumping. Protective vests are required attire for jumping, and Custom Sport has created a niche in making them. "We have sold vests in every state but Alaska and Hawaii, so far," Chris says. "And since my son is going to school in Alaska, we will probably find some customers there, too." The vests require special equipment. Chris says visitors to her workroom are often surprised to see a bandsaw

and a drill press. Employees cut the thick foam with the saw and drill each piece with the press, for ventilation.

Custom Sport began its mail-order business in 1978. In addition to the various lines of activewear Chris offers, she also does patternmaking for other small manufacturers and is happy to work as a manufacturing facility, if her schedule permits. Between Chris and her two sewing employees, they make hundreds of technical outdoor jackets a year and ship orders all over the country.

Chris notes, "I love to see a guy walking into the shop who is 6'8". I know I can help him, because I know he has never had a good fit in outerwear." She goes on to explain, "I can make the sleeves long enough and can customize anything, depending on what the customer wants. They may see a Gore-Tex jacket they like, but prefer another color. I stock dozens of colors, so I can accommodate them. They might like an extra pocket on a sleeve; we can do that, too. A lot of people like bells and whistles in their coats. If they want to spend the money, well, we can manage it."

Chris uses only industrial machines, except an older Viking she keeps for buttonholes. "I don't know how you can make any money using a home machine," she says. "I don't think it's fair to charge a customer $35 an hour without using high-speed equipment—I can sew twice as fast using my industrial equipment. I have no problem with my machines, especially the computerized industrial. But if it ever has a problem I can just send the control panel out to the shop; the machine part can stay put." This is almost a requirement for Chris, as the closest shop is off the island. Other equipment at Custom Sport includes an old upholstery machine for making horse blankets, a computerized Juki with automatic backstitch and heel-operated presser lift and an industrial serger. All the catalog components are created on a Macintosh computer.

Assess work space requirements

If you intend to make draperies, stage curtains, sails or awnings, be sure you have lots of room, with big cutting tables. Anything less will be impractical. However, some specialties don't require much room at all. Alterations, for instance, can be confined to a small space. You really only need room enough for about a 2' × 3' cutting area, a sewing machine, some kind of pressing station and perhaps a blindstitcher. Bridal alterations take more space, but perhaps you can set up a larger, temporary cutting area only when it's needed.

Teaching sewing takes up a lot of space, too—usually a whole room—unless you are teaching one-on-one classes or at another location, such as the local community center. You'll also need more equipment—sewing, cutting and pressing. However, if you have the space, the communication skills, the desire and ability to teach and a good potential student base, the financial rewards of teaching can be significant.

Some other ideas for you if you have a small apartment or little available work space: custom children's clothing, miniquilts, doll clothes, napkins and other household items, scarves and hats. This is by no means a complete list; the sky's the limit for ideas.

Assess equipment needs

Although many start out in the sewing business using their home machines, this isn't necessarily the best idea (see chapter three). In a production business like Deborah Jackson's uniform service, industrial machines are an absolute requirement, for both speed and efficiency. Traditional tailoring requires the use of pressing equipment with more steam than the average household iron, and both an industrial gravity-feed iron and a vacuum board may be necessary for you to accomplish a professional-looking product. Your specialty and the size of your business will determine your equipment needs.

Consider your personal abilities and limitations

Upholstering requires strength, as does sailmaking. The sheer effort of heaving furniture and heavy canvas around can sap limited strength. Are you exhausted by long hours of hand sewing? You may want to avoid making heavily beaded bridal gowns.

Are you good at math? Precise fit requires good arithmetic skills, not only in custom clothing, but in window treatments and slipcovers, as well as fittings for RVs, motorcycles, tents, banners and many other sewn products.

Determine your accessibility to raw goods and maintenance resources

Running to the fabric store for a spool of neon orange thread at 2:00 A.M. isn't an option for most people, but there are sometimes problems that need to be resolved quickly. Most mail-order services can and will send orders out by next-day delivery service; it just might cost you more. You may also have to travel far to find equipment. Be sure to get as much maintenance information as possible, particularly if your business is in a rural or otherwise inaccessible area. If you live in the remote hinterlands of Wyoming or Maine, it may be difficult to find a good repair facility for your industrial machine. However, this sort of obstacle is easily overcome.

Sometimes a specialty chooses you!

Is this situation familiar to you? You have been sewing for others for awhile and you suddenly realize that most of your time is concentrated in one or two specialties? You have acquired a reputation for creating beautiful wedding decorations, or well-fitting, high-quality suits, or the cutest children's room decorations anyone's ever seen. Well, go for it! If this is acceptable to you, back up and regroup. Change your marketing focus so it reflects this change in your business, and hone in on that area. Accentuate the positive.

What kind of income can you expect?

This depends on several factors, geography, for instance. What is profitable in one area of the United States may not be in your area, and vice

Traits for Success & Possible Income

Specialty	Traits for Success		Possible Gross Income Ranges
Dressmaking	Ability to sew quickly and accurately Patternmaking skills Fitting expertise Diplomacy and tact Self-confidence	Good taste Knowledge of fashion and fabrics Creativity Excellent spatial ability	$2 to $40 per hour
Alterations	Same as dressmaking, plus: Good to excellent sewing skills Knowledge of how garments are made Ability to judge fit	Communication skills Problem-solving skills Knowledge of proportion	$5 to $30 per hour
Custom Design	Same as above, plus: Excellent patternmaking skills Couture-level sewing skills Advanced creativity	Exquisite taste Knowledge of better fabrics and their use	$7 to $45 per hour

Bridal	Same as dressmaking, plus:
	Excellent sewing skills
	Alterations skills
	Good design sense
	Excellent hand-sewing skills
	  (for beading)
		Knowledge of recent trends
		Patience and good
		  communication skills
		Ability to hold up under
		  extreme pressure
		Large work space, especially tables
			$8 to $45 per hour

Tailoring	Same as custom design, plus:
	Excellent tailoring skills,
	  including pressing
	Thorough knowledge of
	  tailorable fabrics
		Thorough knowledge
		  of shaping techniques
		Excellent customer service skills
		Good understanding
		  of body complexities
			$8 to $50 per hour

Costumes	Good to excellent sewing skills
	Patternmaking ability
	Excellent fitting skills
	Alterations skills
	Ability to translate ideas into reality
	For body puppets: engineering skills
		Ability to create illusion that
		  holds up to stage lighting
		Dyeing and other fabric
		  manipulation skills
		Thorough knowledge of fabrics
			$2 to $10 per hour
			(nontheatric)
			$6 to $40 + per
			  hour
			(theatric)

Home Decor	Good eye for color and fabric choices Knowledge of home decor trends Good to excellent sewing skills Dressmaking skills, for certain details Speed and pattern-matching abilities	Large work area Industrial machines Excellent math skills Good communication skills	$6 to $40 per hour

Specialty	Traits for Success		Possible Gross Income Ranges
Crafts	Creativity and originality Tolerance for duplication of effort Good selling/marketing skills Good sewing skills	Knowledge of current trends Willingness to travel to shows Access to lower-priced raw goods	$0 to $40 per hour (depending on craft, market)
Embroidery	Willingness to work with computers Desire to make many of one design	Good mechanical ability Large work space for the machines	$10 to $70 per hour

Sport Goods	Excellent design skills
	Knowledge of the sport
	  and the customer
	Knowledge of the marketplace
	  and trends
		Originality
		Desire to make many of one design
		Access to appropriate fabrics
		Engineering ability
		Good marketing skills
			$6 to $35 per hour

Quilting	Excellent hand-sewing or machine skills Knowledge of quilt patterns Good eye for color and design Good eye-hand coordination	Large work space Excellent spatial ability Strong eyes	$4 to $30 per hour (more for machine quilters)
Flags/Banners	Excellent spatial ability Good eye for color and design Good eye-hand coordination Large work space Desire to make many of one design	Factory sewing skills Access to wholesale fabric sources Knowledge of musical and religious information Good selling/marketing skills	$6 to $35 per hour
Liturgical	Excellent sewing skills Knowledge of religious symbolism	Access to fine fabrics Patternmaking skills	$5 to $50 per hour
Teaching	Excellent communication skills Empathy for beginners Good understanding of the material Pleasant, clear speaking voice	Access to large work space for hands-on classes Sense of humor Ability to inspire others	$6 to $40 per hour

Piecework	Ability to sew quickly and accurately
	Tolerance for duplication of effort
	Large work space
	Willingness to work to a deadline
		Industrial machines and access
		  to repair facility
		Proximity to industry that needs
		  your services
			$5 to $30 per hour

versa. In some parts of the South, less is paid for dressmaking than in the North. On the other hand, heirloom sewing is valued much more highly in the South. In New York City, even though it's a big, cosmopolitan area, it may be more difficult to charge a higher amount for a custom suit than in a Midwestern city. Why? There are still many sweatshop situations in a big city, and labor is sometimes very cheap.

Many people in rural areas or small towns believe they can't charge as much as their big-city counterparts. This may or may not be true. If you have the only alterations business in the area, you can almost charge whatever you want. Your customers' only alternative may be to do the work themselves. It's just not true that "things are cheaper in the country." A gallon of milk, a loaf of bread, a tankful of gas, a haircut—these may actually cost more in rural areas.

There's only one surefire way to figure out what to charge: Do your market research. It's more labor intensive than the "guess-and-by-gosh" method, but it's the only way to attain a true picture of your earnings potential.

Skill level and personality also factor into income potential. See the chart on pages 18 and 19 for more specific information, as well as an income range for each specialty.

Hiring employees

If you decide to manufacture a product on a larger scale than a one-person operation, consult your local Internal Revenue Service office, as well as your accountant. Hiring employees creates more paperwork than working solo, but it may be worth the effort if you have a hot niche market you need to pursue.

Be wary of employing sewing subcontractors, those who sew for you in their own homes. There are federal restrictions on hiring contract sewing help for ladies garments, and the law changed substantially in 1994. The onus is on you, the business owner, to make sure those working for you also have other clients; if they work only for you, they are considered employees. In more than one case, this has caused serious problems for business owners who, during a seasonal lull in assigning work to their subcontractors, were notified that one or more of them filed for unemployment. Since the business wasn't paying for unemployment insurance for these people, it caused the authorities to scrutinize that business more carefully. Stiff penalties are levied against those who break this law, including high fines and seizure of all goods and fixtures.

Some states have restrictions that differ from the federal laws. Wisconsin, for instance, mandates an immediate $1,000 fine for *hiring* sewing contractors. To make sure you stay within the law, research both the local statutes and the federal requirements.

CHAPTER 3

Equipping Your Business

The first step in establishing any business is to equip yourself with the tools you need to get the job done. If you plan to make a living with your sewing, your sewing machine must be appropriate for the type and amount of work you'll be handling. There are three main classifications of sewing machines on the market today.

- *Domestic machines* are those used in the home. They are usually portable, (although some have tables), weigh very little and use household current.

- *Industrial machines*, those that are true industrials, typically have one function they perform extremely efficiently. They are not portable—in fact, some of them are enormous—and they have heavy-duty motors that normally have either oil pans or self-oiling systems. Many industrial machines are inappropriate for the typical home-based sewing business, but there are some smaller machines that are used frequently.

- *Commercial machines* are hybrids of industrial and domestic machines. They perform more than one function, usually both a straight stitch and a zigzag, and often have the capability of sewing in reverse (true industrial machines rarely sew in reverse for backstitching). Needles and feet may be interchangeable with domestic machine parts, and motors are normally smaller than the true industrials. However, these machines are not portable and require heavy-duty shop tables for their use.

Choosing the correct machine for your workshop

One of the most appealing reasons to begin a sewing business is that you already have most of the equipment you need. However, for a long-term business, you might want to consider buying a stronger machine. Most domestic sewing machines carry warranties that guarantee their trouble-free use for as much as twenty-five years. This presumes the "normal" wear and tear that any typical household appliance might receive over the course of its useful life. In the case of a sewing machine, this means no more than twenty to thirty hours of use in a month. When that same machine is used in a business, the usage could soar to as much as eight hours a day, or nearly eight times as much as the same machine in even the most avid hobbyist's pursuit.

The generous warranties of domestic machines are not meant to cover such heavy wear. Therefore, most companies specifically exclude any kind of business usage in the wording of their warranties. Before you buy a machine, be sure to ask about any such clause; it could mean that if you burn up the motor of your expensive machine, you alone are responsible for replacing either the parts or the entire machine.

If you already have a machine you want to use, make a decision about how you will feel about any problems down the line. Are you prepared to simply buy a new machine if this one begins to show wear and tear? Or would you prefer to save that machine for certain tasks only, such as buttonholes or decorative stitching, and purchase a heavy-duty machine for utility stitching? Many alterations shops keep a home machine set up just to make buttonholes and use industrial and commercial machines for all other sewing. Some use relatively inexpensive home machines to make alterations and have a blindstitch machine for hems. The owners are prepared to replace their home machines when they wear out.

Advantages of industrial/commercial equipment

Speed

With the average speed of a home sewing machine at between 700 and 900 stitches per minute (spm), a change to an industrial speed demon at 3,500 spm can mean a dramatic increase in productivity and efficiency. For long seams like those in draperies, bridal and special occasion gowns,

Industrial bar tack

and tents or awnings, these faster speeds can make a great deal of difference in your hourly income.

If your product is small, however, the speed may not make as big a difference in your overall efficiency. Doll clothes, for instance, are less efficiently made on an industrial machine, as are other small items. For such short seams, it would be overkill to use anything faster than a home serger. (Industrial sergers are as much as four times as fast as their domestic counterparts.)

Power

In the quest for piercing power to sew such items as heavy-duty canvas or multiple layers of any fabric, you may want to look to industrial machines. Their heavier motors allow them to make the most difficult jobs easy. There are machines built for specific tasks—to sew leather, for instance.

Industrial and commercial machines are rated as to what kind of work they are best suited for, and this information, on "spec sheets" for each machine, is available from anyone who sells them.

Maximum efficiency

If your needs require specialty machines, the sewing industry has them. For example, you may want to consider buying a buttonhole machine. These are not petite additions to your sewing room. Buttonhole machines are about the size of an undercounter refrigerator (though they sit on a table so you can operate the machine while standing). However, if you need the capability to sew thousands of the same-sized buttonholes, the purchase of such a machine can save you hundreds of hours and pay for itself many times over. Each buttonhole is made identically, based on a set size, in less than the time it would take to reset a typical home machine for each buttonhole. You can literally make hundreds of buttonholes in an hour. In addition, there may be an opportunity to rent the services of the machine to other sewing professionals in your area. Conversely, some tailor shops have buttonhole machines you can rent, or you can pay them per buttonhole for special projects or garments.

Other machines offer specific task completion, such as coverstitch machines, to seam and decoratively finish stretch seams; blindstitch machines, to make professional-quality hems; button-sew machines, to sew on buttons at blinding speeds. Double-needle machines are especially useful to create perfectly parallel rows of stitching, such as those used on hems for knit clothing.

There are even computerized industrial machines that allow you to preset the stitch length for specific tasks. For instance, production specialist Deborah Jackson can, with the help of her Hisico computerized industrial machine, sew hundreds of pockets onto hundreds of pants. She presets the machine to lock the beginning stitches, sew a predetermined number of stitches for the seam, then lock the stitch again, cut the thread and suck the thread end down beneath the machine into a waste receptacle. Now that's efficiency!

In addition to specialty machines, feet for hundreds of specific tasks are available to make your life more efficient and your work speedier. Piping,

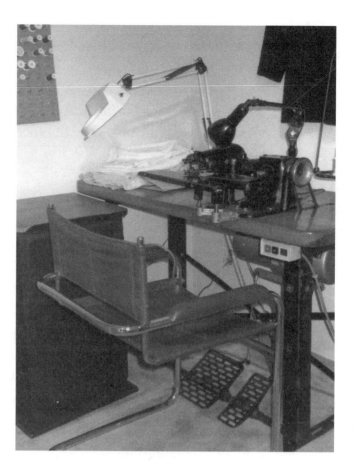

Industrial blindstitch machine

cording, folding and zipper feet are just a few of the ones available. How would you like to sew on miles of bias binding without ever lifting the presser foot and have none of it curl or twist? It's possible with the aid of folders that attach to the front of the machine to guide the bias onto the fabric perfectly. Hemming is another process made easier by specialty feet and folders. Hemmers are available in many widths for all sorts of applications.

Duty use and maintenance

Because industrial machines are meant for factory use, they are also meant to run nearly continuously, often around the clock. This duty use, as it is known, makes for a virtually indestructible machine. Many models have self-oiling wicks, which keep the all-metal parts from heating too much and allow them to run without frequent maintenance interruptions.

Industrial buttonsew machine

On the other hand, the newer home machines have enclosed systems, using little or no outside lubrication. Although many of their parts are made of nylon or plastics, they are generally of a type that withstands the friction of "normal," or home, use. When they are used more frequently, these materials break down more readily, in particular the more sensitive computer parts of many electronic machines.

Although it's possible to maintain your own machines, it is generally better to have a qualified mechanic service them for you, especially for the more technical problems such as timing. Since industrial machines are less likely to break down for overuse and overheating but more likely to break down for timing problems, having a trustworthy mechanic nearby can be important. Machine stores generally have mechanics on staff or on call. Ask about this service when you purchase your machine.

Buying a used machine

Although nothing lasts forever, most industrial machines can live almost forever. If you want to investigate using a factory model, consider buying a used machine; often they are in excellent condition and present a great value to the sewing professional. Such a buy could save as much as 60 percent of the original cost.

The chief disadvantage may be that the previous owner had the machine set to do tasks that aren't important to you. If you are buying directly from the owner, ask if she had the machine modified in any way to suit her work. Sometimes this will be a good thing, for example, if she had the motor speed set slower or faster than average and the new setting fits your needs. It could be important if she had specialty feet or attachments built, as parts aren't available at your corner fabric store. When considering buying a used machine, ask if you can also purchase the needles and bobbins that go with it. Having extras of each is a great time-saver.

Another disadvantage would be if the machine has not been properly maintained. Most factory machines are maintained by staff mechanics. However, smaller businesses may not take the time, money or energy to make sure their machines are running well. It's a good idea to check this.

Space requirements

Industrial machines are usually much larger than their domestic counterparts. If your workroom is small, be prepared to give a large chunk of it to your industrial helpers. They are generally heavy, and definitely not portable, so plan ahead. Design a layout of the room, and keep your machines in that configuration for awhile (see "Space Needs for a Sewing Workroom," chapter four).

Along with being big and clunky, these machines aren't dainty and pretty like domestic models. The factory decor look will probably never hit the pages of *Architectural Digest*. Function is the key here. The all-metal, one-piece casings on the machine make it heavy enough to need a special table. These tables are made of heavy-duty Formica (you get your pick of green or woodgrain tops) and have steel adjustable-height legs. The motor mounts beneath the table, and the foot pedal is straddled between the

Industrial straight stitch machine

table's legs. To the right, also beneath the table, is usually the knee lift for the presser foot, a wonderful convenience for speed and control.

Most tables include a drawer or two for parts, as well as an extrawide top for supporting the fabric. If you find your product needs a larger table, a "corral" can be built to keep the fabric or garment off the floor.

Pressing equipment

After sewing, pressing is probably the next most important process in a workroom. The need for heavy-duty equipment for this process is just as great, and in some cases, it's essential.

Heavy irons with gravity-feed water bottles for steam can make an enormous difference in the quality of your work and in the amount of time spent achieving that quality. In addition, a vacuum board is helpful

Kim Lawrence

Kim's Custom Creations
Lanexa, Virginia

In 1991 Kim Lawrence wanted to work part-time. She had small children and needed a little extra income. A custom-decorating shop owner who had worked at Colonial Williamsburg hired Kim for awhile and taught her how to make window treatments and other items. When the owner decided to go back to Williamsburg to work and closed the shop, Kim continued the business from her home.

"I made up flyers advertising my new business, and my children and I placed them in newspaper boxes in the three secured neighborhoods in Williamsburg. I averaged one call for every 100 flyers we put out," Kim says. She spent about $20 for 500 flyers. At this rate, her cost per customer was about $4. And although these first few jobs were small jobs, they led to better assignments. Kim also ran twice-a-week ads in the Williamsburg community paper for $45 a month.

She originally worked with a home machine, right on the kitchen table. Kim recently bought both an industrial lockstitch and a blindstitch machine and is converting the garage to a sewing studio. Now Kim makes window treatments and other home accessories. She says, "I can sew anything for the home, including slipcovers, except upholstery. I make dust ruffles but send bedspreads out to be made by Virginia Quilting, about an hour away." Kim has done upholstery work, but admits "I'm not facile in it, and I don't quite know how to

charge at this point."

Kim's initial goal was to make $10 an hour. Some jobs bring in more than others. On one commercial rush job, she figures she made about $50 an hour, a rare event. This was for her best commercial client, who likes the quality of her work so he feeds her business. He often requests rush jobs, but he is positioning Kim to work for him more. "This was a $2,500 job that needed to be done in ten days. The fabric didn't come in for four of those days, so I only spent about six days sewing." Kim adds, "I would love to have more like that. There is lots of expensive commercial space in this area. For instance, I made three pairs of sheers for one building. I prefer the commercial jobs because I talk too much, and Mrs. Smith talks too much, and I end up not making any money on the time I spend with her."

Trial and error determined Kim's pricing. She got pricing information from bigger workrooms, and for jobs she didn't make any money on, she made sure she charged more the next time. According to Kim, "If people paid the price, I went up $10 next time. I got to a certain point where people wouldn't go for the price, so I kind of stuck there. There's a lot of major competition in my area, lots of top-of-the-line furniture stores." Kim adds, "To this day I can't say how long anything takes because I hardly ever get a chance to sit and finish something beginning to end."

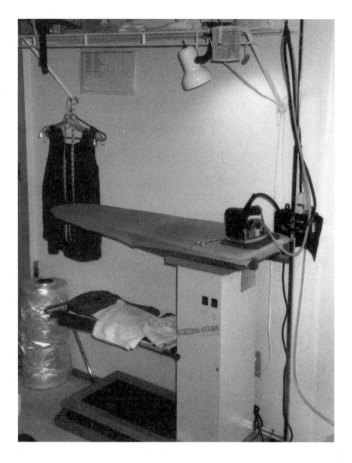

Vacuum board and industrial steam iron

in tailoring. It's an open secret that removing the steam from the fabric quickly and completely is key to creating a perfect press.

Just as it shares the unattractiveness and ungainliness of the industrial sewing machines, industrial pressing equipment also shares the efficiency of that equipment. It's also more expensive than the iron you can buy in any discount store, but well worth the extra expense and effort. Household irons are not meant to stay on all day, but the industrial versions' heating elements are well insulated from burning out. Their excellent steam is ready whenever you are.

Finding sources

Larger cities have stores that sell industrial equipment, as do any smaller cities that have had any kind of textile industry in recent years. Companies that supply dry cleaners and tailor shops are also good sources for machines and other necessary supplies (see the appendix for specific sources).

To find a reliable local shop, ask other sewing professionals where they buy supplies. Your local dry cleaner may have information about a shop, as will any department store that has an in-house alterations department. This is also a great way to find maintenance specialists.

CHAPTER 4

Setting Up Shop

Should your business be in your home or in a separate shop? Most sewing specialties work well as home-based enterprises. If you have the space, and the inclination, working at home is often the best way to begin. Naturally, if you decide to make massive stuffed costumes or theatre curtains and you live in a small apartment, home is probably not the optimal work space. However, if that is the specialty you've chosen, stick with it. Anything is possible—Deborah Jackson (see chapter one) has a factory in what was once her family room.

Home-based business vs. a shop

There are many factors to consider when deciding whether or not to strike out to the "street," as an outside shop is often called. First of all, can you afford to pay rent? Can you afford not to? If your customer base is dependent on a visible presence in the community or on foot traffic past the shop, then a shop would be advisable. But when you're just starting out, it might be best to wait awhile to take this step. Here's an example of someone who has experienced both ends of this situation.

Gay Costa's alterations business began simply. She had worked in alterations at a department store that eventually went out of business. Gay found other retail store business, which she began doing from her home. When business increased, she remodeled her single-car garage to accommodate a couple of sewing machines, pressing equipment, a small fitting area and a customer area with phone and desk. Her daughter and her mother helped out with the business as needed.

Within a few months, Gay realized the garage wasn't going to provide enough space for her quickly growing business, and when a storefront near her home went up for lease, she contracted for the space. The best part about the location was its position directly in front of the drive-in window of the only bank in her small town. It wasn't long before everyone in the village of Greenhills, Ohio, knew of Galina Alterations' existence!

Becky Reeves

Reeves Manufacturing/Xander Wear
LaSalle, Colorado

Reeves Manufacturing sews a variety of products, but the company started with sportswear for bodybuilders, which is still its main product.

In the summer of 1992, Becky Reeves opened Xander Wear, a shop in the small farming community of LaSalle, Colorado. The shop specializes in attire for bodybuilders, who have difficulty finding clothing that fits, as their necks and upper torso are generally much thicker than the average consumer's. Xander provides workout wear, some street clothing, bike shorts, baggies and big tops for kids. Becky makes all items in the line.

Originally, Becky worked from the basement in her home, and she worked at the business part-time. However, she soon outgrew the basement and took over the garage. She has been working full-time for the past couple of years, since her youngest child went to school.

Becky now has an 800-square-foot workroom attached to Xander Wear's store. This has worked out well; since customers must enter her shop through the store, they can only see Becky during store hours unless they have scheduled appointments, a boon for this mother of three school-age children. Also, Becky feels safe working alone, and if she has to leave for an hour or so, as she does at the end of every school day, the Xander personnel can take messages from walk-in customers or direct them to wait for her return. Becky says there are pros and cons about working in a storefront business, but her arrangement has many benefits.

"I have a section for sewing, a section for cutting, plus an office space. It's nice to have all the machines out of my home," she says. Becky has eight industrial machines, including a walking foot, a tailor's machine, a zigzag machine, a waistbander (for sewing several rows of stitches at once), a serger, a coverstitch machine and a blind-stitch machine. In addition, she has a cutter with an 8-inch blade and chain mail gloves for safety.

Terry Reeves does all the cutting, although this isn't his full-time job. He and Becky have decided he will keep his "day job" as an electrician while the children are in parochial school, mainly for the benefits. Becky says the income from the business has doubled every year, but it still isn't enough to totally support them and provide tuition for three kids. Eventually, though, they would like to work together full-time, as well as hire employees to share the workload.

Becky's advice to anyone interested in her kind of business: "Make sure you love it. You will invest both time and money in the business; make sure you want to do both."

Gay Costa's corner workstation

Gay Costa's reception area

Business boomed, and Gay hired employees to help with the work, as by now her daughter had married and moved away. Several years later, Gay's daughter moved back to town with a new baby and decided to work with her mother again. They closed the store and moved back to the garage so they could keep the baby with them, and since Gay by now had a loyal customer base, they no longer needed the visibility of the storefront.

Advantages of a home-based business

Lower initial and operating costs

A commitment to a lease or expensive retail space could sink a new business before it really has a chance to get off the ground. With a home-based business, you can test the waters for awhile and see if your idea has merit. You can find out if your perceived market is really there, and you don't have to spend much more than the cost of a few hundred business cards to do so. In a home-based business, you can use the equipment you already have, including your existing phone line (see chapter nine). Any retail space would need a business phone (with a yellow pages listing), business utilities, rent, additional employee costs, more advertising money and other hefty expenses.

Easier transition to starting a business

Home-based operations allow you to ease into business. Unless you know you have a solid market ready to beat a path to your door immediately, there may be some lag times at first. Many people start sewing for others part-time while working at other jobs until the sewing business begins to create a substantial replacement income.

Less financial, physical and emotional commitment

Having a retail storefront costs a great deal initially, plus there are ongoing expenses, the largest of which is likely the rent. It's unusual to find monthly leases for retail spaces except in low-stability areas, so one- to three-year leases are more common—which may be a long time for a sewing business.

Operating a retail outlet also requires a tremendous amount of your physical and emotional energy. Someone needs to be at the store for all the stated hours, and someone has to be able to handle every need of the business. At first, this is usually the owner, unless ample start-up business or capital allows for employees to do these chores. This would only be possible in rare situations, though, and generally the owner is on the line for such time-consuming jobs. A big emotional drain is the constant worry over whether enough money will come in to cover operational costs, many of which would not exist for a business conducted from home.

Close proximity to family members

Home-based businesses offer a way for many people to "have it all": to provide an additional income to the family while still maintaining a presence in the home. If you need to stay home with children or an older family member, a home-based business can be very helpful. In fact, one study suggests that a second wage earner working outside the home in the U.S. actually costs the family money, because of expenses such as car fare, child care, work-related clothing and meals eaten away from home.

While Becky Reeves's factory is outside her home, she still closes her shop to drive her children home from school every afternoon. Many store situations would not lend themselves to such a setup, however.

Your own health problems or unusual schedule requirements may also make it more desirable to work from home. You can work whenever it's convenient to you. If you're the type who doesn't really come alive until the kids are in bed, being able to sew quietly into the night can be a tremendous advantage over outside work. Kitty Stein's husband works the night shift, and she enjoys working when the house is quiet and there are no phone calls.

Use of existing equipment and space

Buying equipment adds more financial burden to the start-up of your business, as does adding on to a house or renting another space. Keeping your current setup of machinery and space will work for awhile (unless the specialty has additional needs), and you can always expand later.

Disadvantages of a home-based business

Possible illegality

Although many communities have loosened their laws on home-operated businesses, it's wise to find out what the law says in your particular area. Some towns, especially planned communities, have stringent rules about what types of businesses are allowed and about how these businesses may be conducted. In order to comply, you might have to change your focus slightly, or even apply for change in the laws. Also, be careful to check what permits are required.

Constant presence of your work

If you're the type who obsesses over unfinished projects or who can't seem to quit work, a pile of work awaiting you in the next room may be difficult to ignore. When phone calls come in or customers come to the studio, having a little space between your work life and your home life is often desirable. It can be achieved; it just may be difficult.

Customer drop-ins and phone calls at odd hours

This doesn't have to happen. If you're clear with customers about your business hours, much of this problem won't exist. Having a second phone line and an answering machine or voice mail helps, too. Simply avoid answering calls to that line after hours, and include your business hours in your answering machine message. A direction to customers to call back during that time is helpful.

Judy Pagenkopf has an alterations shop in a separate area of a laundromat and a home-based alterations and custom dressmaking business. She tells her customers her hours and insists that outside of those hours they see her on an appointment basis only. "I'm busy after dinner," says this single mother of three. "I have a report on Australia to work on, posters for art and long division to figure out. My customers have to understand that my children need me in the evenings."

Interference with your family life (and vice versa)

When deadlines loom, trips to your child's school for special occasions often take a backseat. That bride who loses fifteen pounds in the last month before her wedding may need her gown altered just as your seventeen-year-old child is choosing a college. A large order for backpacks for a hiking club may have to be set aside when a family member has a serious illness. Self-employment means being prepared for these sorts of emergencies. A home business often causes collisions between the domestic and the business sides of your life.

If your business needs to function in a part of your house that was previously available to the rest of the family, that disruption of the rhythm of the home could mean discord for awhile. Usually, this doesn't last. As my own business grew and changed, it migrated through various parts of the house, from spare bedrooms, to half the basement, to the end of the living room, to the entire family room. My family adapted, although they grumbled a bit at first.

Sometimes family members who are unhappy about the business purposely get in your way. Preparing the whole family in advance, and enlisting their cooperation, may forestall such a problem.

Inability of your home to support the business

Do you have enough room for the business you want? Or, if you have the room, is it comfortable enough? Most homes aren't equipped with enough overhead lighting to accommodate the high lighting needs of sewing and pressing. You may find it's difficult to safely plug in enough lighting and sewing appliances in the space you have. A boost in the home's electrical capacity might also be in order. The same cool basement studio that was comfortable for a class of six sewing students was too chilly for my own office, which had to be moved elsewhere.

How about an attractive area to greet customers? For dressmaking and alterations, a private area for trying on garments is the bare minimum of publicly accessible space you need. Do you really want customers going to your bedroom area to change in the only bathroom? Is it possible to create a private spot for this purpose with a screen or some other method? Would you feel better if customers could enter the work area directly, without access to the rest of your home? If you decide to teach sewing, is there a convenient place for students to try on their garments?

Some specialties may have tremendous storage or other physical needs. For instance, an embroidery business that requires storage of hundreds of spools of thread, two computers and five large embroidery machines may not be welcome in the typical home. Neither will the traffic of customers coming in and out, if your family is used to having more privacy.

Space needs for a sewing workroom

Often, a business gets started before the owner realizes what is happening, or it grows so quickly that space is soon cramped. In a situation like this, little initial thought goes into planning the workroom. And if employees are added to the space, everything may soon change from varying degrees of efficiency to total chaos.

If you find yourself in one of these scenarios, it is probably time to consider rearranging things.

- Do you have trouble finding things immediately?
- Are you constantly maneuvering around furniture to get from one task to another?
- Must any tasks be completed in another room or on another floor because space is so limited?
- In order to cut out projects, is it necessary to clear off a space? (Or do you find yourself crawling around on the floor to hem draperies or tents?)
- Is the clutter beginning to bother you?
- Have you ruined anything lately because of clutter?
- Have you found yourself buying duplicates of notions you already own?

Planning a work area takes a little effort, but in the long run it saves time. A well-thought-out workroom design can make an enormous difference in your efficiency, no matter how much or how little space you have available.

Beginning to plan your work space

First examine the space; take stock of its physical features. Are there windows (or a lack thereof) that offer wonderful light part of the day? Do those windows let in too much glare or the heat of the day? Would a different covering make a difference? Do the dark walls feel oppressive?

How about the rest of the lighting? Is it sufficient to keep your eyes from fatiguing, or would more light help you work longer? (Tip: Almost no room has *too* much light!) Are dark walls or furnishings absorbing what light there is? Do the fixtures have sufficient wattage to illuminate the area? Note any areas you feel need more light.

What about your work flow? Would it be better to have a cutting area set up nearer to the sewing machines, or would you prefer to have a pressing station closer to the machines? What tasks require you to get up from the chair most often every day? Would it help if you could sit down for them, or would a shorter walk make it easier for you to accomplish these tasks? Think of the different things you do in a typical workday; how would you improve the flow of such a day?

Storage is everyone's problem. As amateurs twenty years ago, we didn't need much more than a machine and a sewing basket to accomplish all kinds of wondrous things. Today's professional workroom boasts many labor- and timesaving devices and requires storage space for a long list of supplies: interfacings, trims, threads, machine supplies, bolts of fabric and completed projects. Organization is crucial to efficiency and profitability. List all the items you need to store and where they need to live in relationship to the rest of the workroom; for example, all the press cloths, tailor hams, clappers, etc., need to be near the pressing area.

Ergonomics is a buzzword today that means adapting the working environment to the needs of the human body. Better chairs, higher cutting tables and more comfortable tools all help make your workday more pleasant. What are your particular difficulties in the present space? Is your current chair uncomfortable after an hour or so of sewing? Does your back scream with pain after a cutting session? Are the scissors you use giving you blisters? Look for ways to make your work more comfortable. And don't forget to take breaks! Sitting too long is hard on the body; changing position every forty-five minutes to an hour is beneficial, and reduces eyestrain as well.

List various space needs of your particular business.

- Sewing—can be divided into various sections, such as seaming, hemming, embroidery, serging, buttonholes, buttons, topstitching
- Pressing
- Cutting
- Customer reception/consultation
- Fitting
- Paperwork/telephone/messages
- Computer/office
- Storage—for customers' goods
- Customer and/or employee restroom
- Shipping/packaging

Measuring the work space

The next step is to measure the room(s). This isn't difficult, but it needs to be accurate. Begin at a corner. Measure along each wall, writing each measurement as you take it. In a rough drawing, indicate each door and

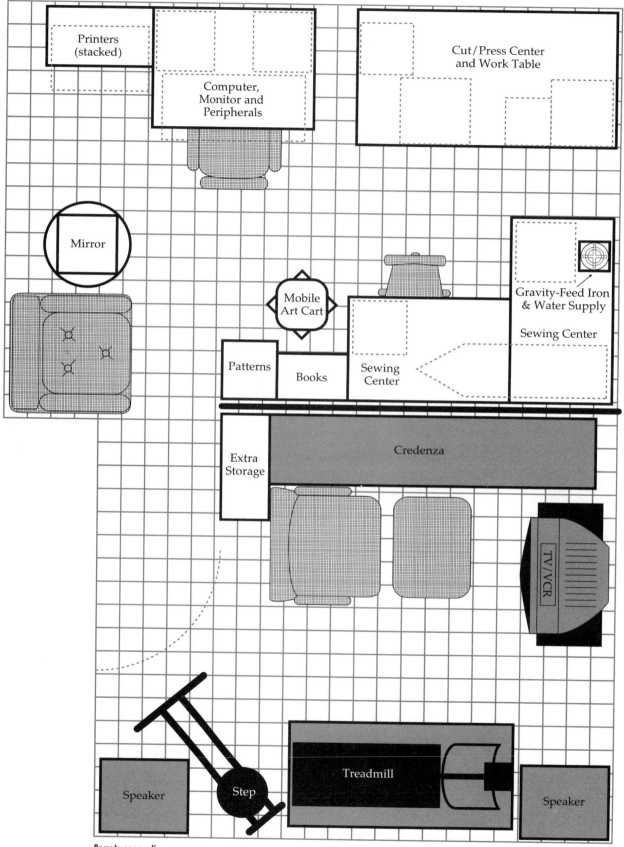

Sample space diagram (One grid square = 6")

window opening and their positions along the wall, as well as wall outlets, lights and switches. Measure from the floor to the bottoms of these features, also, so you can tell how much room is beneath each one. Using a good metal rule like the ones carpenters use, measure to the nearest ¼ inch.

Plot this on graph paper, using ¼-inch grid, with a scale of one square equaling six inches. Since most rooms are not perfectly square, don't be too concerned if your measurements aren't exactly right, unless your home or building is fairly new or the dimensions are off by more than a couple of inches. A good scale ruler can help with drawing the room. Triangular rulers are probably the most common, available at an office or art store in the drafting department. Draw a circle on the plan to indicate each overhead light so you are sure to take them into consideration. Note any architectural features you need to work around, such as poles and heaters. Also indicate closet areas and dimensions.

Now that you have the room drawn, you can begin to plot a space diagram. Make several photocopies of this graph so you can write on them and discard them without redrawing the measurements. Now you are ready to design a plan. Since paper is easier to move than actual furniture, especially if the furniture is in another room or on another floor, make scale drawings of everything that will go in the room, and cut them out to use as templates. (Tip: If you cut these from different colored paper, they will be easier to see against the graph paper.)

Note: You may prefer to use one of the many CAD-based drawing systems for designing your plan. Input the measurements of the room, and create your own furniture pieces from the library included in the program. (Many programs allow you to edit the dimensions of the icons in the library.) Using such a program will allow you to save many versions of the plan, and you can also "see" the plan in the program's 3-D view.

Considering the different areas you need for your business, begin to look critically at the actual area. How can you place each center for maximum efficiency? For instance, ask yourself whether it might be best to keep customers out of the sewing area, which may be messy. If the answer is yes, decide how to locate customer reception elsewhere. If your work is particularly neat, or if you haven't any additional space, you may decide that your customers can just as easily be greeted in the workroom. Some specialties, production sewing or many craft-type businesses don't require this type of area. Do you require easy access to a washing machine? Factor that into your plans as well.

On one of your photocopied room diagrams (I'll call this Plan One), draw circles where you would like to locate various work centers. For instance, if there is a nice bright window you'd like to take advantage of, place a sewing area circle there. Nearby should be pressing and storage and any other work processes that pertain to your business.

Next, consider how you need to work. Is it really efficient to have the cutting table across the room from the sewing area? It is if you do all your cutting first and then sew. For some quilters or wearables artists, that wouldn't be practical. In order to add color and pattern as the creative urge strikes, they may need a cutting area adjacent to the sewing machine.

When thinking about your work flow, consider the work triangle. For most sewing processes, the three "legs" of the triangle would be cutting, sewing and pressing. Production sewing is usually done on precut fabric and is rarely pressed by the manufacturer, so only the sewing area is needed. However, a place to receive the cut goods and to prepare them for shipping or pickup may be equally necessary. In addition, somewhere to lay out the various pieces in order of sewing is desirable.

Note: If you have employees, the ideal setup gives each person, or group of persons, a work triangle that won't be intersected by someone else.

Various layouts

Basic layouts for the ideal work triangle include L-shaped, U-shaped, one-wall and corridor. These options offer varying degrees of efficiency, and your choice will depend on the room's physical features and your personal preferences.

L-shaped and U-shaped layouts

These are the most efficient of all setups for a sewing workroom. Everything is easily accessible, particularly if the operator is using an office-type swivel chair with wheels. A mere twist of the hips will propel the operator from the sewing machine to the pressing station. This is an ideal setup for anyone who needs to work quickly at multiple tasks, for instance, making doll clothing or other small items. The operator could cut out the

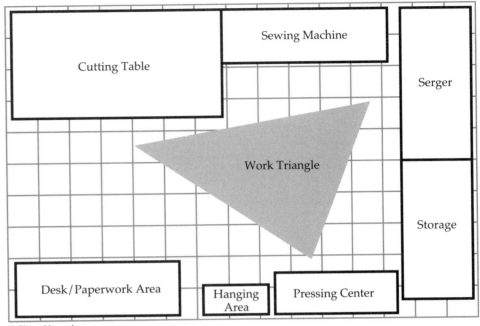

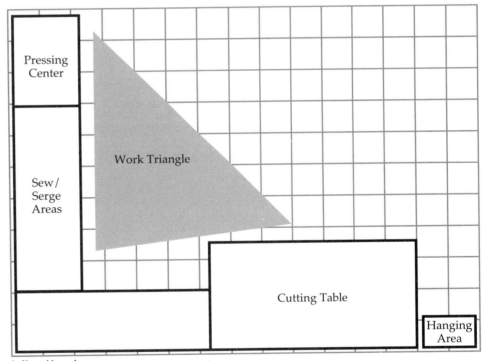

U-Shaped Layout (One grid square = one foot)

L-Shaped Layout (One grid square = one foot)

pattern, then go immediately to the machines to sew the garments. Pressing requires only another movement, particularly if the ironing board or pressing board is set at chair height.

The main reason these layouts work best is because they keep traffic

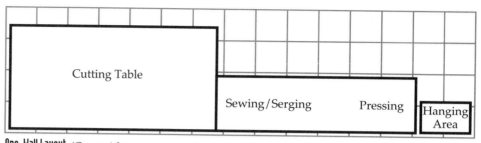

One-Wall Layout (One grid square = one foot)

out of the main work area; traffic tends to flow around the L or the U rather than through it.

One-wall and corridor layouts

Since traffic can flow past or through this type of arrangement, plan carefully so tasks aren't subject to constant interruptions. Also, unless a chair with well-lubricated casters is used, the operator must physically get up and move to various stations to perform other tasks. Sometimes all you can find is one wall, though, so it's better than nothing.

Even with only one wall, an L-shaped or U-shaped layout can be created using various furniture arrangements. Cutting tables and pressing stations that can be moved to the operator's side can create either of the more efficient arrangements temporarily. For small areas or where nothing can sit out except work in progress, this is an ideal solution.

Storage

Everyone struggles to create efficient and sufficient storage, in any kind of business. But sewing especially creates storage problems because of the many kinds of notions and patterns used every day.

What kind of workroom do you envision as the ultimate work space? Does it have everything at your fingertips, displayed in the open? Or do you prefer to have the neat, clean look of closed storage, with everything behind doors or in drawers? Most people will end up with some combination of the two preferences.

Identify your storage needs. List the things you use frequently, and prioritize them in order of importance. On the photocopied plan you designed earlier, add a few more circles to indicate storage space. Using colored ink or pencil, define where you think various items should be kept for the highest efficiency. This will give you a better idea of how to organize the space.

Open storage

If there are no closets, or if seeing all your supplies gives you a creative boost, open storage is ideal. Residing on shelving that reaches to the ceiling or on racks hanging from walls, fabric and supplies can lend their color and form to the decor of the room. Small items can be placed in colorful bins or other containers available at any of dozens of stores who cater to office and home storage needs. Open baskets are wonderful for holding quilt fabrics, and wire shelving actually allows air to flow around anything kept on them—perfect for fabric and other fragile supplies.

Closed storage

Fabric and thread are both susceptible to damage from light, heat and dust. If this is a concern in your work space, then by all means consider keeping them protected from these factors. You may also prefer the uncluttered look of having everything stashed away. But what do you do if your space doesn't have walls and walls of closets?

Can you create storage under tables? Cutting tables afford a large space for storage. One designer has a lovely, light-filled workroom with absolutely no clutter. When asked where she kept everything, she swept aside the fabric draping the edges of her cutting area and other tables. Boxes, drawers and shelves were holding fabric, notions and other supplies. Velcro holds the draping to the tables' edges, allowing easy access to anything beneath the surfaces. The draping also contributes color and a designer touch to the decor and provides a bit of soundproofing as well.

Is a closet available for your use? If not, how about creating one? If there is an area of the room that can be enclosed, you can create wonderful closed storage simply by installing a floor-to-ceiling miniblind or cellular shade. Shelves and cubbies can be erected behind such a blind, which can also add decorative and perhaps sound-insulating value. A useful hiding place can even be created with a simple folding screen.

Kitchen cabinets can be modified for use in a sewing room. They don't necessarily have to become a permanent part of the room. If you only use base cabinets, many times they can be freestanding units, perfect as a base for cutting tables. Topped with some kind of sturdy surface, they are the perfect height for comfort while cutting, and they offer lots of storage possibilities. Research the many cabinet options available—pullout shelves can be utilized for machine storage; drawer dividers are great for grouping threads; extra-deep drawers, such as for pots and pans, offer great space for storing rolled-up interfacings, and these drawers can be opened all the way so with one glance you can see everything inside. Use your imagination; you may surprise yourself.

Lighting

Now that you know where you will work and where everything is to be placed, plan how to adequately illuminate those areas.

Did you know that your eyes use about 25 percent of your body's energy? Even more endurance is called for during activities with high lighting requirements. Activities such as sewing, cutting, writing, reading and ironing, performed over sustained periods of time, can sap your energy under poor lighting conditions.

You may have already experienced fatigue during a workday and wondered why something as seemingly innocent as sewing would tire you out so. The solution could be as simple as adding more light to the room. The better the lighting in your workroom, the more quality time you'll spend there, and the more efficient you'll be.

Wall color

Another problem affecting a room's lighting may be that the walls are too dark. One way to take advantage of the available light, even magnify it, is to paint all the reflective surfaces, such as walls and ceilings, a light color. Even on a bright day, a room with ample lighting and windows but dark walls will still seem dark. Walls painted a balanced white, between stark white and cream, potentially reflect as much as 80 percent of the ambient light back into the room. Compare this to dark walls, which may reflect as little as 10 percent of the available light. Be sure to use flat or semigloss paint, as high gloss can cause a glare that can actually reduce the effectiveness of the light-colored walls—and give you a nasty headache to boot.

Natural light

Windows are natural light emitters, except on gloomy days or at night. And if the window is facing south, the resulting glare on sunny days can have a negative effect instead of enhancing the room's lighting.

Window coverings are almost as important as lighting. Use your window coverings to cure any insufficiency in the window. For instance, if there is a glare on some days, a cellular shade in a light color will soften the sunshine without reducing its light value, as well as insulate the room from the sun's heat. That same shade will help augment the room's lighting at night, too. Nighttime windows with no coverings can have the same effect as a dark wall; you will notice light actually being drawn away by the blackness of the uncovered window.

Don't forget office duties when planning lighting. Allow for some kind of direct illumination of the desk or other workstation.

Kinds of lighting

General lighting

- Grouped as two kinds: direct and indirect
- Includes ambient light, or room light—can come from windows, wall and ceiling colors or mirrored surfaces
- "Washes" a room with light

Task lighting

- Used for close work—includes any direct light
- Pinpoints the light
- Illuminates the work without throwing shadows over it
- Helps avoid shine or glare in your eyes

On your Plan One diagram, which already includes circles indicating work centers and storage, draw additional circles with a highlighter to indicate where light is needed most. Determine where direct lighting should be located, for example, over the sewing machines (to augment any other light there), over cutting tables, near pressing stations. Don't forget that dressing and fitting rooms should also be well lit, with strong general lighting. The one rule to follow: Accept no shadows.

Now you're ready to implement Plan One. Lighting should be installed first. There are a variety of bulbs and fixtures available; your needs may be met best with a combination of light types.

Incandescent bulbs

Today's incandescent bulbs are more versatile than ever before. With options ranging from cool white to full spectrum, most existing fixtures can be made to perform well in a workroom. Incandescent light, which tends to be more direct than fluorescent, is best for task lighting.

Look for clamp-on fixtures for industrial sewing machines. These are perfect for not only machine sewing, but for directing light on hand sewing and ironing as well.

Choose full-spectrum incandescent bulbs for better perception of color values when making color matches in fabric or craft materials. This can also be a health benefit if you suffer from Seasonal Affective Disorder (SAD). Full-spectrum bulbs mimic the color of real sunshine and are often recommended by doctors for anyone with this problem.

Fluorescent fixtures

In addition to their energy-saving benefits, fluorescent bulbs offer a more even wash of light, and manufacturers have made major technological advances. Today's fluorescents offer the same range of choices as incandescents, including red-band, blue-band and full spectrum. Some even fit into lamps meant for traditional light bulbs. When augmented by incandescent or halogen task lighting, fluorescent fixtures are especially good for lighting large areas.

Kateri Ellison

Designs by Kateri
Washington, DC

Kateri Ellison's work space

Because of limited space in her Washington, DC, townhouse, custom clothier Kateri Ellison designed her workroom/office for total efficiency.

In a space roughly 8½' × 14', Kateri has everything she needs to conduct business on a typical workday. Because she works alone, Kateri has taken advantage of the size of the room to make it work best for her. Without leaving her chair, she can sew, serge, press and answer the phone or fax. Ample electrical outlets supply power to the workroom and office equipment and lighting.

Two closets, one on each side of the room, offer clutter-free closed storage. Also,

Kateri uses the space beneath the work and cutting tables as storage. Filing cabinets and drawers store all kinds of sewing paraphernalia.

A comfy chair with a stack of current fashion magazines nearby makes a pleasant spot for customers to sit while planning their next wardrobes. An attractive wall divider affords the customer privacy during fittings, and it breaks the room into two parts so one portion is also available for the Ellison family's use. An Oriental carpet over the room's wall-to-wall carpet further divides the room visually.

One side of the divider makes an excellent backdrop for the bulletin board used as a project control center above the sewing machines. Pattern envelopes and swatches of customers' fabric pinned to the board allow Kateri to monitor work in progress. Above the wall over the cutting table, inspirational photos and draped fabric stimulate the creative juices and add an attractive accent to the room.

To augment the natural light that streams in from the two windows, generous track lighting illuminates the work areas. Miniblinds disappear when open during daylight hours then reappear to preserve Kateri's privacy when she is sewing in the evening.

Halogen bulbs

Relative newcomers to the lighting scene, halogen bulbs offer a wonderfully true color of light, perfect for the sewing room. Though they are initially more expensive than either incandescent or fluorescent bulbs, halogen is less expensive per hour to burn than incandescent, similar to fluorescents.

There is a drawback to using halogen lights: They are very hot; in fact, they are often used as highly efficient heating elements in kitchen cooktops. This unfortunately makes them not only uncomfortable but also more dangerous to use. If you choose halogen for your workroom, make sure the bulbs and fixtures are labeled *UL approved*, and be extra careful to keep the lights away from curtains, walls and anything else flammable. The recommended distance is twelve inches or more. Also, choose fixtures that have guards over the bulbs to help protect fingers or other objects that might hover too close.

One particularly effective use of halogen bulbs is in torchère-type lamps aimed at the ceiling over a cutting table. With a white ceiling this efficiently illuminates a cutting area. And if you choose the type of torchère fixture that has a clear or frosted shade, the light also illuminates the rest of the room. One of the most effective of this type is the fixture with the light on a swing arm. This can be positioned nearer to the cutting area than the stationary standing light.

Professional attitude and image

When customers come into your workroom or your shop, they will immediately form an opinion about you and about your work. Unless you will never have anyone come to your workplace, a clean, organized workroom can mean the difference between gaining your customer's respect and not getting it at all. Not every customer feels this way, but there will be some who will not work with you if they feel your studio is dirty and untidy. There will also be those clients who know that creativity comes from chaos—those people are to be cherished!

When you greet clients for the first time, you should make an effort to dress neatly and at least have the floor swept and the most serious clutter banished from sight. Instill confidence from the beginning. While it is normally not necessary to wear a suit and heels, contrast your own reaction to someone dressed neatly with a touch of makeup to that same person with uncombed hair, dressed in ragged sweatshirt, faded, baggy jeans and grubby tennies. Which person would you feel better about handing a project that could cost you hundreds of dollars? If the external clues of dress are all you have to go on, you would probably prefer the one who is better groomed.

Make sure the rest of your family conforms to the business attitude also. This doesn't mean your seven-year-old should wear a business suit, but it does mean that children don't compete with you for their share of clients' attention. Bridal expert Karen Howland's five children knew that when "the pretty ladies" came to be fitted for bridal gowns, the kids weren't to disturb their mother unless it was an emergency. A door between her studio and the rest of the house was shut during fittings, which emphasized the need for privacy, but Karen could still hear what was going on. When the youngest child was alone with her during a fitting, he was occupied with small toys kept just for that purpose.

Clients should not be greeted at the door by a sticky kid or on the telephone by, "Who is this?" If your business is home based, having both a separate entrance and a separate phone line that are only answered in a businesslike manner could be beneficial. If these are not possible, regular reminders to the family might be necessary for awhile until your priorities are remembered consistently. I'm speaking from personal experience here. My own family was forbidden to answer the line reserved for my sewing school. When I answered that line, it was with a cheery, "Hello, this is Karen," or, "Good morning, this is Karen." Voice mail on that line took care of answering machine messages gone astray due to overzealous little message erasers. ("It wasn't for me" or "I thought you heard that message!") Be sure your answering machine message also reflects a business attitude.

When phone calls come in and you're in the midst of taking care of another customer, it's common courtesy to wait on the person who was there first. Is there anything more infuriating than waiting for a salesperson in a department store as he answers the telephone? If you don't have an answering machine that can field calls, take a message and return the call when you aren't as busy. One excellent reason above and beyond customer service: Interruptions cause mistakes. Because of a phone call, I once cut an entire faux fur coat with half the grain going the wrong way.

About customer service: Ascribe to the idea that "a bird in the hand is worth two in the bush." Don't alienate the paying customer in front of you in your anxiety to get new business. You could end up losing both. Return phone calls right away, regardless of whether they involve potential sales or problems with current or previous projects.

Service problems tend to grow; nip them in the bud immediately. If there's a conflict between the service you feel you rendered the client and the service she perceives she has received, resolve it as soon as possible. Problem resolution is difficult for some people; if this is your own weak point, refer to your library for help. Many books have been written about sales, and many of them have chapters on this issue. This is also a common discussion topic of professional sewing and other networking groups.

Keeping track of your work

As your workload increases, it will become more difficult to stay organized, unless you have a way to keep tabs of the status of each project. Patricia Anthony, of Wyldwmn Custom Clothing, uses a calendar as an organizational tool. She explains, "I have a project calendar on which I mark out all my 'personal' time and business appointments. Then as each client or project comes in, I schedule the hours right on the calendar. Unless I am expecting a specific, important call from a client, I am unavailable by phone during my production time." Patricia returns calls first thing in the morning or between 7:00 and 8:00 P.M. when people are home from work.

To fill in blank space on your calendar, Patricia advises, "What you can do is schedule in your own personal projects . . . the clients don't know that they are your private projects. That way if you need to reschedule them, you can do that easily by telling your client that you know that the deadline on that project is far enough off that you can easily reschedule it. It gives your calendar a successful look right from the beginning."

Patricia also offers her customers "overtime" hours at premium rates. She says, "I do limit the number of overtime hours each week so as not to lessen the quality of work I do on other projects. I make it a point to explain this to my clients so that they don't go away thinking that at some time someone else's emergency may impact the quality of time I spend on their garments or my ability to meet one of their deadlines." Patricia goes on to say, "I *never* suggest that I might 'put off' someone else's work, because then that client may think I will do the same to them at some point and then rush through their project."

Another suggestion for staying on top of all projects: Attach an input slip to all parts of a project as soon as it comes in. Keep that slip with all other paperwork related to the project—work orders, time records, order changes, receipts for any supplies pertaining to this job—until the customer picks up the finished work. A plastic zip-top bag is a good receptacle for these items: Enclose smaller projects in the bags with the paperwork, and for garments, punch holes in the bags and slip them over the clothes hangers.

Regarding supplies you purchase for customers, I suggest including a markup in the prices you charge customers. If you purchase zippers in bulk, for instance, and use one from your stock for a client's order, you should charge the customer for the zipper plus a set charge, perhaps 30 percent of the cost of the zipper. If you pass on the exact cost to the client, you will not be reimbursed for the additional costs of processing mail orders or driving to the store. Additionally, the markup will protect any discounts you might get from suppliers.

Recordkeeping and taxes

Every business has to keep records for a variety of reasons. In the United States, it's necessary to keep records of all transactions for at least seven years (some accountants recommend keeping them longer). It's important to record the right data, though, or those records won't mean anything.

Because you will need to report all income to the government and pay taxes on any income over expenses, bookkeeping is the most important type of recordkeeping. Be sure to account for everything—every dime that comes in and every dime that goes out. Anytime you buy anything for the business, get a receipt. Sort the receipts per the categories specified on your tax forms. At the end of each day, add up each category of receipts and enter the totals in a notebook. At the end of each month, total each category of expense, and at the end of the year, there will be no more than twelve figures to add in each category. It's that simple.

In order to keep your business and personal expenses and income separate, a business checking account is a necessity. Several years ago my husband and I were audited in a routine periodic audit for sole proprietors. Since I handle all the bookkeeping for both our businesses, I asked the auditor more questions than she asked me! She told me that, for each bank account, the Internal Revenue Service (IRS) determines the total of deposits less withdrawals and then compares that figure to the net income reported on Schedule C. In this way the IRS can see if self-employed taxpayers are fudging their incomes. The auditor advised keeping all business and personal accounting strictly separate, in order to make it easier to keep track of it, and in order to avoid problems with the IRS. In addition, a separate account makes it easier to evaluate the business. If you ever need to arrange for a loan, the business's account activity provides important data for the financial institution that's considering your loan request.

Every check should be deposited. Record what each deposit is for so you will have the same kind of record of income that you have for expenses. This will make it easy to complete your tax return. A self-inking rubber stamp with all your account information will simplify check depositing.

In addition to keeping a separate checking account, have one credit card account that is used for nothing but business purchases. This makes it easier to pay the balance; write one check from your business account each month. It also makes it much easier to see where your money is going; if all the charges are mixed in with clothing and entertainment purchases, it's difficult to separate them. Overly high operating costs are easier to ignore when they're hiding among other expenditures.

Typical expenses in a one-person or partnership sewing business

- Rent or mortgage (or the proportion of your home rent or mortgage your space represents)
- Telephone
- Utilities
- Office supplies (stationery, software, pens, etc.)
- Sewing supplies (zippers, threads, interfacings, etc.)
- Postage
- Advertising and other marketing costs
- Fees and licenses (checking account fees, professional dues, etc.)
- Taxes, including quarterly estimated income taxes
- Interest on loans
- Depreciation on equipment and furniture used in the business
- Cost of goods (fabric and other raw materials used in your products)
- Mileage
- Insurance

Don't forget mileage costs when you're keeping business records. This is a hidden cost, but it can certainly add up in a hurry. At this writing, the IRS allows you to deduct $ .30 per mile—it takes a very short trip to create a $1.00 deduction. In general, you are allowed to deduct mileage for any trip from your home or business to run business-related errands, such as to go to a client's home or to make trips to the fabric store. Even a short trip to the post office or copy store can be business related. Keep good records, and ask your accountant which kinds of trips apply to your particular business.

Depreciation is another hidden cost, and an often forgotten tax deduction. Everything has a useful life, including sewing machines and other equipment: telephones, computers and even software programs. Depreciating this property helps you to spread the cost of these items over a period of time, usually three to five years. The IRS has a list of various depreciation schedules for different kinds of property. What about machines and other equipment you already own? Ask your accountant whether a depreciation deduction is appropriate for you, and if she will

57

prepare a depreciation schedule for you to follow in preparing your tax returns. Your accountant can also advise you whether it is more advantageous to take the entire cost of new equipment in the current tax year, in a special deduction called Section 179.

Getting advice

Be aware that some businesses take longer than others to show a profit. It may take two to five years before you can get by with no other income. Be prepared for this; many people get discouraged and give up after just a few months. However, planning well and zeroing in on a specialty right away have a positive impact on profitability. Do your market research, seek advice from financial experts and be careful with your spending until you begin to see profit coming your way. Keeping careful records will help you identify ways to improve the bottom line more quickly. If you wait until tax time to analyze the business's progress, it could be too late; your business may already be beyond resuscitation.

Ask other businesspeople who their accountants are, and choose someone from these recommendations. Call the accountant to schedule an "interview" to see if you and she would work well together. (Most accountants do not charge for this time.) Feeling comfortable with the accountant is important; you will share your most personal financial information with her. Ask if the accountant has audit experience; home businesses do get audited, and accountants can accompany their clients to the IRS audit.

Until your business begins to take hold, an initial meeting should be all that's necessary *if* you have your accounting system set up properly. A one-hour session with an accountant at the start-up of your business could be one of your best investments. Inquire about fees, and make an appointment for an hour, with the agreement that the accountant will help you set up your recordkeeping systems.

Make a list of questions for the accountant, and prepare as much information as possible ahead of time. This will help contain costs, and you can spend the time listening to her answers and making notes. Ask for tips on the best methods for keeping your books and what expenses should be tracked. Remember to ask about mileage; this often-overlooked expense is somewhat tricky to calculate.

If you have any misgivings about any aspect of local and state sales or income taxes, this is a good time to seek clarification. Some accountants will even make up a tax payment calendar that indicates when certain types of taxes are due. In some parts of the country, dressmaking and other services are taxable; other places have no such sales tax. Here in Cincinnati, in addition to the quarterly estimated federal income taxes, I also must pay sales taxes at least twice yearly, and once a year personal property tax is due on any business property or inventory. If you hire employees, it adds a whole new set of tax payment requirements.

If your business will carry inventory, inquire about necessary record-keeping and taxes. Inventory has to be counted every year at a certain time, and separate records need to be kept for reporting how much is left at the end of the tax year. Find out how that applies to your business and if inventory is taxed separately in your state.

Be sure to file a federal tax return even if you didn't have income. If you have other income, your business losses can offset your tax obligation and save money for you. Usually filing Schedule C is sufficient, unless you have chosen to incorporate your business (see "Should you incorporate?"). In addition, some businesses qualify for a home office deduction, which may reduce your tax obligation further whether you have additional income or not. Ask your accountant how this should be handled in your case. Be prepared to give her an overall measurement of your home and the square footage of your work space. These figures are necessary in order to figure the amount of deduction.

Should you incorporate?

Unless your business employs several to many people or manufactures products that may carry a liability, incorporation is often an unnecessary expense. There are filing fees for incorporation plus separate annual taxes. Sole proprietors have none of these expenses. During your meeting with the accountant, check to see what the best business format is for you and for your specialty.

Insurance

Whether your business is in your home or in a shop, it is always important to protect yourself and your business assets with insurance.

There should be three concerns uppermost in your mind, no matter where your business is located:

- The possible economic loss of property, both yours and your customers'
- Liability, in case someone is hurt on the premises or off
- Ensuring you have enough money to continue in business should you ever have a disaster

Note: Be sure to talk to your agent about what you read here, as laws vary widely between states and provisions vary between companies.

Your first priority is to make sure you *have* coverage for your business. Unless your home business is minimal, a rider on your homeowner's policy is not going to be enough. You need to contact your agent and tell him, honestly, what kind of equipment you have and what quantity of customers' goods are on the premises at any one time.

Why do you need to cover your property? Suppose your home or business were in a fire and you needed to buy all new equipment to get back on your feet. Total how much it would cost to rebuild the business. You might be surprised to find how it adds up. Insurance is meant to put you back in the same position you were in before the claim. An insurance policy that reflects the amount of money you have invested in your business will help you get back to work quicker. If you need to economize, a higher deductible is better than less coverage.

Most companies have a special class of insurance policy called a Business Owner's Policy (BOP), which is designed especially for small companies. These policies are packaged with all kinds of goodies that used to cost a lot extra as add-ons, and they are quite reasonably priced.

One of the special coverages added to the BOP is Customer's Goods, sometimes known as Care, Custody and Control. If a fire or a tornado or another covered event destroys your customer's fabric that's waiting to be made up or her finished goods, this rider would cover their replacement. Consider how useful this would be if you have several thousand dollars' worth of commercial drapery fabric in your workroom or a valuable bridal gown awaiting alterations.

Make sure you get the maximum after a loss, too. Keep good records—photos and receipts—of what you have and *keep them off premises*. It won't do you any good to have meticulous records if they burn up with your business.

Liability

When you think of the term "liability," sometimes accounting comes to mind, but in this case I'm talking about being liable for an accidental occurrence. Consider the consequences if you were measuring windows or teaching in someone's home and accidentally injured the customer or her child. People sue for that sort of thing. Liability insurance would provide an award to the injured party and other benefits as well.

First, in the case of an accident, you should immediately call the agent and report the incident. The insurance company often offers the injured party an immediate cash payment for any first aid expenses incurred. This does two things: It makes the person who was hurt aware that you care about what happened, and it often defuses any potential difficulty later. Many times, this payment keeps people from suing. Of course, if it does come to a lawsuit, the insurance company will pay the judgment award, up to the limits of the policy. Make sure these limits at least cover your assets, that is, your personal net worth. (To figure this, total all your assets, including the value of your business and business property, then deduct everything you owe.)

Don't worry about losing your insurance as a result of filing such a claim. Accidents do happen, and that's why you buy insurance. Unless you file claims often, a reputable insurance company doesn't cancel for using your policy.

Also included in Business Liability is damage to a customer's property while you're on her premises. For instance, suppose you lose your balance and fall off a ladder while measuring a window. The broken window would be covered under your business policy. (Your injuries would be covered under your health insurance or Worker's Compensation. Check with your insurance agent for how this should be handled, as every state is different.)

If you have employees who sometimes run errands for you, you should specify that they be covered under a liability known as Owned and Non-Owned Autos. This provides protection for you if they have accidents on your time. Be aware, this does *not* take the place of auto insurance.

Another benefit of liability insurance includes the payment of legal expenses should you be sued. As you know, this can be incredibly costly.

Another reason to carry a good insurance policy is to be sure you can get back into business after a serious loss. To insure this, most BOPs cover what is known as Business Income. This provides for a payment by the insurance company of any amounts you would have netted over the period of time your business is unable to operate. (However, you need to supply records of that projected income to the insurance adjuster—another reason to keep records off premises.) Another coverage is Extra Expense, which helps you with other costs of getting back into business, for example, rental of a temporary location.

Other coverages typically included in business policies (but not all, ask your agent if you need one of these):

- Fire Legal Liability: This is important if you rent your space and you cause a fire. Some leases require proof of such coverage.
- Money and Securities, and Employee Dishonesty: These cover you in the event of a robbery or if an employee walks off with your money.
- Accounts Receivable and Valuable Papers: These two riders are very important. They provide coverage to not only pay you what moneys you would have been paid before the loss, but also to recover and restore the records.
- Outdoor Signs: Some of them cost a lot to replace.
- Liquor Legal Liability: If you have a Christmas party or other kind of reception and serve wine, you might need this rider. It covers you in the event one of your guests later has an accident because of partaking of your refreshments.

There are many other policy provisions, but they may or may not be included in your company's policy, as each company differs widely. Also, some states file different versions of Business Owner's Policies than that described here.

Finding an insurance agent

Be aware that the same agent who handles your home insurance may not know how to cover your business needs, especially if that agent works for a company that traditionally covers mostly family insurance. Ask if there is someone at the agency who specializes in commercial lines. If not, call around to other agencies, either from the yellow pages or from friends' recommendations.

There are two kinds of insurance agencies: the independent agency, where they carry at least two and usually more insurance companies; and the captive agency, who writes insurance exclusively for one company. An example of a captive company is State Farm, whose agents are only allowed to sell that company's products. Usually, captive companies specialize in insurance for families, but not always.

My recommendation is to request a bid from several agents, including one with a captive company if you already have a relationship with it. The benefit of dealing with an independent agent is that he can more easily find a competitive bid for you, depending on the companies he does business with. Also, in case your policy is canceled for some reason, the independent agent has somewhere else to go with your business.

Tell all the agents the same information about your business and the coverage you seek, and ask them to give you two bids: one with exactly what you asked for, the other with their recommendations. This gives you an opportunity to compare apples to apples and allows you to see which agent is willing to listen to you. This is *very* important. Having the right kind of coverage is crucial when you have a loss. In nine years of selling insurance, I saw many policies that had gaps in coverage because the agent hadn't taken the time to get to know the business.

Copyrights

If you aspire to creating new and different products to sell, be sure these products, whatever they are, are your own creations entirely and do not violate any kind of copyright of another's idea.

This is an extremely volatile area in sewing, in particular because several nationally known companies have begun to vigorously defend their own copyrighted materials. Some companies employ violation spotters, who actually attend craft fairs to find any unauthorized use of their copyrighted images and names. Disney, in particular, has been known to prosecute, which results in hefty fines, seizure of merchandise and lawsuits. Be especially careful of using likenesses of Mickey Mouse, Winnie the Pooh or any other licensed characters. Even the use of fabric bearing these characters is banned, and such a statement is often printed right on the material.

Ideas cannot by copyrighted, but the execution of those ideas falls under copyright law. Just because you change the color of an original quilt

Dee McCarthy

Dee McCarthy Designs
Park City, Utah

Dee McCarthy's career began before she was even out of elementary school, when a friend of her mother offered her $100 to make a bridal gown for a Madame Alexander doll. That was a lot of money in the early 1960s. Dee continued to sew for others throughout high school and college, earning spending money by hemming garments for other girls in her dorm. "I charged more for rush jobs, even then," Dee says. She graduated from the University of Delaware with a double major in art and art history, then she went into the tour and meeting planning business, although she continued to sew for customers part-time.

After several years, Dee realized the tour business wasn't her calling. She decided to go back to school for a degree in design, and her research brought a shocking revelation: "Schools that teach design don't teach you how to sew. There were thirty students in my class at Harper College [Palatine, Illinois]. Out of this class, only the five of us over age thirty knew how to sew. Not many instructors knew how, either, and I ended up helping to teach the tailoring class."

Dee feels the greatest gift design school gave her was a freedom of design. She says, "I grew up in a conservative area, and these classes helped free my creativity and liberate my design ideas. I still have those designs; it's hysterical to see how the design process opened up. It was fun to see you could take a really good piece of fabric and you could put a little bit of design element to it."

Moving to the resort town of Park City, Utah, has freed Dee further; her clients' larger discretionary incomes free her to be creative in design and allow her to take on different kinds of projects. There are finally people willing to pay what she feels her experience and talent are worth, and now she can afford to do some pro bono, or charity, work. For example, a local public radio station has two fund-raisers a year, and Dee donates a custom ski suit for each event. This has had a side benefit of making her work known to the locals and has given her custom skiwear business a good start.

From the skiwear came other custom work. As Dee is an avid horsewoman, she soon became involved making saddle covers for endurance riders. Then she made leg wraps for Ride & Tie events. This relay team involves three members: two runner/riders and a horse. ("The United States always wins this event in the Olympics," says Dee.) Because the leg wraps, which protect a runner's legs while he is on the horse, have to be removed quickly, Dee designed a special kind of wrap that attached to the saddle. In addition to eliminating the need for the rider to carry the wrap while running, it also made using the wrap more efficient.

"I don't get frustrated by difficult jobs because I often learn in the process; it provides a cheap education," Dee remarks. One alterations job for a wealthy client didn't bring much in the way of hourly income, but it was a distinct learning experience. This couture jacket needed extensive alterations, requiring Dee to unpick quite a bit of the construction. "It was like peeling the petals of a flower," she says. "I learned so much from the handwork in this garment. It was a great learning experience, though it took me twelve times as long as I thought it would. However, because of the job I did with it, this client trusts me with most of her other alterations. For some reason, custom work seems to bring alterations work, rather than the reverse."

Custom work is Dee's first love. This type of clientele uses her service frequently, and they can pay the price for the work. But Dee says there are clients for everyone: "There's a market for $300 bridal gowns, $3,000 bridal gowns and even $30,000 bridal gowns."

Dee also makes custom Polarfleece sportswear, a popular line in her ski resort community. A couple of times a year Dee hosts a home party where she shows her latest styles to interested parties. "My customers enjoy coming to my home, having a glass of wine and some good conversation, and choosing from my line. The benefit to them is they get the colors and styles they want, and the clothes fit them. From my viewpoint, the stretch tights take little time to make, and I do very well with this aspect of my business."

"If you don't learn from it, and you don't enjoy it, you should be doing something else," she says. "I feel very fortunate that I have this business I find so fulfilling, and from which I make a very nice income."

---

pattern, for instance, doesn't mean you haven't violated the law.

In addition, fair use of patterns of others dictates that they are not used to manufacture products to sell as your own creations. The "Big Four" pattern companies, Butterick, Vogue, Simplicity and McCall's, expressly prohibit such use of their patterns.

Commercial pattern companies do, however, allow the use of their patterns in making garments and other sewn articles for customers. Essentially, their policy is this: For each item you make, you should buy one pattern. If you make three dresses from the same pattern for one individual, that's fine, but if you are making the same dress for three different people, you should purchase (or the client should provide) a pattern for each person.

Use of commercial patterns in manufacturing is not only illegal in most cases but also inefficient; cutting apart and using tissue patterns for wholesale manufacturing would be a terrible waste of time. In the industry, oak tag patterns are generally used. If paper is used at all, they are computer-generated patterns printed on the paper in a layout that allows for as little fabric waste as possible. (See the appendix for information on pattern-making software.)

Especially for those who want to manufacture many of something, whether it is a craft, a toy or a garment, the design should be original to you, or you should pay someone to create an original design for that specific item. Many smaller design companies are happy to give you permission to use their patterns, or they will create patterns to your specifications. Some designers ask for a small fee, and others ask simply that you request permission; each has a different policy. This includes designs in magazines; always write or call the publication to get in touch with the designer.

It is a courtesy to ask first; these designers make their living from their designs. Using their patterns for your own gain reduces their ability to profit from their own designs, so be prepared to pay for that right. And never, under any circumstances, copy another's pattern for sale. One woman who did so was levied a fine of $60,000 for attempting to sell six patterns she had copied. A federal marshal who was at the craft show just to watch for this kind of violation caught her in the act of selling them. It just isn't worth this kind of monetary risk. Create your own designs, or find something else to do.

So what do you do if the pattern is from an old book or magazine? If you wish to use such a pattern, at least make an attempt to contact the designer; often the publisher will know how to reach that person. Copyrights belong to the author for many years after her death. In the case of a book that was published in the early 1950s by someone who was thirty-five years old, for example, this copyright would still be in effect long past the millenium. Don't assume that an old book is safe to copy from, except for personal, noncommercial use. "Commercial," in this case, means that you profit by it somehow. These restrictions would also apply to any original patterns you create for sale and protect you from others profiting from your original ideas. Same goes for class handouts; don't copy anyone else's materials without permission, and even then mark the handout clearly to show where the information came from.

Copyright is a tricky part of the law, and this section of the book is not meant to take the place of good legal advice. Please consult an intellectual property rights attorney or the copyright section of the federal statutes at any larger library for more information.

CHAPTER 5
Basics of Buying and Selling

Anytime you deal with the public you're in a sales situation. Luckily, most sewing professionals don't have many of the problems normally associated with sales. There are few situations where a hard sell is necessary, nor would such a tactic succeed. In general, sewing services are a rare commodity, and the more typical situation is that you have to turn down business than the other way around.

Overcoming objections

However, there are several basic sales ideas you should know in order to succeed in a sewing business. One is the idea of overcoming objections. As I travel around the country speaking to sewing pros, the questions I get the most begin with, "What do I say when my customers tell me . . ." These are a customer's objections to the sale. Sometimes people just want you to overcome their objections, to give them a reason or justification to spend their money. The only way to get past this is to counter each objection with a benefit to the customer.

- "I can get it at Wal-Mart cheaper."
  Answer: "Yes, you can, but it won't be custom-made, just for you, with the fabrics and color and quality you prefer. It won't fit nearly as well, and you might see the same garment on everyone else at the dance."
  Answer: "If you could find what you want at retail, why are you here?"

- "Your price is too high."
  Answer: "Perhaps I can reduce the price by changing the design. I could delete the lining, which would reduce the price to $X, or I could eliminate the ruffles from the skirt hem." (See the sections on pricing for more help.)
  Answer: "I offer a customer service. Your garment will fit only *you*, it will be made in the color and fabric of *your* choice and will include the

features that *you* choose, rather than what manufacturers choose to sell this season." (Say this very sweetly.)

Answer: "My individualized, custom service should cost more than mass-produced garments, which are made in enormous quantity of inferior fabrics, often in overseas factories by underpaid labor and with lower-quality workmanship."

* "I can make it myself for less than that!"
  Answer: "Perhaps." (Period. Don't say anything else. Let her get herself out of *this* one!)

Always answer objections with benefits to the customers, but without being argumentative. Sometimes they honestly can't afford your services, and they really have no business asking you to sew for them to begin with. In cases like these, it's best just to allow them to gracefully bow out of the situations. But be kind; you never know when their financial statuses will change, and then they will think of you first as someone they trust to do that type of work for them. Be prepared to admit that not everyone is a customer—not even Wal-Mart sells to every person who walks into the stores.

Once you have chosen your specialty, these sales situations get easier. You know who your customer is, and he knows you have what he wants. All you have to do is to provide it at a price the broadest range of customers will pay and that gives you the most comfortable profit.

If you develop a patter about your product or service, many of the objections your customers might raise can be quashed before they are ever voiced. You can anticipate the objections forming in the customer's mind as you talk about the window treatments you will make for her, for instance. She might be preparing to complain about having to hang them herself, but when you mention during the course of your discussion that *installation is included*, that objection is satisfied ahead of time, and it dissolves, never to become an issue. This idea can be applied to many other products as well. Shortening pants, for example: Your competitor does them by hand; you have a blindstitch machine that *duplicates the more professional, ready-to-wear method*. Or your stuffed bunnies are *made of genuine mohair, and their eyes are created with safety-locked components*.

When the customer has no more objections, stop answering them. You can literally talk yourself out of a sale by talking too much. Silence is golden, and nowhere more so than in a sales situation. Let the customer make the next move, and if that next step is to say, "I'll take it," all the better.

Closing the sale

Sometimes you can get to the sale quicker by asking, "When would you like this to be completed? My schedule is open for either May 1 or the following week. Which is better for you?" This is called a close, and there are many ways to close a sale. (See the appendix for recommended reading for more information on selling, or go to the business section of any good bookstore or library.)

Extra income

Add-on services can make a tremendous difference to the bottom line of your business. Michael LaBoeuf, author of *The Perfect Business*, calls such add-ons PIGs, which stands for Passive Income Generators. For example, alterationist Judy Pagenkopf cheerfully accepts leather repairs, which she then hands off to a leather repairperson who picks up and delivers work to her. Judy pays the repair shop and charges the customer the cost of the service plus a surcharge for handling the repair. The customer doesn't know about the surcharge, but since the leather shop is not generally known to the public, it is unlikely he could access that company. It is not labor-intensive for Judy, so she increases her dollar per hour income by offering such a service.

What type of PIG could you offer your customer? Many drapery work-rooms also sell hard-to-find hardware. One designer in Ohio rents crinolines to her bridal and formalwear clients. She also has made up several styles of faux fur capelets that fit over voluminous bridal gown sleeves. Because of the uncertainty of the weather in the Midwest at any time of the year, she makes a tidy income renting these capes to barely covered brides. Another bridal designer also sells satin dyeable shoes to her bridal customers, as well as veils, ringbearer pillows and other specialty items. None of these services take much time to manage.

Pricing your services

The biggest human temptation is to settle for too little.

Thomas Merton, 1917-1968

As in any other kind of business, how you price your sewn products or services can mean the difference between success and failure. If you overcharge, you might have a tough time finding the customers, especially when the business is new. But underpricing is much more serious. *Not charging enough is the worst pricing mistake you can make.* Businesses with no income at all can survive easier than a business with too little income for the work. There will always be someone with a lower price and some-one with a higher price. Don't be the one with the lowest price.

- Underpricing forces you to work harder for less. (If your shop is the busiest one in town, your prices are probably too low.)
- Underpricing taxes your resources; you are too busy, and too tired, to find new income streams.
- Too-low prices tell customers you aren't serious about business. When you pay more for something, you think of it as more worthwhile.
- Underpricing makes your competitors angry and can ultimately pull down all prices in town. Every business will suffer, including yours.
- If you charge too little to begin with, it's difficult to raise prices to the proper level.
- Low prices equal low profit, and thus you can't afford to invest in new equipment and more education.
- The *best* mistake a new business can make is *over*charging.

Rule of thumb: If at least 30 percent of your customers aren't hemming and hawing about your prices, they are probably too low.

Karen Howland, the author of *Unit Pricing for Dressmaking*, says, "You're giving up your hobby when you sew for others. If someone asked you to give up sewing for good, what would it take?" This logic helped Karen decide to raise her own prices.

Pricing strategies

Depending on your specialty, you may have several choices of how to price your products or services.

In the case of craft manufacturing, as much depends on the salability of the product as on the cost to produce it. And if you plan to sell your product to retail stores, prices must be low enough to allow the stores to double that price. Before you begin production, find out if you can make the item cheaply enough to do this and still sell that item. If the item is fairly inexpensive to produce, you can use the "eight times" rule of thumb for pricing: Set the price at approximately eight (sometimes ten) times the amount it cost for the raw materials. If the resultant price is too high, rethink the whole idea. Perhaps it just isn't economically feasible to produce. Or perhaps a different production method or fewer features will increase its profitability.

In order to profit from custom sewing, you need to plan ahead. Use the formula given here to determine what hourly rate you need to charge. I recommend trying to make at least $15 per hour to start; $20 is even better. This gives you a fair margin for overhead, labor and profit. Remember that customers value more highly services for which they pay more.

Pricing formula

    _____ Monthly salary

+ _____ phone

+ _____ utilities

+ _____ rent

+ _____ insurance

+ _____ depreciation

+ _____ taxes

+ _____ equipment/maintenance

+ _____ profit

= _____ monthly income

÷ _____ number of hours worked per month

= _____ hourly price

For dressmaking and other custom services, there are several ways to price. In some parts of the country, you may have to compete more strongly than in other places, and one or more of these methods could be used to give you an edge on the competition.

Price lists

There are several price lists available for purchase, and you can also use the lists used by dry cleaners and alterations departments. However, you should use these as guidelines only. Some price lists have a strong geographical emphasis; the prices reflected may either be way too high or way too low for your own area and situation. Prices from department stores are sometimes very low, reflecting the store's desire to offer a value-added service to their customer.

If you choose to use a price list as your guide, try to determine what hourly wage it represents. Take some time to change the list to allow you to make what you need to make.

Garment (or "experience") pricing

Many bridesmaids' dresses are priced by the garment, with a set amount for set types of gowns. This is more a reaction to what the market will bear than any other reason. There are, however, some inherent problems in this pricing method:

- It may take you longer to make garments that others are able to crank out more quickly.
- Certain styles may take much longer than others to make.
- Certain fabrics may be more difficult to sew.
- In the case of experience pricing, you might not remember all the details of the garment you sewed before. Also, each garment and situation have a tendency to differ from one another just enough that it's tough to predict how the project will go.

Susan Khalje, a couture bridal designer who lives in Baltimore, Maryland, feels garment pricing works best for her. After twenty years of sewing for others, she is confident she can predict how long each project will take to complete. She also makes the price high enough that she feels comfortable taking the time to add the couture details she and her customers like best. (For more about Susan, see pages 145-147.)

Pattern piece pricing

In some areas of the country, every seamstress charges the same amount for the same garment; the price is determined by the number of pattern pieces. For each individual piece of cut fabric, there is a charge of $5 to $15 for labor. However, this doesn't take into account the difficulty of the fabric, so a surcharge is added (20 to 30 percent) for working with slippery satins or tricky velvets. If you use this method, remember to charge for all the pattern pieces used in the lining, too.

A drawback to this method is that it doesn't take into account the skill level of the clothier, nor does it allow much flexibility in pricing the garment. And if there are many fittings, that isn't factored in. One way around this is to charge a flat fitting fee, but that isn't necessarily workable either.

Hourly rates

Although this method is an excellent way to keep your eye on the bottom line, especially if your sewing is speedy and efficient, it also has some potential pitfalls. First of all, many customers are opposed to paying a set hourly rate; sewing isn't always perceived as a valued service, and if your hourly rate is higher than what the customer feels your service is worth, there may be price resistance, no matter what the rate is. Conversely, if your hourly rate is low, the customer may try to take advantage of your low prices. If you choose to use an hourly rate, avoid revealing the figure to your customers.

Other disadvantages to hourly rates:

- If you are especially slow and methodical, your prices could be impractical for nearly all your potential customers.
- It's easy to underestimate the time it will take for a garment. Since the human body is so complex, a first effort at fitting someone may take longer than subsequent projects for them. And customers tend to downplay the complexity of their projects, both to themselves and to their dressmakers—"It's just a simple dress." (It always is!) Don't be swayed by their opinions—remember, you're the professional here.

If you set up an hourly system, have a timer and a logbook nearby to record every minute you spend on each customer's project. (Having these records can make it easier to experience price later projects and to evaluate your rate periodically.) Be sure to include consultation and fitting times in your log, unless you choose to charge separately for these meetings. But do charge something; your time is valuable, and charging for it communicates that fact to the client.

Combination pricing

This method combines the garment pricing system and add-on pricing for various details. For instance: A typical jacket with a two-button front, lapels and patch pockets would have a base price. If the customer requests linings, vented sleeves, vent back, welt pockets and bound buttonholes, an additional charge would be made for each of these. This works in the opposite way as well. To save the customer on labor, you can show how stripping these details from the garment estimate will lower the price.

Pricing for beading

When asked to do beading, be very careful about giving a price. Estimate your time only, and aim for somewhere in the range of $20 to $40 per hour. Beading is very hard on the eyes and is a highly skilled activity. Make sure the customer knows this, and don't sell yourself short by giving a low price for this service.

Alterations

Pricing alterations is somewhat less complex than pricing custom garment sewing. It's also more competitive in some towns. Using an hourly, or unit, cost works best to develop your own price list.

Begin by timing yourself doing some simple alterations. One expert suggests buying secondhand clothing to inspect and take apart. Practice sewing various types of hems, letting side seams in and out, changing the waist size in men's pants and shortening sleeves. These are the most common alterations, along with replacing zippers and shortening bridal gown hems. (See *Time and motion studies*, page 78.)

Occasionally, dry cleaners or department store alterations departments have price lists posted or available. This might be a good place to start investigating how much is charged for various alterations in your community. Sometimes pant hems are considered "loss leaders," that is, a competitive service to advertise to bring in business. Judy Pagenkopf tries to keep the cost for doing pant hems just about the same as her nearest competitor's charge. The rest of her alterations price list doesn't conform so closely to any other, but it doesn't have to.

Window treatments and home decor

This is another area where hourly charges work well, but you should probably not call them that. A price list that reflects your targeted hourly income for various kinds of services is normally expected, particularly if you work with decorators as a wholesale workroom. Retail customers don't expect price lists as much as designers do. Designers need to know your cost so they can pass on that cost plus a markup, often 30 to 50 percent, to their customers.

If you choose to act as a wholesale workroom, be especially careful not to compete with the designers for the same customers. Nothing will ruin a business relationship faster than undercutting someone else's price for the same business. Decorators will be more willing to send you business if they know they can trust you. This kind of business is actually easier for you; you don't have to do any of the design, and you don't have to work with the customer or do the installations (unless you choose to do it for the decorator, in which case you should be paid an additional amount).

Most draperies are charged by the width, but there are many variables now with the newer treatments. It would be beneficial to you to keep up with the market by subscribing to one of the industry magazines (see the appendix). These magazines sponsor trade shows around the country all year long, with seminars on marketing, pricing and other workroom issues.

Embroidery

With the availability of newer, less expensive and more compact embroidery machines, entry into this field is easier and more economical than ever. Many businesses struggle with how to charge for this service, however.

Beth Hodges

Soft Furnishings
Elberton, Georgia

"I have a gift—I can figure out how to do anything I see. If a customer brings me a photograph, I can nearly always determine how it is made and then duplicate it," says Beth Hodges, who from her home in rural Georgia furnishes draperies, window treatments and all manner of fabric decorative items for the home. About half of her business now is selling "hard" treatments: shades, blinds and decorative hardware. Probably half of her soft business comes from outside her own area. Her tiny community boasts a population of 12,000, with the nearest bigger town about forty-five miles away.

"I wasn't afraid to meet my competitors' prices when I was trying to recruit new business. I told potential customers, 'I charge more, but how about if I use your current price list for six months and we renegotiate then?' They had been dissatisfied with the service they had been getting, and I met their demands more efficiently. After six months, they were willing to meet my price scale (kicking and screaming all the way!)." As Beth points out, "You have to be prepared to eat jobs sometimes to satisfy customers, and be willing to work really hard to keep their business. A happy customer tells three others; an unhappy customer tells twenty!

"If a customer criticizes others' work in front of you, be careful," she warns, "they will also criticize your work. Never say anything bad about a competitor. And don't say anything negative, especially about the cus-tomer's home." Beth says many people are insecure about their homes, and your comments may make them even more so.

Beth credits her success in sales to three things: making sure her clients are happy with her work, her advertising and her method of selling window treatments. She advertises in the local newspaper, typically with a photograph of some recent work she has done.

When Beth is selling a treatment, she uses a drawing on graph paper, on a ¼- to 5-inch scale. An exact picture of the customer's window is drawn to scale on the paper, along with the window's relationship to both floor and ceiling. Then every treatment is drawn onto onionskin overlay. The overlays are laid over the graph paper so the customer can see exactly how the treatments will look. "This eliminates so many communication errors," says Beth. "The client doesn't envision puddled drapes, when the treatment I'm showing is actually just floor length. There is a computer program that shows treatments, but it uses a stock window; my method shows the window as it is in real life. I make a sale every time."

"Get it in writing," says Beth about work agreements. Her husband is an attorney, and he advised her to use written contracts, even though under Georgia law a cash down payment is as good as a written document. However, this isn't true in every state, and you should check your own local laws. Beth uses a three-part form and gives one part to the customer at the time of the sale.

Two full-time employees help Beth run her business. On the subject of employees, Beth advises hiring someone with no experience, then training them to do things your way. She says, "I'm not a blamer; I take responsibility for anything that goes wrong, both to the customer and to the ladies who work for me. And I tell them every day that they do a good job."

Beth has a rule for her own and her employees' work: If we can see it, the customer can, too. If it's wrong, do it over. And nothing leaves her workroom with raw edges; everything is finished properly. According to Beth, "We want our products to look custom-made; not homemade and not store-bought. I view everything we do as a stepping-stone to something else, so it's important to make a good impression."

Many commercial embroiderers charge by the stitch count of the embroidered design. For example, if the design has two thousand stitches, the cost to the customer would be $2.00 to $3.50 per item, depending on pricing in the area. Up to five colors would be included in this price, with higher prices for more colors. Since part of the cost is in the setup of the design, you could pass on a savings to the customer for multiples of the same design, with price breaks at various points.

An embroiderer in Florida uses the following formula in pricing embroidered clothing items: cost + markup + number of stitches = contract price. It's especially important to include markup (30 to 50 percent) in this type of work so the price includes enough profit to cover other expenses. Because commercial embroidery machines are so expensive to buy new ($3,000 to upward of $30,000), the cost of the equipment should be spread out over the price of the goods embroidered.

Rush jobs

In addition to charges for services rendered, don't forget about *implied* service. If a customer wants a rush job, charge for it. Many shops charge from 30 to 50 percent additional for rush work; at least one shop charges 100 percent. Remember, if you set time aside from your other work, that makes those other customers wait. Decide what constitutes "rush" for your business: Is it anything that must be completed in less than two to four weeks, or are you willing to take rush orders in less time than that?

Other professions charge a premium rate for overtime; this is essentially what your rush customer is asking for. You may have to work unplanned nights or weekends in order to finish all the work you have to do because of this order. Charge for it.

Do not undervalue your service; that is the worst thing you can do.

Time and motion studies

In the late 1960s, while working my way through college, I happened to be a time study clerk at a large Ohio factory, Mosler Safe Company. The mere fact that this factory had an entire department for efficiency studies says how important it is to know how much time each operation of a job takes. If you choose to do production sewing, time studies will help you determine how to set your prices accurately and fairly.

To make any money at contract sewing, speed is essential. Speed is usually the result of repeating the same function many times. However, there is generally a plateau where increasing speed levels off and performance remains static. When preparing a bid for a contract job, time yourself performing the same operation at least ten times, then take an average of that function. Calculate all the parts of the job, and use that as your time estimate. And be sure to add in the time it takes to time your work; this is an additional cost to you.

This method will work with making any kind of multiples, whether they are garments, pot holders or awnings.

Tip: When making multiples of anything, it's faster and more efficient to complete one step at a time for the full quantity of items than to complete each garment or project one by one. For example: Add all the sleeves to a pile of doll dresses (all the right ones first, then all the left ones) before adding the collars.

Get real!

Be sure to use a realistic hourly figure. As appalling as it may seem, some people equate their services with hourly wages in the marketplace. This is unrealistic because hourly employees don't have to pay their own taxes from that money, nor do they have to pay any overhead at all. As a self-employed individual, you are obliged to pay all these expenses and more (see chart, chapter five). If you only charge $5 to $10 per hour for sewing, your actual "income" could be a negative figure! Consider how much it costs to get your car fixed or to have a plumber unclog a pipe. Most sewing pros have at least as much education or experience in their field as these professionals, yet they often have a more difficult time charging for what that experience is worth. Based on that comparison, reconsider your pricing structure.

Charge enough that it is profitable for you to continue in business. If you find yourself saying, "But my customers won't pay that much!" you might want to find different customers. What is the sense of being in business to lose money? Sometimes it takes a few years to get to the point of making a profit; that's different. But if you have been self-employed for a while and have lost money from the beginning, go back to chapter one and regroup. Research the situation and figure out why your business isn't profitable. If "no one will pay," perhaps you should change your focus and find the clients who will pay. They do exist; sometimes you have to shift your sights ever so slightly to see them. Just because no one in your town wears custom suits and evening gowns doesn't mean that no one wears Civil War reenactment costumes or church clothing or specialized leather wear.

Perceived-value pricing

An alterationist in Florida told me that she charged double the dry cleaners' prices for alterations because she was relatively new to the field. She said, "I tell my customers they have to pay me more because it's hard for me and takes me longer." Her clients have the option of not having her do the work, but they ask for her services. She had the guts to ask for it, so she gets that price. There's a lesson here, I think.

Kenneth King, San Francisco "designer to the stars," author and former cohost of PBS-TV's *Sewing Today*, has my all-time favorite pricing method. King says, "I just figure out what it would cost in retail and add a zero to the end!"

If clients consider your work valuable to them in some way, they are

Paula O'Connell

Luxurious Alternatives
Oakville, Ontario, Canada

web site?

Paula O'Connell is an accountant who got tired of doing the same thing for so long. She was in a position to do what she wanted to do, without the pressure of having to earn a living, and decided she would rather be an artisan than a profiteer. "Although I do make a profit from what I do, I'm not doing it for groceries. My hobby is self-supporting, and I can work with the quality of materials I want to work with. I couldn't justify buying the latest fancy computerized machine for a hobby, but with the business I could," explains Paula.

"I saw Donna Salyers at a conference in Toronto, and I liked the way the faux furs looked so I bought a kit," says Paula, who, along with many people in Ontario, wears furs. She was sick of replacing them when they wore out, and she was amazed at how well the faux fur wore. "No one could believe it wasn't real, and everyone who saw my coats asked me to make coats for them. I decided to make the coats as a business." She notes, "I'm still doing the fur coats, teaching classes, selling yardage and other activities." Paula feels that if she spent the time to actively market the coat business it could support her without any additional income, although she prefers not to do so at the present.

Paula sells a good portion of her merchandise at consumer shows and one-of-a-kind gift shows for retail stores. She has two children at home, and focusing on shows allows her to concentrate on production and sales without spending a lot of time fit-

ting and seeing clients. She has a large warehouse attached to her and her husband's retail display business, so this is where she cuts the furs and sews. They can be messy to cut at home.

Another unique service Paula is focusing on now is dressmaking for cross-dressers. She says there is a market in her area, with no one to serve it, and she feels she is especially qualified to do so. Both her pattern-making training and an open mind allow her to be successful in this type of market. She views it as a costume business.

"Some of these guys want to get a little fussier than the basic patterns or styles available in larger sizes," Paula says. "They want really super designed stuff, some of the same styles they see on the runway." She plans to use her costume, bridal and special occasion wear experience to help her with this specialty, as well as her love of beadwork. This idea also dovetails nicely with her preference for working with one-of-a-kind garments.

Paula has chosen to publicize her business by several methods. One is to send press releases to local newspaper editors. She writes the article herself; many times the paper prints what she submits to them, verbatim. There's a lesson here: Be extra careful about what you submit for publication. "You find out who the editor is, and you send it to that person," she says. "Include everything you want in the article, and don't include anything you don't want to see in print. They won't ask you for permission ahead of time, and they will assume you sent it to be included in the article. Be sure you proofread what you send them first!"

Having an accounting background helps Paula charge what she's worth, she feels. "I know what I have to give up to do this kind of work, so I'm not afraid to charge for that. For instance, it's worth it to me to pay someone else to do my housework, because it's a $7 an hour job. I can spend my time sewing and make more than that," she explains. "You have to figure out how much you want to make in a year and how many hours you are willing to work to make that kind of money. It's nice to say you spent last weekend painting the house, but," Paula asks, "what didn't you do to make that same amount of money? Although, it's hard for me to justify just sewing for money; I have to be able to make really special cre-

ations for a lot of money, to satisfy both my needs."

She reminds others that the cost of machines, power, overhead, full-spectrum bulbs and so forth needs to be factored into the cost of doing business. "You need to charge for it, or you're subsidizing the business. It's hard to do," she admits. You have to ask yourself, "Are you a seamstress, a dressmaker or a sewing machine operator? Choose the skill level at which you are, and decide how much you're going to charge based on your self-description." Paula points out what may seem obvious but often isn't practiced: "More skilled work should command higher prices. Those doing custom work should make more than an operator who is given piles of seams to sew, with no real decisions of fit or style to make."

often willing to pay more. Don't be afraid to think of yourself as a professional—and price your work accordingly.

Note: To reduce price resistance, and to remind yourself of why your prices are what they are, make a poster of this saying, and hang it on the wall of your studio:

> The bitterness of poor quality remains long after the sweetness of low price is forgotten.
>
> Anonymous

Consignment

A good way for a small business to get started is to sell on consignment to small stores, including boutiques. This means that no money is exchanged until after the items are sold. Usually, accounts are settled once a week, but that depends on the store and how its bookkeeping is set up. Some stores prefer to pay about 40 percent of the retail amount to the designer; others pay as much as 60 percent.

While it may not seem fair that you, the designer, get so little, remember that the store owners have enormous expenses to keep the doors open. In exchange, you get the benefit of their advertising, their yellow pages ads and their excellent retail locations—none of which you had to commit to paying for. Not only that, but the store owners take a chance on anything they put in stock; if it doesn't sell, it gets shopworn and it makes the rest of the merchandise look tawdry. Should that happen, be prepared to again do some honest soul-searching about how well your designs will sell.

Consignment selling is a good way to test the market. If you think you have a hot product, making just a few to sell in a well-placed shop makes better sense than just jumping into a full-scale manufacturing venture. One preemie wear manufacturer in Michigan began her business this way. In three years she has expanded to a catalog of goods she now sells nationally.

Buying supplies

One of the most important aspects of being profitable involves *not* spending money. Every dollar of income you don't spend becomes profit to you. Reducing your everyday expenses makes sense. Pay less for what you buy.

If you're making articles for customers, try to purchase all raw materials for those products at a price lower than retail. If you pay regular retail for these components, the resulting product will have to cost too much. Finding a better price helps lower your cost, and therefore the price of the item. Maintaining wholesale resources will help contain costs and allow you to maintain a competitive edge in price.

However, sometimes you can be too conscientious of the bottom line.

"I had to learn how to spend money before I could learn to charge for my services," says Karen Howland. "Like many of us, I learned to sew to save money. We mistakenly try to apply our own frugality to our customers, who don't always care to be frugal." Often, when Karen told her bridal clients how much yardage to buy for their projects, she noticed they wrote down more than the recommended amount. "For instance, if a blouse took two and a half yards, invariably the customer wrote down 'three yards.' If I told them they needed four and three-eighths yards for a suit, it amazed me to see them write 'five yards.' " Karen says, "This taught me a lesson and helped make my sewing much more efficient, too. I no longer worried about how to squeeze a layout into a small amount of fabric; this saved me a lot of time."

Knowing that her customers valued her service enough to blow a little money on extra fabric helped Karen place more importance on her own services and charge more for them. Be careful not to ascribe your own values to your customers.

What are resale numbers?

In order to buy goods at wholesale, you first need to purchase a vendor's license (in most areas) and apply for a resale tax number. This allows you to purchase supplies for the business without paying sales tax, as long as the supplies are to be used in a finished product.

How does this work? Say you manufacture tablecloths. When you purchase bolts of fabric, thread and any embellishments to the cloths, as well as packaging materials, you do not pay sales tax on any of these items, which will all eventually be sold to a customer. The customer, the end user, will then pay sales tax. In most cases (not all, check your community's laws for local compliance), sales tax is meant to be paid by the end user. Whoever is selling the goods collects the tax, then remits it to whatever taxing body demands it. For instance, in my own community the State of Ohio requires sewing professionals to collect state sales tax from anyone who contracts for such services. The business owner then must pay that tax to the state periodically.

No one, except some nonprofit agencies such as schools, is exempt from paying sales tax as an end user. This includes you when you purchase equipment; you are still required to pay sales tax on machines and other items used in your business, even if you have a resale number. Because these items are not going to be sold to someone else (unless you have a retail store selling such items or live in a state with no sales tax), you must pay tax on them.

This is perhaps the least understood aspect of resale numbers, and your insistence on not paying sales tax, if it is required, will earmark you as an amateur. Familiarize yourself with this part of doing business before setting out to buy wholesale goods.

If you are required to collect sales tax, be careful to also then remit the amount you collect to the taxing authority. Keeping that money could be an actionable offense. It just isn't worth going to jail or getting a big fine for the small amount of money typically involved. Keep good records in order to stay within the law.

Many taxing agencies send employees to craft shows to see if all vendors are charging tax. They occasionally purchase goods simply to check compliance. Be aware of such a practice, and make sure you have the proper vendor license or other required documentation.

Sources of wholesale goods

Finding wholesale sources is one of the most difficult tasks for any business, but in the past it was especially tough for sewing workrooms. Nowadays, with access to the Internet and other resource centers, that part of conducting a sewing business is easier than ever (see the appendix for resource information). You can expect to pay from 30 to 50 percent less from a wholesale resource, typically, with the higher discount available to those who buy larger quantities.

Pitfalls of buying wholesale

Many wholesale sources have minimum purchases—either a minimum number of yards (of one fabric) or a dollar minimum, usually $100 or more. Some resources waive the minimum purchase amount after the initial purchase, but not all. Don't expect to buy a couple of yards of fabric or a mere package or two of certain notions; that isn't wholesale buying, and asking for special terms for such low quantities is insulting to the wholesaler. Many companies make it difficult to buy from them because they have had home sewing enthusiasts or part-time businesses waste their time with unreasonable requests. Be careful to know their guidelines and stay within them.

Because of the minimums, you may be forced to accept goods in a far larger quantity than you expected to buy. In a case like this, it might be better to purchase the fabric at a retail sale price, or better yet, have your customer purchase the goods. (Note: Many workrooms charge extra for using COM, or Customer's Own Material. This is especially important if the customer brings you unsuitable fabric for a project. Customers also might purchase too little fabric, flawed goods, goods printed off-grain or material that is more difficult to sew.)

Another problem with buying fabric wholesale is that you may have to accept whatever the wholesaler has on hand, even if it's much more than you need for the project. Karen Howland cautions, "Make sure you charge your customer the equivalent of the retail price. Very often when you buy wholesale fabric, the wholesaler doesn't have exactly the amount you need and you're obliged to take more. If you need fifteen yards for a wedding gown, the smallest piece they have may be twenty-two yards— and they don't cut fabric in these places—you get what they have. In this case you would be out quite a bit of money if you had charged your customer the same price per yard you are paying."

Not only are you sometimes forced to buy more than you need, but if there is a flaw in the material, it is more difficult to get a refund or a replacement bolt. And if you've already cut into the fabric and then find a flaw, wholesalers won't take it back at all, unlike some retail fabric stores. Karen says this is also a good reason to take the twenty-two yards; from bitter experience, she automatically adds a couple of yards to her estimate to cover such contingencies. Moreover, if you wait to check the goods until you're ready to cut and sew, there may not be time to reorder. Get into the habit of checking materials right away, to forestall such a situation.

Carol Hawkey, owner of a sewing school in Casper, Wyoming, and publisher of Directions Patterns for children, has some advice if you need a large quantity of goods for a one-time project: "Make the best deal you can with your local fabric store. Minimum, they will give you 10 percent off, maybe up to 25 percent, if you pay up front on the order for one or two whole bolts (usually twenty-five yards)." She further adds, "Think of the risk for the fabric store if you order on promise and then change your mind. They would be stuck with a huge quantity of fabric they didn't want." Thus up-front payment gives them some financial security while it gets you a lower price.

"Manufacturers and mills have huge minimums of several thousand yards," Carol says. "The smallest I've found was five hundred yards, rolled on tubes." A better option for many sewing businesses is to order fabric from a distributor—the ones who sell the folded bolts we're used to seeing at fabric stores. Some distributors have minimums as low as $50, and the wholesale price is about 35 to 40 percent less than you would pay at retail. You will have shipping costs to pay if you order fabric this way, but if your order is large enough, the distributor will absorb the shipping cost. In order to do business this way, you must have a business and a resale license.

Carol advises those who plan to continue to use large quantities of fabric or other goods to start with the *Thomas Register* at the local library. Many fabric distributors (and thousands of other resources) are listed in this mighty reference work of U.S. and Canadian resources. The *Thomas Register* can also be accessed through the World Wide Web. Other sites contain additional European resources and some trade organizations (see the appendix). The Web has many other resource centers as well. Search for *sewing* and any other words that describe your needs: *fabric, trims, beads,* etc.

Crafts supplies

Because so many people make crafts casually to sell a piece or two at a time, many suppliers are leery of selling "wholesale." In the past, retail stores, embittered by the hard economic blows sustained when retail superstores opened in their competitive range, complained to suppliers who were selling some of the same merchandise to individuals. They felt business was hard enough to come by without the suppliers "stealing" these sales from them. However, the retailers were also reluctant to sell discounted supplies to crafts professionals.

This has changed somewhat in recent years. A new awareness of the problems of all parties has come about, partly as a result of new professional associations. These groups have sponsored seminars to educate their members on how to buy supplies. By opening the lines of communications on all sides, they have also made inroads in opening the eyes of the various retailers and suppliers to the potential sales these professional crafters represent.

Attitude is everything

When ordering from a company for the first time, a businesslike attitude is a must. Before you call, have your resale license number, reference addresses and phone numbers handy, and know what you want or are willing to accept. (Of course be realistic about your expectations.) A calm, professional demeanor will go a long way toward getting what you want.

If you write to a company, spend a little extra time to make your "company" look like one. Scrawled messages on scratch paper will be ignored, with some justification. A more businesslike approach will open more doors to you.

Also, if you're unsure about how the sales tax situation works, find out what you're required to do before you call or write to a company about buying wholesale. The local taxing authority usually has brochures or other written material about this, or you can call the Small Business Administration for suggestions about where to get information.

Contracts 101

Why should you have a contract? Well, consider this true story: A work associate of Julie Davis's husband asked Julie to make costumes for a weekend singing group in Illinois. It was a big order—forty-eight dresses—and the singers were providing the fabric, so Julie didn't ask for a deposit. "I always require a deposit when I am covering the materials; this way I'm only out time and labor, not actual funds, if anything goes wrong," says Julie, who lives in central Illinois.

"We had a measuring session," explains Julie. "I made up the dresses with a loose fit, then I pin fit them in a second fitting session. When they came to pick them up, everyone was twirling around in their new dresses when one of the mothers remarked that the style, which had a fitted, shirred bodice and a flowy, circular skirt, made her daughter look fat." Suddenly everyone thought the girls looked fat, and the lovely garments they had just been admiring on themselves no longer looked as lovely to them. On that sour note, Julie let them take their dresses with them, along with an invoice for the work.

"My contact, who worked with my husband, called a few days after that to say they hated the dresses and they weren't going to pay for them.

Later, we saw promotional flyers all over town advertising the group, and they were wearing my dresses!" says Davis.

"I took a flyer with me to a lawyer for advice. He said it would probably cost as much to fight for the money as what they owed me, which was $3,800, because I would have to sue each singer individually. They didn't have any kind of organized business, unfortunately, or I could have just sued the company," says Julie, who decided to drop the idea of trying to prosecute the group members for the money.

"With a project that big, I wasn't able to work on any other items during that time. When they wouldn't pay me, I not only lost the money from this job, but from any other jobs I might have been doing then." Julie laments, "I really needed that money, too, as I counted on my sewing income to augment my husband's teaching income at the time." Julie feels she learned some valuable, if expensive, lessons from this experience: Never take on a job without a signed and dated contract, always get a deposit and never let the work go out of the shop without getting the balance owed you.

What is a contract?

A contract can take many forms, but basically it is just an agreement that one party will do something for another party, by such a time and for a specified consideration, or fee. Actually, oral agreements are contracts, but they aren't as easily enforceable as written ones. Oral agreements, in the case of a dispute, often hinge on one person's word against another's, and it's difficult to prove who said what.

One good way to create your own contract is to take advantage of the sample contracts (see the appendix), adding or subtracting parts to suit your own business. Then take the result to an attorney for help in tweaking the document to conform to your local laws. Because laws vary widely from state to state and from country to country, no one document can apply to every situation. Consider having more than one contract if your business offers more than one type of sewing service.

Why should you use contracts?

Having a signed contract for every job is the ideal situation. Not only will this protect you from your customers' whims, but honest businesspeople should consider their customers' protection as well. If there is a dispute, a copy of a signed contract will go a long way toward showing who might be the injured party. It also keeps misunderstandings to a minimum and makes for good customer relations—everyone knows what everyone else is supposed to do.

Spelling out every detail in a contract also allows you to charge additional amounts for add-on work. Often a customer will decide that a further embellishment or more details or additional parts should be added to the job. This is an excellent opportunity to make a change or addendum to the contract, and you should not be shy about telling the customer this. Have the addendum signed so that both of you know without a shadow of a doubt what this extra work will cost and how it will affect the other details previously specified in the contract.

Having everything in writing also helps you plan your workload in advance. Knowing when projects are due simplifies scheduling additional projects, making it easier to know when to turn down work. Home decor projects, bridal gowns and other jobs that are occasion related sometimes seem to come to you in clumps. Knowing that you are already close to overload will allow you to refer business elsewhere or to leave time open for other possibilities, whether work related or for your own social or family calendar.

Using a contract also sets a tone for the relationship you have with your customers. They know from the get-go that this is a business deal and that you are not just a hobbyist. In short, it saves a lot of energy, in communicating both what you expect of the customer and what the customer can expect of you.

What a contract should include

- Basics: This is a statement that says who will do what, by when and for how much. Fully describe what these contingencies are.
- Specifics: Spell out who will provide the materials; who will preshrink them, if necessary; what is expected at fittings; what payment methods are acceptable.
- Fine print items: Address what happens if the customer changes her mind—or her weight (brides are notorious for changing dress sizes).
- Policy sheet: This includes your "rules."

Policy sheet

This is an addendum to the contract that further details your expectations of the customer and what he can expect from you. Have the customer initial each section as you review the information together at your initial meeting.

- When the raw materials need to be delivered
- When the first fitting or measuring is scheduled
- What clothing, shoes, undergarments, etc., are to be worn to the fitting
- How checks or charges are handled (including your policy on bounced checks)
- How payments are to be made and when
- Amount of deposit expected for different types of work
- Suggested calling hours, appointment times
- Cancellation policy
- How missed or late appointments are handled

Like the contract, the policy sheet shows the customer you are a serious businessperson. It reduces the possibility of misunderstandings. However, should any arise, having the customer's initials on the policy sheet should help smooth over any problems. (See a policy sheet example on page 150.)

Show me the money!

Consultation fees

Many dressmakers and tailors charge consultation fees for initial meetings with new clients. This fee is later applied to the cost of any work performed for that customer. This practice helps you to establish from the beginning that your time is worth money, and the customer is less likely to waste valuable minutes for you. If you're like Kim Lawrence, who likes to chat with her drapery customers, it will also keep you from wasting your own time!

Joyce Murphy

JSM Tailors
Bainbridge Island, Washington

Joyce Murphy

For nearly twenty years, Joyce Murphy has been tailoring designs and altering tailored apparel. After creating career wear from her home for four years, Joyce moved to her current shop in 1985. She sold made-to-measure suits for eight years and employed an in-house wardrobe consultant. "I kept looking for ways to provide career wear for women and had hoped to work into the custom area," she explains, "but I don't like not being paid for the time to shop for fabrics, and now I've stopped making custom, as well as the made-to-measure. The business wasn't growing on its own because of the dress-down trend of the nineties. I would have had to beat the bushes for business, and it wasn't something I wanted to do."

Now Joyce focuses on alterations and tailoring. She has spent a lot of time revising her price list and making it work best for her business. She does show this to her customers if they want to see it. It gives her a backup, and since the list looks quite official, it offers credibility to her pricing structure. Prices reflect the different methods required, especially the variances between men's and women's alterations techniques.

"At Seattle Central Community College, I took classes for my apparel design degree from a tailor." Joyce says, "I use that course more than anything else I took; it was extremely beneficial." There are standard ways of altering certain types of garments in menswear, and Joyce says many people aren't aware of them. "I think there's a real need for this level of understanding tailoring." She notes, alterations done in this manner turn out better, and use simpler, more cost efficient methods. But most dressmakers who have a home sewing background aren't aware of these techniques. Joyce feels that the ability to do alterations helps anyone doing custom work to fit better. The difference between the professional and the amateur is that the professional follows through on the garment, taking the extra time to make it fit properly.

Owning a storefront allows Joyce to lend a helping hand to the other sewing pros in her small island community in Puget Sound. Joyce hires others from the area to work in her shop and showcases local talent in her shop's window. "I feel the impor-

tance of providing serious part-time work for talented employees," she says. "Not everyone wants the responsibility or time commitment of owning a shop. In a time of corporate downsizing, one of my goals is to 'upsize' sewing businesses." As part of JSM Tailors, these part-time employees are on-site for referrals when customers ask for work that Joyce doesn't do. Paula Shelkin, who works for Joyce three seven-hour days a week, says she gets about 80 percent of her home decor business as referrals through JSM.

Joyce has set up a payment system that allows the employees to share in the income from the pieces they alter. "Every alteration requires both fitting and sewing, so I pay employees 42 percent for the sewing done, 14 percent for the fitting. That adds up to 56 percent, and there's another 5 to 6 percent in payroll taxes, so we're up to about 60 percent." And, she adds, "There's another amount of cost in zippers, thread and other parts and pieces that go out the door with the garment, about 5 percent. This is all added into the cost of goods. So my gross profit margin is about 35 percent," which is what she aims for. Joyce also points out, "With increased volume, I pay slightly more, because the basic costs don't go up. I pay a quarterly bonus based on the percentage of sewing work done by each person."

Joyce enlists the help of her employees to make her business profitable, in a system sometimes known as MBO—Management by Objectives. She also runs her business in an open book accounting method; the employees all know how the company is doing every month, and everyone strives to help maintain a healthy profit picture for the business. Joyce pays herself an administrative wage to make up for the training she gives the employees and the bookwork she must do to keep the business running.

Joyce does get help doing the payroll forms, but other than that she does everything herself in a Lotus 1-2-3 spreadsheet and pays bills with Intuit QuickBooks. She says, "I do a profit and loss statement with the help of these programs so I know how my business is doing. You have to under-stand the bookkeeping part, otherwise how can you track your progress?"

Joyce adds, "Specializing in one or two things makes it much easier because then each business has its own slot for expenses, etc. From a bookkeeping standpoint, it's much easier to run a singularly focused business. You understand what you're doing, and can make it better." The same applies to your specific jobs. She explains, "If I'm hemming jackets and I get them five days a week, I'm going to get faster at it. If I see one a month, it isn't quite the same. We do want to see variety, though, to keep our interest."

Deposits

When you take on a job, it is wise to get a deposit before starting the work. Kateri Ellison, like many dressmakers, never begins new work without a 30 percent deposit. In some specialties it may be necessary to charge 50 percent to start a new job, especially if the work requires special equipment. Rule of thumb: Specify in the contract how and by whom the up-front expenses will be covered, especially fabric costs to you. All deposit provisions should be negotiated and spelled out in the contract.

Final payment methods

Never release work without a final payment; as Julie Davis's contract story so painfully illustrates, you may never be paid for the job. Sometimes buyer's remorse sets in and your customer is reluctant to pay for what may have been an impulse purchase he couldn't afford. Special-occasion garments are notoriously subject to nonpayment, especially after the big event is over. Or a spouse finds out how much something cost and forbids payment. This is a touchy situation; you deserve to be paid for your work, and you have no control over the client's marital or domestic situation. In cases like this, contracts are your only way of proving you are owed the money.

Many brides are so preoccupied with the flurry of getting ready to be married that they forget they have closed their checking accounts. It is unwise to take a check from a bride the day before her wedding!

If you never release work without payment and always require a deposit up front, you will only lose the profit part of the payment. This isn't an optimal situation but is better than not being paid at all.

Final payment options

- Payment by check one week before release of work (or however long it takes checks to clear with your bank)
- Money order or cash, then release
- Check payment, then release
- Credit card payment, then release

In the case of a bounced check, you should definitely pass on the fee to the customer. Your bank charges you for this, and you shouldn't have to absorb that cost just because the client is a lousy money manager. Find out what the fee is, and post a sign that says "Returned check fee: $XX." (Many banks now charge as much as $40 per check.) Add this same wording to your contract, in the fine print area.

Credit cards

In the case of a large installation for window treatments, it may be necessary to ask for final payment at installation. In this industry and for other specialties with large financial outlay by the client, access to merchant credit card services is beneficial. Check with your bank to see if such a service is available to your business.

Most banks require a business to show them some sort of track record indicating sales strength before they commit to issuing a credit card service. Be prepared to show financial records of at least one year; some banks require two years' information. To ensure payment of the costs involved, banks require companies with credit card services to set up accounts in those same financial institutions. These may be merely DBA, or Doing Business As, accounts, which are lower-cost checking accounts that normally don't pay any interest on the balance. Because true business checking accounts can be costly, this is an economical option for a small business. The credit card costs are then transferred directly from the account; and the transaction deposits, directly to the account. Because there is no waiting for the deposit to clear, the businessperson has the money in the account within twenty-four hours of when the deposit is made.

Protect yourself

If you follow all the steps I've described, your chances of success will be greater than if you run your business haphazardly. For businesses that begin slowly, these procedures are sometimes difficult to segue into, but the rewards are great for taking the time to put these precautions into place. There may still be times when you are forced to consider a customer's account a dead loss. In such a case, remember you can take the amount as a business loss deduction. Ask your accountant how this should be handled.

Also, sometimes it just isn't worth fighting for a few dollars. The lesson learned may be worth the money lost, in the long run. As Julie Davis says, "I learned many things from my experience. I look at this as a lesson I couldn't have gotten anywhere else." There are very few classes in sewing business management, and though experience can be a painful teacher, here's an optimistic thought: Experience can also offer a relatively inexpensive education.

CHAPTER 6

The Business Plan

Having a plan is always a good idea, whether you're plotting out your future business or just going on a picnic. Consider the consequences of beginning a trip without consulting a map: Who knows where you'd end up? The same is true of a business: Unless you have some idea of your objectives, your energy will be too scattered to accomplish your full potential.

In a start-up business, having a plan can make an enormous difference in how quickly the business fulfills the owner's goals. However, even existing businesses benefit from a business plan. Taking stock is a good thing to do, especially if the business seems to be stagnant, or if profit is low, or if the owner is so busy working she doesn't seem to have any other life. Developing a business plan forces a redirection of energy, one way or the other.

What is a business plan?

Despite the official-sounding name, a business plan is nothing more than a list of actions. Call it an action plan, if that sounds friendlier. This plan outlines all the steps needed to get a business going and to keep it running smoothly. It spells out the goals of the business owner and affords a "track to run on," or a road map for the business. It helps keep the owner from wasting time and energy doing anything that won't move the business forward.

Your business plan should provide, in whatever form you desire, a list of priorities and plans for your business future.

Action list

This list details the first things that need to be determined.

Where will the business be located?

- Are there any local zoning problems? If so, can anything be done to change them?
- What changes to that location need to be made?
- If the business will be in your home, does this mean some remodeling should be done?
- Is the location convenient for customers, if they will come to you?
- If the business will be in a "street" location, is one available? What kind of lease is required, and do you need to hire an attorney or real estate agent to help with this?
- Is any furniture needed to create a comfortable work environment?

Is your skill level up-to-date?

- If not, what needs to be done to get up to speed? Classes, or an apprenticeship? Where can these be obtained?
- What do you know about the specialty you picked? Will networking with other professionals help?

What kind of help will you need?

- If your business needs additional employees, are there possible candidates in your community, or will you need to train people?
- Will you need professional help, such as an accountant, lawyer or other specialist? Where can this be obtained?
- Is there an SBA office in town that can provide additional business assistance?

What kind of licenses or permits are required?

What state and local ordinances and laws do you need more information about?

- What is the current information about sales taxes, income taxes and any additional requirements, such as labeling laws, in your area?

What equipment do you need?

- Can it be obtained locally, or do you need to find other sources?

- Can this machinery or equipment be serviced easily, or do you need expert service? Where can this service be found?
- What kind of supplies do you need for this equipment? Where can they be obtained?

What office supplies do you need?

- Can these be obtained locally, or is a mail-order source needed?
- How about business cards and stationery? Will a simple design suffice, or would you like to hire someone to design a logo and use more interesting paper supplies? Whom will you hire?
- How will you handle paperwork? Can you get by with boilerplate forms, or will you create them from a computer program? Do you have a computer, and do you know how to use the program?

These are just suggestions to get you started; it's important to carefully evaluate your own needs and adjust your action list accordingly.

Your business time line

Decide when everything on your list needs to be completed. This doesn't have to be a hard-and-fast date unless you want it to be, but it helps to have some kind of target. If you never make a goal, you won't ever complete all the tasks.

The simple act of committing a date to paper helps to establish it in your mind. It's surprising how powerful this action is. Try it and see how it works for you.

Business specialty: Who are you?

As discussed in chapter two, having a specialty defines your business. It keeps you from wasting time and energy doing anything that doesn't forward the goals of your specialty.

Also, when you have a specialty it makes it simple to know what to list on a business card. This is helpful when you're getting started; every card and every marketing device will say who and what you are, right from the beginning.

What's your name?

It's all in a name, and your business name should give a clue as to what your business is about. Even something as simple as "Mary's Tailoring" is sufficient, as long as it tells what you do. A good name defines your business, just as a specialty does, and eliminates time-wasting phone calls.

It amazes me how many different ways there are to cleverly use the word *sew* in a business name. However, there is a limit to possible combinations, and someone else may already be using an idea that comes to you in a dream some night. Most states allow you to register your business name so there won't be more than one business with the same name; some states allow you to use your own name without registering, as in "Karen Maslowski School of Sewing." Contact the local SBA office for information on what the laws require in your area.

Your target market

If you have chosen a specialty or a couple of areas in which to specialize, it's easy to figure out who your target market is. If you've chosen to make wedding gowns, you already know that parents of young children will be less likely to need your services than will college-age women or younger businesswomen. However, a less likely, but probably beneficial, place to advertise custom bridal work is in a community of older, more settled people: They often have daughters and granddaughters who may need your services. (See chapter nine for more information on advertising and marketing.)

Knowing who your target market is helps to further focus your attention on that group of individuals. Get to know them and their needs, and offer them solutions to those needs.

How to reach that target market

Once you know who you want to reach, determine where to find them. This is not always easy, and sometimes takes a little detective work on your part. Include in the action plan how you intend to get your message to these potential customers.

How (and what) to charge

These are two different things—how to charge may actually be more important. Review the pricing methods described in chapter six. Decide which you will use and how much you need to charge to make a profit. Include the whole gamut of pricing situations in your action plan.

Where to get supplies

What supplies are available wholesale, and which do you need to make arrangements to purchase locally with a discount? Try to have this information written in your business plan.

Equipment needs

Is your current equipment sufficient for your business, or will you need to expand in the near future? If you need more equipment, where can you get it, how much does it cost and who will service it? Estimate how long it will be before the business can afford to make such a purchase.

Expansion plans

What will this business look like in six months?

- How do you think you want to do business in the future?
- Do you always want to do the same thing, or would you like your business to evolve somehow?
- What kind of income do you want in six months? Do you hope to break even by then? Write it down; it won't become reality unless you have a plan.

Future plans

Where do you want to be in one year, five years, ten years? Maybe you would like to be on the beach in Cancun. Who wouldn't! But maybe you'd like to have a staff in a few years so you can still have the business *and* take a vacation periodically. Would you hope to have a specific annual income at a certain future date? This is the time to plan for it and write it down.

Do you have a finite plan, to accommodate a particular life goal? Perhaps you only want your business to continue until a certain date or event.

- The kids are in school or in college or still at home.
- Your spouse retires.
- You get divorced or married.
- Your house is paid off.
- You win the lottery!
- You _____ (fill in the blank).

Plan for personal and business growth

This is very important: Be sure to include plans for your own development. Whether you want to take classes to improve your skills or join support groups, be sure to accommodate these interests. And don't forget to make time for social activities. Remember, all work and no play made Jill a very dull girl.

That's it, that's all there is to a business plan. Just because it's on paper doesn't mean it's set in stone, however. You can always change your mind—it's *your* business! But for now, this is your plan. Review it periodically, as your goals and business needs change.

Catherine Bennett

Carina
Kirkland, Washington

Catherine Bennett

In late 1992, after a sixteen-year career in interior design, Catherine Bennett initiated her custom design line, Carina, in her home in Kirkland, Washington. Her plan was to provide the type of clothing she herself had trouble finding: well-fitting, smart, career wear of natural fibers, coordinated in groupings of pants, skirts, jackets and blouses. Bennett had a lifelong interest in sewing for herself, and she had taken classes in fashion design in the late 1980s, including some patternmaking courses. She thought she could make this type of clothing for fellow professionals and they would fit everybody.

Word-of-mouth referrals from her colleagues from interior design brought in the first trickle of clientele. Then her first big break came in February 1993, when a feature article about her new business was published in the "Scene" section of *The Seattle Times*. Customers from these two kinds of referrals made up her core clientele. "The news articles were most successful as far as marketing—this is the kind of advertising you can't buy," Catherine says. "Fashion shows weren't as good for me; the ones I did were too expensive to put on, with space rental, guest speakers, refreshments, invitations, programs and the expense of creating two dozen garments. Some shows ended up netting nothing at all." Another good way to bring in business was sending brochures out to names from a mailing list she purchased. This list included women in the vicinity who made under $100,000 a year. At $1 a brochure, plus mailing costs and the expense of the list, this was less expensive than other types of advertising, although still pricey.

As to the division of labor, Catherine created the designs, then hired a patternmaker to correct the fit, fine-tune the patterns, then grade for different sizes, usually from size 2 to size 12. Catherine also did some of the patternmaking, sewed, supervised, cleaned, serviced machines, did the marketing and made the sales. In addition, she also purchased fabric for the line each season. There were usually three to four other employees who assisted with production and other tasks. Catherine's husband, Dan, did the paperwork for the business, including payroll. "I paid my employees quite well,

and they were all excellent. If I had it to do over again, though, I wouldn't have employees," she now says. "It was expensive, and I had to constantly work to keep them busy. It was insane."

In fact, Catherine admits she made many mistakes, and she hopes her story helps others who want to produce clothing. Although she had been self-employed previously, she realizes now that she didn't have the right kind of business experience to make the business successful, and it has taken her several years to learn hard lessons about developing a line vs. making custom clothing. "I thought it would be easier than it is. You don't need formal education, but you do need to know more than I did," says Catherine. "Our customers, like everyone, had lots of fitting problems, and each garment had to have a custom pattern. Contrary to what I originally thought," she recalls, "every fabrication required a new pattern, because different fabrics had to be fit differently. It took about eight to ten hours to develop a pattern, then make a muslin and then do the fitting. It was hard to get enough for a custom garment to cover those costs." Although Catherine had a stated pricing policy, it was not adhered to, and she admits, "This was a mistake—it cost me money as well. We couldn't price our line high enough to cover these costs—fitting time and client contact alone took from three to five hours. My jackets were around $500 to $700 apiece, but this wasn't enough for the quality of workmanship, and the time and care spent in making the garments fit." Some customers thought Carina's prices were too high, saying there wasn't a designer label. Catherine says, "It made no difference that my garments were equally well made, one-of-a-kind and custom fitted. Not only that, but they were made in the U.S., by hourly employees." It was difficult for Catherine, an admittedly poor self-promoter, to overcome customers' objections (see chapter six) and educate them to see the benefit in buying from her, as opposed to buying goods made overseas with exploited labor.

Other mistakes Catherine feels she made: purchasing too much fabric (she still had $15,000 of fabric in inventory at the beginning of 1997); hiring a rep who didn't have Catherine's best interests at heart; and having her business in her home. As she points out, "There's no walk-in traffic in a residential area; your customers have to plan to be at the studio. I had no way of getting accidental business."

Catherine offers this advice: "Don't fly blind like I did. Do your homework; talk to other designers and other people who are doing similar things. Make a plan." She also feels there isn't anything wrong with hard work, but you do have to eventually get a reward for it.

CHAPTER 7

Financing the Business

Any business needs money to start with, if only to pay for a few supplies. How to find this money depends on how much you need, plus a variety of other factors.

First, determine what your needs are, based on the decisions made while creating a business plan. Then use the following methods to decide how to accumulate the capital to get started.

Financing a business

There are two ways to finance a business: with your own money or with someone else's money. How much capital is needed and how much is on hand will have as much bearing on this decision as anything else.

Bootstrapping, or "baby steps" method

A common term in small business circles, "bootstrapping" refers to using whatever resources are on hand to make the business grow, then pouring any profits back into the business. What are the advantages of doing this? First of all, there's no need to go through any formal loan proceedings. If you began the business to add a little extra income to the family, the added burden of debt is generally not desirable. It may also be the only option, if your credit record is less than sterling.

When I started my sewing school in 1987, I used a small nest egg I had accumulated. This allowed me to invest in sewing machines and even to remodel the part of the house where the school was to be. I didn't have to pay anyone back but myself, which I did within a few short months. I used new income to purchase additional supplies and equipment and to beef up the minimal initial advertising my meager budget allowed. This method worked well for me; I didn't want to grow quickly. Too many students at once would have been too overwhelming; this slow beginning gave me a chance to figure out the best way to run the school.

With this method, new equipment and other upgrade decisions are made based on what kind of income the business is getting. The use of existing equipment and supplies pays for new purchases. If business is slow, it may take longer than planned to achieve all of the acquisition goals you have. It may mean your business grows even more slowly, without the added push a yellow pages ad or a faster industrial machine might provide.

Many people in sewing businesses get their start this way, with a minimum outlay of start-up capital. The advantages are many: No loan to pay back; the business can use the machines and other equipment already owned; and there is less pressure to immediately make lots of income. There is a disadvantage, however: If your business idea is so hot that it takes off right away, you could be facing an immediate crisis not being fully operational from the beginning. As you work on your business plan, decide whether or not this is something that will give you trouble.

Financing, or the "giant leap" method

One of the major causes of business failure is lack of capital, not only for start-up, but for covering day-to-day expenses. When a business is financed from day one, it gets a head start at success. From the first day, the owner has the money to pay for advertising, new and up-to-date equipment and a business phone line.

A danger of financing is that the business may take a long time to succeed, and the intensity of the need to make a loan payment each month may be more pressure than you want to accept. Having the business start out "in the hole" financially sometimes makes a difficult obstacle to overcome.

Also, the learning curve of new equipment and methods may counteract any benefit of starting out so well equipped, unless you can get training first. If after you have worked for awhile you decide you don't like the business, you could be stuck with unneeded equipment plus debt that isn't paying for itself. Think this through carefully before considering financing.

If you decide you need to have more capital than your own reserves can provide, dust off that business plan and head over to your local bank to arrange financing. Be sure this version of your plan is typed and legible. Your banker can tell you whether or not he needs any further information.

One thing he will probably want to know is how much income you project each year for the next five years or so. The bank will also want to know the particulars of your personal finances: how much money you owe for loans; the amounts of mortgage and equity on your home; estimated monthly bills; and any financial assets you own, including life insurance, retirement accounts, investments and personal property.

An alternative to bank financing is that old standby: Mom or Dad. Borrowing from a family member is a time-honored tradition, but tread carefully in this mine-filled territory. Be conscientious: Use a written contract and be ultracareful to make the payments you say you'll make. And be prepared to accept unsolicited advice: It's an unwritten law that anytime you ask parents for money, you automatically invite their interest in your life. If you don't take advantage of them, hopefully, they will return the favor.

How to decide which method of start-up to use

Questions to ask yourself:

- How much of a risk taker are you?
- How strong is your market?
- How refined are your skills; will there be a period of learning?
- How much stamina do you have, both for the work and for the concept?

How much of a risk taker are you?

A typical entrepreneur profile seems to indicate a penchant for risk taking, but that's not always the case. Many business owners would prefer to plod along and keep the money they make without taking any kind of scary gambles. Others prefer the thrill of taking an idea, throwing caution to the wind and building it into a fabulous empire. Perhaps you fall somewhere in between these extremes.

My husband, Steve, also has his own business. He's a conservative person, hates to spend large amounts of money and refuses to have any kind of installment debt. It just makes him too uncomfortable to think it might not be paid. I, on the other hand, sometimes like to plunge right in with ideas and tend to look less at the bottom line than at my visions of success. Naturally, our styles clash occasionally. Steve would prefer that I didn't spend so much money up front sometimes, and I have encouraged him to deliberate a little less about major equipment purchases that would pay for themselves in better time efficiency and higher-quality output. And I make sure I have enough cash to purchase any new equipment or service for my business. Talking about this over the years has benefited both of us: We each have a more balanced risk-taking profile as a result of the other's influence.

You have to decide your own level of tolerance of installment debt, which can be critical in any business. Consider other alternatives if it would be too uncomfortable for you to finance your sewing business. Perhaps you could sell an investment or other property, trim certain expenses or scale back your plans somewhat.

How strong is your market?

Again, if the market is there for your product or service, and if waiting until you have the money saved could cause you to lose a timing advantage, financing would probably be a good idea for your new business.

On the other hand, if you're not sure whether your heirloom christening gowns will be an immediate hit, a slower start is probably a safer business bet.

How refined are your skills?

If there will be a period of learning, you might want to operate such a business part-time for awhile, until you're more comfortable with the process. The computerized embroidery business is a good example. According to a professional embroiderer, there is a high potential even for experienced machine operators to damage embroidered garments. Learning to use the machines could mean a big difference to the profit picture of a commercial embroiderer. Also, having designs digitized for embroidery can be costly; learning to do this service yourself could also shave costs.

How much stamina do you have?

What kind of staying power do you have? Can you sustain your interest in this idea long enough to pay off a loan? Will the work entertain and interest you that long? Or will you be bored with it, but stuck with a seemingly endless string of payments?

Hiring professional help

When you are setting up the books for your business, you can ask your accountant for advice on financing. An accountant can also help you refine your business plan so it conforms to any guidelines your lending institution may prescribe.

Partnerships

If you decide to start a business with a partner, be sure to consult both an accountant and an attorney. Under no circumstances, even if the other person is your best friend or close relative (perhaps especially in those cases), enter into a partnership without formal partnership documents. Many lawyers go as far as counseling their clients to never enter into a partnership. Some professional advisors suggest incorporating as a way of limiting potential problems, as well as personal liability.

Liability

Most small sewing or craft businesses work best as sole proprietorships. Unless your product line has a liability exposure or you have several employees, incorporation is probably unnecessary. Examples of products that might require protection from liability suits are baby carriers, some types of toys, protective garments (for firefighters, police officers or auto racers, for example) and parachutes. This is by no means every possible product with exposure to product liability lawsuits. Consider how your product will be used, and make sure your professional advisors, including insurance agents, know of any pitfalls related to your product's use. Be sure to have adequate insurance—and be aware in advance that such high-risk coverage can be costly.

Kitty Stein

Workroom Concepts
Clearbrook, Virginia

Kitty Stein

Kitty Stein began her career in a department store that made draperies and slipcovers in its home fashions department. She was there for two years and realized there was no chance of advancement. She was bored sewing only drapes, so Kitty began making window treatments from her home for another designer.

"At the time, 1978, I didn't think of this as a 'business'; I thought it was fun, and I could make some money sewing. The designer taught me quite a bit; she had had a workroom for some time, and already had a price list," says Kitty.

"After about a year or so, she suggested I hire someone else to help out. I put an ad in the paper and hired someone. The day Nancy came to work for me," Kitty says, "it occurred to me that I should check with my attorney to see if my home was zoned for employees. He said it wasn't, so I fired her the same day she started working." After that, Kitty's attorney arranged it so both Kitty and Nancy operated businesses from Kitty's home, and the customers paid them each directly. "Sounds good," says Kitty, "except I wasn't smart enough to make any money from the situation. I was training her, and she was getting the benefit of everything I knew, but I didn't get reimbursed for my part in bringing her work. It didn't dawn on me that I should get a little more for training, and my attorney assumed I knew to do so."

Things changed in 1980 when Nancy and Kitty became partners. "We had industrial sewing machines and a lot of other equipment, all in an 11′×16′ room," recalls Kitty. "We bought all the equipment the salesman told us we needed; he told us we could make all kinds of money because the equipment would increase our production." The salesman was right, but soon the partners worked themselves out of jobs and had to implement marketing strategies and canvass for new customers. This was something they really didn't want to do or know how to do. Retailing to individuals was not their intended focus.

"One of the best things we did was to have a professional brochure made, describing our services; it gave us something to hand to potential clients. We went to the Washington, DC, area and walked into businesses, literally knocking on doors." As Kitty tells it, "I remember walking into a

fabric store, hiding behind bolts of fabric and arguing about who *had* to go talk to this person. We didn't know what we were doing; it's hysterical to look back on it now and remember this. We actually walked out of some of them with work, and I have no idea how we did that!"

Business did start to come in regularly, and the two decided to move into a store. "Again, we didn't consult with any of our consultants; we just told them after the fact." Kitty says, "Our accountant about had heart failure. He said we didn't have enough income yet." But the partners thought the price was right and rented a 6,000-square-foot store. Since it was more space than they needed, they set up part of it as retail space and hired decorators. "We had no experience hiring, so we hired everyone who applied," which could have been costly, but, Kitty says, "Fortunately, we were paying them on commission, so we didn't have to pay them unless they sold. However, we didn't know how to sell, so we couldn't teach them how to sell. To actually get Mrs. Jones to sign on the dotted line was harder than just handing over what she came in for."

Nancy handled the retail business, and Kitty managed the wholesale business. Though, according to Kitty, "Neither of us had any business managing. We were sewing at first, and eventually we hired as many as four seamstresses. That was a problem. We both got into the business because we loved to sew, but with all our responsibilities we didn't have time to sew anymore."

By the end of 1990, both of them were weary. "Nancy was tired of the employee problems that had begun to spring up with a couple of our decorators, and I was tired of the whole thing," says Kitty. "We decided to close the business, rather than to sell it. Nancy kept the van, and she has her own installation business now. I kept the equipment, and did work for designers from my home."

At this point, Kitty was hoping to share her business experiences by writing about them. "I spoke to the editor at *Draperies and Window Coverings* magazine, who asked me to send them a proposal. I sent it, along with ideas for about six articles, and they said 'write it.' They haven't told me to stop, so I'm still doing it," she says. "I write about the kind of information I wish I'd had, and I hope it helps others from making the kinds of mistakes we made." Kitty also presents seminars for the magazine and consults with people setting up window treatment businesses. She developed a packet of forms for photocopying for drapery workrooms. These forms can help workrooms with ordering, measuring, pricing and many other day-to-day operations. Kitty also writes a regular column for *SewWHAT?*, a newsletter for drapery workrooms, and she is a regular contributor to DraperyPros, an e-mail list with a weekly

online chat (see the appendix for more information).

Kitty's advice to those interested in succeeding in a sewing business: "Research what you want to do. Be prepared, businesswise, for the roadblocks, because they're going to be there." She emphasizes, "Educate yourself, so you're prepared for it. If you have employees, you especially need more information. And when you learn something, be willing to share with others. It will make the road easier for someone else, and will make us all more successful." You need to realize you're in a business, and that you are selling something. Kitty knows now that you can't expect to learn everything at once; the education process is ongoing.

Kitty feels the most important step toward success is to plan ahead. "Make time to plan; know where you want to go. Don't just let your business take you wherever." She says, "If you don't know where you want to go, you won't know what kind of education you need to get there." Kitty says she made goals for each upcoming year, then didn't think about them again until the following year. "I did part of it, but didn't take it far enough. You need to lay out all the steps it will take to get to your goal. If you don't get focused, you don't get real good at one thing, or a couple of things. And you won't get the reputation you need to further your business."

CHAPTER 8

Advertising and Marketing

"There's a difference between *work* and *business*," says Karen Howland. "Business leads to more business. Work, on the other hand, just keeps you away from business." In other words, work that will not further your business goals is undesirable. Business not only takes you farther on the road to success, but it keeps coming back to you in other ways. When you have good clients, they continue to bring even more business to you.

How do you get business, as opposed to work? Never lose sight of your goals, keep them firm in your mind and focus everything you do on that vision. It's just that simple. If you learn the basic tools for effective advertising and marketing, success will come to you faster.

Focus, focus, focus

You already know what your specialty or specialties are. Now your job is to determine how best to reach the customers who want you to provide those services.

Obviously, if you make couture custom bridal gowns, setting out your business cards at the local sports bar or restaurant is going to net little return. However, if one of your services is sewing tackle twill on team jackets, that is a great way to get the word out about your business. Sponsoring a kids' soccer team could be a terrific use of your advertising dollars. For bridal experts, having a booth at the annual bridal show would be a much better use of your money, netting customers you might not have access to otherwise.

Tell everyone about your business

When beginning a business, it's a good idea to let everyone know what you are doing. Wait, however, until your plans are ready to be put into action; it dissipates your energy to tell others too soon. Sometimes significant others are threatened by your dreams; in cases like this, it is often better to present an accomplished feat, rather than a pie in the sky plan for "someday."

Regardless of what you do, everyone knows someone who needs, or will need, your service someday. From the beginning, set up a way to reward and thank anyone who sends referrals your way. There are pre-printed thank-you cards with slots for business cards—this is a gracious way to show your gratitude. Include a card or two for your friend to pass along another time. Always say thank you, no matter how small the job that results from the referral. As a former boss always said, "You can't thank someone too often."

Learn, too, to ask for referrals from your satisfied clients. Some dressmaking customers are reluctant to refer their friends to their custom clothier. If you find this to be true, gently remind them that you need a certain number of good customers to stay in business. It is actually in their best interest that they send other people in need of your services to your studio. A steady clientele helps to even out the normal cycle of demand, too, and will help keep you from getting busy with other kinds of work in those slow times.

And remember: One satisfied customer will tell three people about the service you provided. One unhappy client will tell twenty others about the poor treatment he received from you. Always treat your customers as you would like them to portray you to their friends.

A word about specializing

Many sewing business owners find that after their initial marketing push they don't need to advertise further. In some communities certain specialties are in such demand that there is little need to do much more than put a sign out front that says what you do. Your market research lays the foundation for this kind of success; if you have identified a market no one else is serving, you may find instant success.

Inexpensive advertising

Business cards

A box of business cards is just about the least expensive advertising you can purchase. However, they won't help you if you leave them in the box.

Double-sided business card

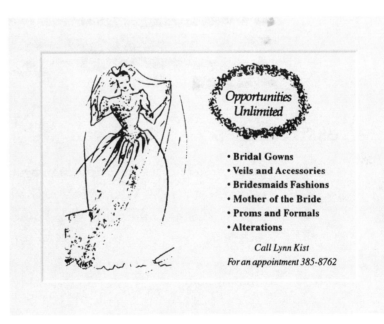

Invitation-style business card

Give them to everyone, even if the people you're handing them to don't seem likely to become customers. People tend to keep business cards, and

115

they often pass them on to others. Also, restaurants, dry cleaners and other local businesses may have someplace to post your business card. Be careful about this, however; if your business card has your address on it, decide whether or not it is safe to leave your card out for anyone to see. You may want to design your card to have only your name and business name, a phone number and the words *By appointment only.*

Creativity counts in creative businesses. One of my favorite business cards sports a gold embossed needle with an actual golden thread dangling from its eye. Dee McCarthy has another cleverly designed card; it is double-sided, advertising two different specialties, in different but related color schemes. One retail and custom bridal shop uses a business card that resembles a wedding invitation.

Bulletins

An inexpensive and relatively effective way to advertise many kinds of sewing businesses is through church and school bulletins. Your community offers many such opportunities. While waiting for church to begin, or while thumbing through a school program at intermission, readers are a captive audience. Make your ad eye-catching enough that it isn't passed over; give the readers an amusing or interesting diversion from their boredom.

Press releases

Send press releases to your local newspapers announcing the opening of your new business. Whenever you change your business in any way, send a press release to the business editor or the fashion editor of the paper, whichever is more appropriate. This is most effective when the local paper is small, or if your community has weekly newspapers. Smaller papers are more willing to report news of this nature.

Flyers

Flyers are great to let potential customers know about your business. Kim Lawrence, who lives near Williamsburg, left colorful flyers about her window treatment business in the news boxes of newer suburban homes. She chose to target an area of more affluent homeowners, who could afford to have custom treatments made for their newer homes. Note: If you decide to distribute flyers, do not leave them in mailboxes. In the United States, this is a federal offense—the interior of a mailbox is considered government property. Doorknob hangers also work well, and blank, computer printable hangers are available from paper companies and office supply stores.

If you choose to mail flyers, pick the recipients judiciously, and don't waste time or money sending flyers to people who have no need for your services. While mailings used to be fairly cheap, today's costs are considerably higher. At three stamps for a dollar plus copy costs, mailing can be more expensive than other ways of promoting your business, depending on how much return you expect.

Test your mailing piece for its effectiveness before committing to a large mailing. Ask everyone who calls you for business where they found out about your services, and keep a record of their answers. Also, consider sending out mail promotions a few at a time. Unless you qualify for a second-class bulk mailing permit, it makes more sense to spread out the work, the expense and the results. If you work alone, it might be best to bring in business a little at a time, rather than to be swamped with new customers all at once. People move occasionally; if you plan to use a mailing list more than once, be sure to record any changes in address.

Newsletters

Newsletters can be a terrific way of building certain types of businesses. For instance, drapery workroom owners who send out monthly newsletters with decorating ideas can spur their customers to add to their existing decor. Sewing teachers can let their students and prospective students know about new classes being offered. Wearable artists and crafters can send out periodic newsletters to tell past customers where the artist's next craft show will be. This is an excellent way to boost business for shows; selling to someone you've already sold to is much easier than breaking new ground. This is especially effective if you have garments or decorative pieces that go with or coordinate with things these customers have already bought from you.

Classified ads

Classified ads work better than display ads, for the amount of money that is spent. Use display ads later, when your business is able to pay for them. Classified ads are less costly, by far, and offer a better return on your dollar when your business is new.

Signs

Signs in public places work in certain situations but not others. When you're just getting started, it is helpful to let as many people as possible know what you're doing, but some business isn't worth getting. First, consider your personal safety. Do you want just anyone calling you? If not, the signboard at the grocery store may not be the best place to advertise. Or simply word the sign carefully to reflect a phone number and your specialty only. In some smaller communities, this isn't a problem, but if you live in a large, impersonal city, do be careful. A sign advertising sewing classes at the neighborhood fabric store doesn't need anything but your name and a telephone number.

Specialty advertising

Certain specialties have unique advertising and marketing possibilities. Targeting your efforts to get your business known makes sense.

Alterations

Contact dry cleaners, ready-to-wear stores, bridal stores and tuxedo rental stores. If you don't do any custom sewing and another sewing professional does no alterations, consider sharing business with that person, referring one another to clients who ask for services you don't provide.

Custom clothing

Contact ready-to-wear stores, bridal stores and fabric stores. Press releases to local newspapers help spark business. Consider writing a column for one of the community papers—a column on wedding tips, for instance, or coordinating clothing. Many custom clothiers also do color and wardrobe consulting. This is a wonderful way to introduce yourself to business-people, who have more need for well-fitting, good-looking clothing. Share marketing efforts with another compatible business in your area. If you do tailoring, consider sharing mailing costs with someone who does only alterations. Send out coupons for small discounts to members of the local Chamber of Commerce, for instance.

A note about marketing through fabric stores: This is a good way to get started, but you may not want to continue to get customers this way once your business is established. Fabric store customers tend to be in search of bargains, and in general, custom sewing should cost *more* than ready-to-wear, not less.

Bridal

Many bridal designers began by doing one wedding for a friend, and some have grown their businesses by making wedding gowns for former bridesmaids for whom they had made gowns. Another way to find customers is to have a relationship with retail bridal stores. For those able to create similar styles in larger sizes, many bridal shops refer customers when they can't provide gowns in the right size. If you specialize in bridal alterations, contact the local bridal store. Bridal consultants are happy to refer their customers to both designers and makers of bridal accessories, such as wedding album covers and rice bags. Be aware that many dressmakers and other sewing pros will not make wedding gowns; this is another reason to network with other professionals.

Window treatments, home decor items

Leave your business cards at fabric stores, especially any store in your area that specializes in home decorating fabrics. If you want to work with interior decorators, make appointments with three or four who do the kind of work you also like to do. Ask for a few minutes of their time, and take a portfolio of your work with you, even if the photos are of drapes or other items you made for your own home. (But don't tell them so, if this is the case!) Painters can also give you referrals, and real estate agents are wonderful contacts for locating new homeowners.

Quilts

If you prefer to make quilts on a commission basis, your local quilt store will be an excellent place to make contacts. Quality workmanship is hard to find, despite the number of quilters. Many hobby quilters only enjoy the piecework aspect of quilting; these people often have piles of finished tops that need hand or machine quilting. Other outlets for finding custom quilt work: antique stores (also a good place to find restoration clients), interior designers, specialty gift shops.

Doll clothing, other hobby specialties

Find out where the local hobbyists meet, and make it a point to join them. Don't be shy about showing samples of your work; if this is your target market, make the most of any association with this group of potential buyers.

Baby items

Leave flyers at pediatricians' offices, day care centers, churches and seniors groups.

Crafts

Craft malls are great places to sell your work, especially if you don't have the time to sit at craft shows for weekends on end. Small booths are rented by the month, and the craft mall management retains a small percentage of the booth's income. This allows the craft producer to test different styles or products and is a great way to get started in part-time manufacturing and sales.

Craft shows reflect varying degrees of professionalism. At the bottom of the heap are table shows at schools and other nonprofit institutions. These venues usually have a small table rental fee, some as low as $15 for two days. With fees like this, your only other costs are for supplies to create the craft items and transportation to and from the show.

Larger craft shows, with much higher fees, are sometimes juried, or judged ahead of time. This ensures the participants that their products won't compete with others that may not be handmade and that several of the booths aren't carrying nearly identical products. It also maintains the quality of the booth offerings. This keeps customers coming back to juried shows, year after year. These shows also have a much higher booth or entrance fee.

If you decide to participate in a juried show, the promoters will want to see slides of your work. Photograph your work (with slide film) against a plain background for better visibility. (For more on selling crafts, see the references in the appendix.)

Specialty products

Many products—parachutes, hot-air balloons, riding clothing, skiwear and kites, for instance—have ready-made sales outlets in the form of specialty magazines and newsletters. If you have writing talents, articles in such publications are an inexpensive way to promote your specialty. Press releases to these magazines are another way to advertise new versions of your product. Send press releases to the editor listed on the masthead at the front of the magazine. Other advertising may also be available, depending on the publication, for true target marketing. If there are trade associations in your field, find out if they accept advertising in their newsletters. For a fairly complete listing of trade associations and industry publications, consult your local library.

Pricier advertising outlets

Display ads

Display ads are among the most expensive of all advertising methods. These ads are the ones you see in newspapers and magazines, anything more than the simple classified ad. When you are just getting started, it is tempting to spend a lot of money on this kind of advertising, but avoid doing so. Unless your service depends heavily on foot traffic, many of the previously described methods will have a stronger impact on your business, without draining your budget. That said, display ads do have their place. For instance, if you have a commercial embroidery business and one of your new products is tied in with a major event in your city, a display ad may generate enough business to pay for the ad and more. Not only that, it could lead to other more lucrative work. If you are announcing a sale, this is another time for a small display ad. Be judicious in planning these, however.

Beth Hodges of Virginia uses display ads to great advantage. Her window treatment business is long established, so she adds photos of jobs she has done to her ads to make them more appealing. Because she lives in a small town with a weekly newspaper, her advertising costs are low, and she has the benefit of more visibility. Readers look for her ad each week and try to guess whose house is being featured.

Marketing to a broader market means display ads in major publications. Many magazines offer discounts for first-time advertisers, and some even offer assistance creating the ad. If you want to inquire about rates, call the number listed under *Advertising* on the magazine's masthead.

Yellow pages ads and listings

Any business on the street, that is, a freestanding shop, should have a yellow pages listing for its phone number. Display ads in the phone book can be expensive, so weigh the need for such expense carefully. If your business depends on customers finding you, look into listings under more than one heading, for example, *Dressmaking, Tailoring, Alterations* and any other related topics. Note: In the past, some phone companies insisted that all businesses, including home-based businesses, have business phone lines (which are more expensive than home lines). Find out what the local service provider requires for your business.

Mass mailings

Mass mailings offer good exposure for some kinds of sewing businesses, especially those with manufactured products, such as specialty stuffed toys, custom furniture covers, kites or other sewn products. Access to a list of some kind will help you target your mailing efforts. Many trade, professional and consumer associations rent the lists of their members and may even proffer them on preprinted labels. A set amount per name, sometimes as little as $.10, is charged, with the understanding that this allows the renter to mail to these names one time only. Very often, dummy names are included in the list as a check to be sure the list isn't abused.

Barbara Shelton's banner for music from the Wizard of Oz

Portfolios

Many types of sewing services are easier to sell if there is some kind of visual sales aid. A portfolio is helpful to bridal, window treatment and other home decor, crafts, dressmaking and many other kinds of businesses.

Barb Shelton of Milford, Ohio, has a bulging portfolio containing hundreds of drum corps banner styles created by her company, Banners by Barbara over the last fifteen years. Schools choosing from existing styles, for which she has already made patterns, save money on their total field banner costs.

When another designer has a new skating client, a flip through her portfolio is often enough to give the skater an idea of how his new costume should look. Photos are great aids for customers who have difficulty articulating what they want—they can merely point to photos that come close to the designs they have in mind. Window treatment photos offer this same advantage in client communication.

In order to create an effective and attractive portfolio, first choose a place to take the photo. Barb Shelton reserves one section of her studio wall as a photographic gallery, and she pins one of each of her original banners there for a portrait before it leaves the shop. If special banners are too large for the wall, they are photographed outdoors against a backdrop of greenery. The background should be as uncluttered as

123

possible, with the focus totally on the item photographed.

In the case of bridal gowns, the best photos are those taken by the professional at the wedding. These are sometimes difficult to get, though. Your relationship with the bride often ends when you turn over the gown, unless you make an extreme effort to keep in touch. Some bridal designers make a point of attending the wedding, if possible, just to take their own pictures. Be sure to clear this with the bride ahead of time.

Professional-looking portfolios can be found at art stores; these make wonderful arty additions to your workplace. Some sewing pros prefer to use smaller photo albums. Home decor specialists, especially, benefit from toting idea books to clients' homes.

Image

Whatever method you choose to promote your business, always be aware that the "medium is the message." In other words, be careful to portray yourself in as businesslike a fashion as possible. A flyer that is no more than a smudged photocopy with lots of typos won't make as good of an impression as one that is well thought out, spell-checked, and copied or printed onto clean, nicely folded paper. The difference in cost is slight; the difference in presentation is massive.

Another image maker or breaker is business stationery. Type the form on a self-correcting electronic typewriter (an inexpensive addition to your office), and photocopy the original; or, better yet, print a new contract or quote each time on your computer (see chapter ten).

Business cards are cheap; some office superstores print one thousand for under $30. Business cards can do double duty as hangtags for many sewn products until you get the capital to purchase your own labels. When you are ready to have labels made, many companies can design and produce them in a variety of quantities, from just one hundred to many thousands. Having your own label sewn into customers' garments adds another value-added quality in their eyes.

CHAPTER 9

Using Computers

Today's homes are more likely to include a personal computer than not. If you have one, consider using it to help make your sewing business more professional, more efficient and more profitable. If you don't have a computer yet, you might decide you want one after you read this chapter!

In the early 1980s, when personal computers were fairly new on the scene, the choices available were limited, not only for computers but also for software and accessories. My first system was ridiculously expensive for what it included: a monochrome (green screen) monitor; a very slow processor; and an enormous, incredibly slow and loud printer. I was pretty excited that I had the luxury of having two floppy drives (5¼-inch at the time), but there was no hard drive. To use my limited software applications, I had to memorize dozens of keyboard combinations. If I needed to print anything, I had to start it just before I went to lunch so I didn't waste all day waiting for one letter to finish printing. All these wonderful features were a rare bargain at $5,000. Yikes.

Things have certainly changed. Now even inexpensive computer systems include all kinds of goodies, and the system is ready to use right out of the box, to streamline your daily work and play activities. Not only that, but the learning curve has been shortened drastically by user-friendly programs that literally teach as you work.

A typical late-1990s system includes a color monitor, a hard drive capable of storing dozens of bookshelves worth of information, a fax modem that can answer the telephone, swift processors capable of performing multiple tasks in moments and CD-ROM drives. Massive programs that once would have required the use of many diskettes are now stored on one CD-ROM, including entire encyclopedias. Not only can you now use the CD-ROM drive to access this information, but you can also play music from your favorite music CDs while you work. By the time you read this book, more incredible advances may have been made; the technology is doubling in less than twelve months at this point.

So what does all this technological wonder have to do with a sewing business? It could have much to do with it, making your business more efficient than you ever dreamed it could be.

"Works" packages

When you buy a new computer, it usually comes preloaded with software of a wide variety, some task oriented and some geared more toward entertainment. If you don't like what you get, it is a simple matter to uninstall one program and install another that you purchase.

There is typically an office suite, or "works," package installed. These packages enable you to perform a variety of office duties: composing letters, proposals, invoices and other written pieces; printing special envelopes; compiling address and other databases; developing spreadsheets (to create your own accounting program, if you desire); tracking appointments; designing newsletters, ads and flyers.

Some of the more common packages you will find: Microsoft Office, Corel WordPerfect, Microsoft Works (which is a less powerful home/office version of Microsoft Office) and Lotus Smart Suite. Any of these packages will help you do nearly everything in this chapter, except faxing, accounting, filling out tax returns and patternmaking.

Business cards and letterhead

With the availability of many new printer-ready papers, almost anyone can create business cards. This is especially handy if you want to have a variety of cards to reflect different aspects of your business. For instance, if you alter bridal gowns and also make lacy doll clothes, you won't necessarily want both your specialties on the same card. Also, if you travel with the doll clothing part of the business, it might be more important to have the area code of your phone number on that card. Suppose you just want to try out a new specialty; the ability to print just a few cards gives you the flexibility to change your mind if things don't work out.

Most sewing businesses do not need the amount of preprinted stationery that comes in a minimum order. Not only do most of the word processing programs allow for making your own letterhead, but you can change it at a whim. Paper supplies represent a large investment if they are printed by a print shop; printing your own saves money, time and space. Moreover, it isn't wasted if information changes because you don't have to purchase a large quantity.

Flyers are easily created on computers, and mailing programs allow for efficient mailings. Using your customer database, you can readily inform your clients of any new and exciting changes in your business. Database labels are a snap to print with today's software and printers.

Policy sheets and price lists created on the computer are not only simpler to print than typed lists, they are also easy to change when it is time to raise prices or make additions. Each printed sheet is an original; no messy photocopies are necessary, nor is a trip to the copy shop. I recommend printing small amounts at a time. This reduces your commitment to prices and policies, as well as saves money on supplies.

Also available are cards to use as thank-you notes, referral cards, reminder cards and other promotional and customer service aids. Create your own logo, and repeat it on all your correspondence and marketing papers.

Develop forms for gathering customer information, then input the data into the computer. This also gives you a "track to run on" when asking questions—with a form to check, you don't forget to ask the right ones. (See appendix for templates for contracts and policy sheets.)

Laser printers are much less expensive than they were even a few years ago (and unheard of before then for home or office use). They make your printed materials look fabulous and can save you hundreds of dollars. And the most important benefit: Using your own professional-quality printer forms brings instant credibility to your business and makes you look like the pro you are!

Bookkeeping, tax records, filing taxes

One of the most compelling reasons for keeping books in the first place is to determine your tax liability at year's end. With this in mind, it makes sense to consider a bookkeeping system that works with a tax-filing package. Today's computer programs offer a variety of flexible systems that work together.

Computer programs like this are simple to understand. Many bookkeeping programs work just like a checkbook: You simply fill in a check on-screen, and the data goes into an electronic "checkbook" file. You can even have checks printed from an ink jet or laser printer. For those who detest writing checks, this is a tremendous time-saver. In addition, the computer never makes addition mistakes, and as long as you keep transactions up-to-date, your checking account balance should be correct.

You can code every transaction that has anything to do with your business. Reports on how much was spent and collected in the business are simple to create. This makes it apparent right away if expenses need to be restrained or if a celebration is in order. Another tremendous benefit to the self-employed in the United States is the ability to see when your required quarterly estimated tax payment needs to be adjusted. Waiting until January to add up all the income and expenses could be a mistake; if you experience terrific income, you may end up owing more than you expected. And with that last quarterly payment due only three weeks after the holidays, that could be a hardship to someone who thought he had lots of extra cash that year.

Need a financial statement for a loan, or for your business plan? Most of the personal accounting programs have a preset financial statement template. Choose this from the menu of options, and a statement is printed immediately. These programs can also serve as training for more complex accounting packages.

In addition to the checking account programs such as Quicken and Microsoft Money, there are also several bookkeeping programs that allow you to create and track invoices, pay bills and even keep track of payroll and inventory. Some of the programs currently on the market include QuickBooks, Peachtree Accounting, M.Y.O.B. (Mind Your Own Business) and One-Write Accounting. In varying degrees of ease of use, these programs offer traditional accounting capabilities.

Most of these accounting programs are capable of keeping track of cost by project. This could be extremely beneficial to your business, especially if you find yourself making unplanned expenditures for jobs that seem to lose money instead of the other way around. Simply code each expense to track which job it belongs to.

Tax packages

With two sole proprietors in my family, our taxes are a little complicated. For years I gave figures to our accountant, who then just filled in our return. Since I had been doing all the work anyway, I tried using one of the tax packages. It cost $40 and the accountant cost $300—a no-brainer, we decided. We were audited a couple of years ago, with no problems. The auditor told me the IRS feels that people who are conscientious enough to use computer bookkeeping and tax programs are usually honest—an added benefit!

Many tax packages provide a transfer utility that simply picks up any coded items from the bookkeeping package and merges them directly into the tax forms. However, you have to make sure your checking account or bookkeeping system has the correct coding. Returns are printed just as they would be if you filled them in by hand, only much neater.

There are several tax packages, including TurboTax, MacInTax and U.S. Tax. Because of the annual changes in the Internal Revenue Service tax code, it is important to use only the program meant for the tax year you are working on. Many of the companies that produce these programs offer a guarantee that they will support any errors their program contains. However, they won't support any data input errors you commit.

One caution about using these wonderful cyber helpers: They do not take the place of an accountant. You should still check to see what kinds of records for expenses and income to keep and which deductions to take. Many accountants can give advice about which program will work best for your business. However, once you are on your way, filling out and filing your own taxes can reflect tremendous savings.

Inventory control and management

How many times has this happened: While at the fabric store, you pick up a couple things you need, only to find you already picked them up the last time you shopped. You might use them soon, but more likely that money could be used more productively elsewhere. However, it isn't always convenient to trudge back to the store to return the items.

This situation can be avoided with inventory control maintained in the computer. Most office packages have database programs included, or they can be purchased separately. Some of the most popular programs are Access, Lotus 1-2-3, ACT! and Quattro Pro. New programs are being developed all the time. Check your local computer store or a computer catalog to keep current. These programs offer a way to record use and purchases of various inventory items: threads, interfacings, fabrics, notions, patterns, books, videotapes, machine maintenance records and much more.

Customer records

Those same database programs can be used to keep tabs on customers. Names, addresses, phone numbers, sizes, color preferences and measurements can all be stored in alphabetical order with little effort on your part. If you don't want the expense of a major database program, there are several nifty little personal information manager (PIM) programs for storing these records and tracking your daily appointments. Sidekick, Outlook, Lotus Organizer and Janna Contact Personal are examples of programs currently available.

Business plan

If you want to present your business plan to a bank, sometimes a little more "curb appeal" is necessary. The same process we walked through in chapter seven can be presented in a more appealing format with business plan software, or with a template in an office program. Lotus Smart Suite's Freelance Graphics contains a template with preset headings for a business plan presentation, among others. But even if you don't have special software, most word processing programs today are capable of producing larger fonts and boxes. Transfer the numbers and other information from your notes to a file you create for a more professional-looking presentation.

Telephone and fax machines

Nearly every computer system sold today includes a fax modem capable of sending and receiving faxes. Many systems also include what is called telephony support, which basically serves as a sophisticated answering machine.

Unattended, the computer can answer the call with your voice or with a preset announcement and either send the call to a "mailbox" or receive a fax. If you have caller identification on that phone number, you can even see who is calling, right on the computer screen. Many programs have a feature that lets you preset certain favorite phone numbers—when those people call, a special screen pops up to alert you.

Hands-free phone calling is also possible. Most computers have speakers attached, and a microphone is often included as well. Since every computer now has jacks for headsets, simply hooking up the inexpensive headset to the computer affords a much less stressful way to hold a phone conversation, and provides privacy. (This assumes that the computer is fairly close to the sewing machines.)

Any document created in the computer can be faxed directly from the computer, without first printing the document. WinFax Pro is one program that facilitates this. It comes in handy when sending credit references to suppliers, for example. Most companies today have fax machines, and it looks more professional to have your own fax number on a letterhead or business card. The ability to fax from your office also saves time and money if your other alternative is to run down the street to do it.

Online access

The marvel of the twentieth century is the unlimited access to nearly anything in the world, right from your desk. Every day more businesses enter the worldwide marketing arena of the World Wide Web, which is only accessible by computer modem. This electronic world is populated by millions of content providers, many of them offering either items for sale or educational information. This information explosion is a boon to any business, but for sewing businesses in particular. Resources that were previously almost impossible to find are now accessible in moments.

E-mail offers immediate communication for keeping in touch with resources, other professionals and even customers. With an Internet access account, the solitude of owning a small business need not be as harsh a reality as it once was. Several online support groups have sprung up, which offer peer counseling and assistance in a matter of hours. Message boards on various online services and Internet newsgroups are available for a variety of special interest areas, including sewing and business. On-line chats offer a way to "talk" to others of like mind. Read and type responses to others from around the country and around the world.

The Internet and the online world are a rich source of information, assistance and networking for anyone. The sewing professional has much to gain by tapping into this vast wonderland in cyberspace. As of this writing, a search for the word *sewing* might net more than twenty thousand references. By the time you read this, that figure could nearly double, given the intense growth this medium is experiencing. Don't be left behind.

Patternmaking software

For many dressmakers, new patternmaking software programs have been a boon to their businesses. Packages of varying degrees of complexity allow the custom clothier to create patterns to fit the unique measurements of individual customers.

There are pattern programs for the most rudimentary styles up to very sophisticated packages that allow grading for multiple sizes and layouts for hundreds of yards of fabric. In order to run the most sophisticated programs, more equipment is necessary; the simpler packages print on less expensive printers and run on more basic systems.

There are many ways to compare these programs, but such research will require some detective work on your part. Online services and Internet newsgroups are one outlet to find others who have used various systems; be aware that there is a wide variance of experience levels represented in such forums.

Lisa Shanley, a former professor at Auburn University, created the program Symmetry for use with home computers. This program allows for three levels of usage: creating custom slopers and applying a bank of patterns to them, creating your own patterns, and grading multiple sizes from your patterns. Lisa's company, Wild Ginger Software, also sells plotters for printing patterns for mass-produced garments. In the past, software packages of this kind would have cost tens of thousands of dollars; Symmetry is available in three price levels, the highest priced choice well under $1,000. This revolutionary shift in cost makes such technology available even to very small manufacturing businesses.

If you don't need to grade for multiple sizes, one of the other pattern drawing programs will suffice. (See the appendix for more information about software programs for patternmaking.)

Storage of professional patterns

Choosing a computer

Don't just buy a computer you see advertised in Sunday's paper because it fits your price range; you may be seriously disappointed later. Research what you need and how powerful of a system is necessary to fill those requirements. Change is the most constant factor in the computer field, and you don't want to find that you outgrew your system before you even learned to make it work for you.

Fortunately there's a wealth of information about computers today. Any library or bookstore has literally hundreds of books on subjects from the very basics of what a computer is to getting the most out of various programs.

There are also many magazines on computing, at many different levels of expertise; one of my favorites is *Home Office Computing*. These

Paul and Lisa Shanley

Aegis Design Group/BMFI/
Wild Ginger Software
Old Hickory, Tennessee

Having long-held interests in both clothing construction and outer space, it was a natural for Paul Shanley to apply his knowledge in both areas to developing protective clothing for the aerospace and aeronautics industries.

After three years at Auburn University (including three quarters in clothing design), Paul left school. He went to work as an apprentice in a costume design studio near Miami for seven months. His next job was as a counselor at NASA Space Camp in Huntsville, Alabama. After a couple of years of steeping himself in the space culture and lore, Paul went back to Auburn for a degree in speech communication, with the goal of working in aerospace and aviation public relations.

In 1989, shortly before the end of his degree program, Paul met Dr. Lisa Christman, a professor at the university. Lisa was preparing a proposal to work as a general contractor on a prototype for a Navy flight suit. This contract was based on fiber technology for flame resistance (FR fiber technology), and Lisa invited Paul to help on the project. When the thirty-day proposal project was over, Lisa and Paul began dating. Shortly afterward, they began a business together, called Aegis Design Group. *Aegis* means shield, or protection. This company created "cut and sew" protective clothing prototypes and product development for military and industry use.

As a professor, Lisa, who by now was

Dr. Lisa Shanley, was encouraged to pursue outside contracts. Together, Paul and Lisa became outside consultants to Dow Chemical Company, for whom they did several prototype projects, including putting an insulation fiber into ski jackets and cold weather sleeping bags. In addition, Lisa won a postdoctoral Navy engineering fellowship to do research. They worked on "end product user" protective equipment for soldiers and Marines. They developed a portable climate control simulator suit. Paul calls this "a poor man's heat chamber." It would allow the military to test potential fighter pilots to see their susceptibility to temperature extremes.

During a sabbatical from Auburn University, Lisa invented Symmetry, her patternmaking software, and she and Paul formed Wild Ginger Software, along with Diane Koza, Ph.D., another Auburn professor. Symmetry was the first computer program of this type to offer pattern grading in an affordable package, which allows even small manufacturers to create their own patterns and grade them.

In the meantime, Paul joined the National Guard and is now an end user of the kind of equipment he's been working on. In addition, he has formed a partnership, BMFI, with an inventor. This partner has developed FR fiber technology and an advanced type of insulation, both of which they intend to develop further and market to industry.

publications rate various kinds of hardware (the actual computer and peripheral equipment) and software (programs) and contain great business articles. You can learn a lot from the ads in these magazines, too, sometimes enough to know what questions to ask.

Check your local community education schedule or the computer store in your area for classes. Not only are the classes themselves valuable, but talking at the break or after class with other students can be very enlightening. Find out what they know and where they shop for their systems and programs. While you're at the computer store, browse the aisles to see what types of products they offer. This research time will pay for itself—promise!

CHAPTER 10

The Importance of Networking and Education

Over the years, my career in the sewing industry has progressed rapidly, in large measure due to networking with other professionals in sewing businesses. Without the many wonderful friends and contacts I've made in this fascinating field, I would not have had the courage to believe in myself enough to teach sewing, nor would I have ever written even one book. I really owe a great deal to my fellow Professional Sewing Association members here in Cincinnati. Hopefully, they have benefited equally by their friendships with me.

Today there are more opportunities for networking with other sewing professionals than ever before. Since the early 1980s, several professional groups have sprung up, offering many meeting and seminar options. (See the appendix for specific groups that may pertain to your specialty, as well as more general associations in the sewing for profit arena.)

The benefits of networking with your peers can't be stressed enough. Joining a group of other sewing professionals can make a difference to your business. Not only does it alleviate the loneliness of working solo, but it also helps to be able to compare notes about various aspects of business. Often, the problems you experience are the same ones others have had. It helps to know you aren't the only one who has gone through such situations. In addition, knowing that another business on the other side of town is able to charge double what you charge may help you increase your prices. Sharing wholesale sources and orders could be another benefit of working with other pros. And it pays to let others know you specialize in certain types of work; referrals from other professionals have lent a helping boost to many businesses.

Don't be afraid to join volunteer groups; these can be an excellent source of new clients. People you meet in support organizations for the arts, for instance, often need evening clothing. Builders associations are great resources for new home and commercial office construction needing window treatments or other sewn products. Church and school groups are other places to network with potential customers.

Even volunteering to sew something for a group can lead to new business. One woman made new cushion covers for the children's section of the local library. A small placard placed nearby announced her work. She received several calls within a few weeks from mothers who had enjoyed the attractive and comfortable new seating with their children and wanted the businessperson to do that quality of work for them. Another enterprising young man volunteered to make costumes for a theatre production benefit. His name in the program brought new customers to his door.

Networking opportunities

Association memberships

Professional associations also offer a way to share information with others. It is my considered opinion that no one has all the answers; we can learn a great deal from one another. Who better to learn from than someone who has been in business for awhile? Take a shortcut to success by taking advantage of others' hard-earned knowledge. However, even beginners often adapt new and creative solutions to common questions of technique. It is interesting to see how our different backgrounds help us arrive at different ways of dealing with the same thorny problems.

Another terrific benefit of getting to know other professionals in your area is that you eventually become familiar with one another's work. When a client or potential client asks for a service your business doesn't provide, having this knowledge of how well a colleague sews can reduce embarrassment in making referrals that turn out all wrong. Conversely, your associates are more willing to send business your way when they feel confident of *your* ability.

Joining such a group and attending meetings regularly can help you in many ways. Not only do you make valuable contacts, but most meetings have varying degrees of an educational aspect. Everyone has a slightly different approach to the way he does business, and getting a glimpse of another's methodology can forever change the way you see certain aspects of your business.

Many association members share information about problem customers, too. Forewarned is forearmed. Especially custom clothiers occasionally get hold of a live one: extremely difficult to fit, rude, picky, abusive and sometimes even scary. It certainly is comforting to members to find out they weren't the only ones to have problems with these individuals!

Newsletters

One of the most tangible benefits of membership in a professional group is receiving the association newsletter. Keeping abreast of what other members are doing can give you something by which to measure your own success. Resources and techniques are often shared, as are details of what other local organizations are planning.

Here in Cincinnati the Professional Sewing Association (PSA) also keeps up with events hosted by the local Fashion Group International, the Women's Entrepreneurs group and a new organization of window treatment professionals. Attending these events offers even more chances for networking, but of an entirely different sort. Many of our members have made excellent contacts with professionals in other fields who need sewing services.

Industry events

Also new in the last fifteen years or so are consumer sewing shows. These events are usually held at convention centers or hotels and offer a way to see many new industry products in one place. In addition, these shows feature many classes, seminars and free venues given by a variety of industry speakers. For the most part, these shows do not afford professional-level instruction. However, we are all on a journey through life, and not everyone is at the same stage of the trip. If your personal quest for information includes learning new information, any level is important to you.

For more business-specific instruction, there are several conventions each year that offer this higher level of information. For all kinds of sewing professionals, Beyond Pin Money: A Conference for Sewing Professionals, sponsored by the Cincinnati PSA, provides serious business help. The goal of Beyond Pin Money is to provide a variety of professional-level classes and a venue for networking with professionals from around the United States and Canada. Professional Association of Custom Clothiers (PACC) also sponsors a convention each year in conjunction with its annual meeting. Instruction at this event is geared more toward custom dressmaking. For tailors, the Custom Tailors and Designers Association of America (CTDA) also has a convention annually.

Drapery and window treatment workrooms are in the catbird seat; there are several events for this group, sponsored by the two industry magazines, *Draperies & Window Coverings* and *Window Fashions*. Technique seminars, business meetings and resource booths all appear at these events.

Quilt Market is for anyone in the quilt business, whether you quilt, write about quilting, sell quilt-related products or just want to find new products. This semiannual event is held in Texas and another part of the country each winter and summer.

The International Costumer's Guild, the Society for Creative Anachronism (SCA) and other groups hold costuming conventions around the country. Some of these are massive events, with seminars, product vendor arenas, contests and celebrity appearances. If your area of expertise is in any kind of reenactment or fantasy costuming, these are can't-miss shows.

Dollmakers and doll clothing makers should investigate the many hobby shows for dolls and the products that surround them. Many kinds of crafting are represented at shows presented by Hobby Industry Association of America (HIA), and the Association of Crafts & Creative Industries (ACCI).

For small manufacturers, the premier event is the Bobbin Show, held every fall in Atlanta, Georgia. At this enormous show, companies who sell products that support the sewing manufacturing business are represented. Here you will find everything from buttons to button sew machines, trims to trimmers, monograms to monogram machines. Quilting and embroidery machines are shown, from sizes to fit your basement to enormous machines more suited to traditional factories. Factory owners and small manufacturers alike attend this show, coming from all over the world. Listening in on passing conversations you are as likely to hear Polish as English, Chinese as Japanese, Portuguese as Spanish.

Online chats and lists

The newest way to network is by plugging into the vast possibilities of the cyberworld. With a modem and an online service provider, such as America OnLine or another of the hundreds of companies that have sprung up in recent years, you can instantly access any of several business support systems.

One such group is the SewPros Network. Begun in December 1996, this group now has several hundred members from all over the world, with sewing businesses ranging from dressmakers to heirloom smockers to outerwear manufacturers.

In addition to SewPros, there are also networks and e-mail digests, or "lists," for drapery workrooms, childrenswear manufacturers and many other specialties (see the appendix).

Online "chats" offer a way to "speak" to others immediately—if you can type, you can talk. You merely type what you want to say into a special block on the screen; when the *Enter* key is pressed, the text is presented to the chat group. Because of the immediacy of this medium, chat members are in all sorts of time zones and in a variety of geographic locations, but all are able to communicate at once.

Online message or bulletin boards are another way to network. In 1994 I conducted a survey of 540 sewing professionals; nearly 20 percent of those surveyed were people I had "met" on sewing message boards on Prodigy and America OnLine. Today that number would be much higher, as personal computers have become more commonplace and more afford-able. Message boards offer a place to find out more—more about sources, more about techniques, more about what is happening outside your own four walls. The Internet also has bulletin boards, which are called news-groups. There are two specifically for sewing:

- alt.sewing
- rec.crafts.textiles.sewing

Take a spin in cyberspace and you'll be amazed at the possibilities.

Related nonsewing networking

Sometimes, the best contacts you can make are outside your own industry. Breakfast (or lunch or dinner) clubs set up to share leads with other profes-sionals can offer ample opportunity for finding new customers. For in-stance, drapery and window treatment professionals who network with real estate professionals, interior decorators, builders and office managers are situated perfectly to make client contacts from among the clients of those other businesses. In the same way, tailors and custom clothiers find new customers when they attend Chamber of Commerce meetings or charity functions. Bridal designers can have carte blanche to the contacts made among florists, jewelers, formalwear rental outlets and event planners.

Create your own networking group; arrange a working breakfast twice a month for people you feel might help one another's business. Typically such a club has half a dozen or more members, each in a different but perhaps related industry. Weekly or monthly meetings to exchange marketing ideas and new contact names often lead to more business for each member. Share names, addresses, phone numbers and other pertinent information about clients. Make it clear that each meeting lasts no more than forty-five minutes, and each time, everyone must share at least as many names as there are members of the group. Be sure to find out as much as you can about each member's business, and keep up with new events planned by each company represented.

Another fabulous way to find clients is to hang out where they are. One woman did just this. She wanted to do custom dressmaking, specializing in formalwear and other fine clothing. In order to meet those who would eventually become her clients, she joined volunteer groups in the arts: Friends of the Ballet, the service arm of the symphony, the opera volunteers. She met the movers and shakers in the social scene in these groups. Whenever anyone asked her what she did, a business card was proffered, along with a description of her services. Kateri Ellison found that her membership in the Greater Washington (DC) Board of Trade was a natural source of new custom clothing clients. As a business group, members expect to network with one another, and they make a point of supporting one another.

Educate yourself

Continuing education is mandatory in many fields, but in the sewing industry, we often have to motivate ourselves to continue to learn new things. In the last fifteen years or so, there have been more changes in our field than in the previous eighty years; many new techniques, products and machines have been developed. Taking the time to update your education will make your business more profitable.

Ngai Kwan

Ngai Kwan Designs
Seattle, Washington

Ngai Kwan

Ngai Kwan worked in the sewing industry for awhile, but was disgruntled with her marketing choices. Wondering why nothing she wanted to make for herself was in the pattern books, she decided to take some classes in both patternmaking and design.

At Seattle Central Community College, Ngai enrolled in the Apparel Design and Services program. The sewing, pattern de-

sign and grading curriculum was very intense, more difficult than her bachelor degree. Instead of cramming three years of information into two years, which was normally done, Ngai decided to take three years to finish so she could concentrate on her studies better.

A talent for patternmaking led to a career choice: Ngai now creates patterns for local seamstresses. They give her the measurements of the clients on a form she provides, along with a sketch, then Ngai makes the pattern. She is paid by the job or by the hour; Ngai says experienced patternmakers can make up to about $25 an hour locally.

One of her clients is a Seattle bridal designer who makes about one hundred gowns a year and employs two other patternmakers. Ngai submits the pattern to the customer, along with a sample, then the client corrects the fit and returns it to Ngai to correct the pattern. For her bridal customer, she sends a muslin for the bride to OK, and fitting changes are transferred to the pattern, if necessary. Another client brought her this challenge: to make a pattern for a one-seam hooded robe for prizefighters. In order to manage the robe with one seam, certain fabric requirements had to be specified. Because of the massive necks and shoulders of fighters, this was a thorny problem to work out.

She feels her method of patternmaking from the client's measurements is faster than changing a pattern made from a sloper; it's also more accurate. Because older slopers are slightly oversized, Ngai says the newer, highly fitted styles are impossible to fit with them. With the oversized styles of the last decade, many industry patternmakers have lost the ability to fit the body more closely. Ngai recommends Helen Armstrong's book, *Patternmaking for Fashion Design.*

Not only are there new, speedier techniques, but there are new fibers on the market. Microfibers, Tencel, hemp and many stretch fabrics are all recent developments on the fabric scene. Learn about these products before you are called upon to use one of them in a project; by then it might be too late to get the information you need about handling it. In addition, being prepared means knowing in advance that a certain kind of machine foot or needle is needed; this reduces panic buying, which can cost more of your hard-earned profit.

It is equally important to keep up with fashion and trends. An entire line of kitchen accessories in last year's country colors that won't sell this year could keep your family supplied for the rest of your life. The latest looks in dance fashions are important to competitive dancers; your customers look to you for guidance in choosing styles and fabrications.

Another trend worth paying attention to is individual color analysis. Many custom clothiers offer their customers this service, along with wardrobe planning. Knowing the latest color theories and using them to help your clients could help fatten your bank balance.

Degree programs

There are some fashion design and apparel technology programs in the United States, but few of these schools teach sewing. Many programs have changed from the traditional Home Economics degree programs, and often you have to create your own educational experience. Going to various conferences will help and, additionally, attending as many business seminars as possible. The Small Business Administration (SBA) offers seminars and ongoing classes in many areas of the country. Call the local office to see what classes are scheduled in your area.

Four-year degree programs rarely include the subject matter most germane to a custom sewing business. A better bet might be one of the many two-year programs around the country. Business courses are also offered at these schools, but not necessarily in the same program, though they are equally important. A good grounding in business basics is essential for business success, and you just can't have too much information in this area.

In order to teach sewing, it isn't necessary to have a degree in sewing, unless you plan to teach at an accredited school. However, for teaching at a retail store or in your own school, a love of sewing and a good knowledge of techniques, as well as good communication skills, are much more important than a degree.

Specialty schools

Several schools exist for concentrated instruction in various aspects of sewing. Cheryl Strickland's drapery school offers classes in many different areas of home decor sewing for business. Palmer/Pletsch Associates in Portland, Oregon, has a widely known school for teaching various subjects, including teaching people to teach sewing. Susan Khalje has a bi-coastal school, teaching concentrated bridal and couture techniques in both Baltimore, Maryland, and Portland, Oregon.

Susan Khalje

Couture Sewing School
Glen Arm, Maryland

Susan Khalje and Catherine Stephenson with the Bridal Sewing School

From concert pianist to couture sewing instructor, Susan Khalje has moved from one fine art to another. After a career as a concert pianist that found her living in London, Susan changed her focus and returned to the United States. She went to New York City and found a job as a seamstress with a couture house. Susan describes the experience as total immersion in the world of haute couture. In addition to sewing the house's own designs, Susan was also asked to work on copies of haute couture garments for many of the bluebloods and celebrities of New York City and the eastern

seaboard. She says, "I worked on the best fabrics, with the finest techniques."

Susan went out on her own after about a year and a half, when she was asked to go to Afghanistan to run a sportswear clothing factory there. While in Afghanistan, Susan caught the eye of the factory owner's best friend, and she and Qadir Khalje married. They lived there for awhile until moving to Amsterdam and then to the United States

In the early 1980s, Susan wanted to get back into sewing—she had been away from her piano practice too long to play professionally—and wanted something that would be more amenable to raising children. Susan was featured in an article on dressmakers in a national magazine. Out of this Susan got a job making a wedding dress, which appealed to her sense of special sewing. She continued to make custom wedding gowns and evening wear for the next fifteen years. Self-taught in altering patterns and creating whatever needs to be made, Susan feels her strength is in technique.

The Bridal Sewing School began in October 1993. Susan has since changed the name to Couture Sewing School because, she says, "We're talking about couture treatments, for special garments. Bridal gowns just happen to be white and have a lot of lace. That requires a lot of special treatment. We're basically set up as a European couture atelier. The emphasis is on hand sewing, but they bring machines. Every morning we do couture samples." Susan finds it advantageous to have group classes. She explains, "The beauty of having group classes is that you may not be working on Alençon lace, but someone else might, and you get to see what techniques apply. You really apply your knowledge right away, which I think is the way to learn. My goal as a teacher is to teach them how to think about the decision-making process of sewing in this way and the solid reasoning behind various choices."

Many students bring a gown they're working on, often for a client. The cost, as this book is being written, is $895 tuition, plus hotel, food, airfare or other travel.

Susan says, "It's very difficult to get training at this level. If you want to use the finer techniques, where else can you go? Almost every other school is based on production sewing, except for a handful of classes here and there. I think the pendulum of higher sewing is swinging back, and couture is becoming a more recognized thing again." The desire to create, and to own, very fine things has begun to come back in certain areas.

Catherine Stephenson of Portland, Oregon, helps Susan in the classes. Catherine shares Susan's love of the couture methods, the fine hand sewing and attention to detail that earmark the most custom of garments.

Susan feels that teaching for several years has changed her focus and changed the way she communicates to her classes. She feels she has become more effective as a result of observing how different people respond to what she has to say. Some of her students put a lot of pressure on themselves to complete a garment during the six-day class, and she found that she had to be sensitive to the various goals of the students. For instance, her original advertising suggested that the class was for intermediate and advanced sewists; Susan has changed this to say "advanced and professional."

Susan was elected chairperson of PACC in 1996 for the first two-year term of the organization. Coincidentally, Catherine Stephenson became her successor as chairperson in 1998.

Sample Contract (For a Drapery Workroom)

Your Company Name
Your Company Address
City, State Zip/Postal Code
Phone/Fax Numbers

Proposal and Acceptance

Submitted to: _____ Date: _____
Phone: Day _____ Evening _____
Billing Address: _____
Job Location: _____ Due Date: _____

I hereby submit specifications and estimates for

_____
_____
_____
_____
_____
_____

I propose hereby to furnish material and labor, complete in accordance with above specifications, for the
sum of $ _____.
NOTE: This proposal may be withdrawn if not accepted within _____ days.

Terms and Conditions:

1. Orders for articles, materials or contractor's services will not be placed in work until signed confirmation of PROPOSAL CONTRACT IS RECEIVED, together with any required deposit.
2. Prices of materials, articles and contractor's services are subject to change. Before proceeding with order, notice of any price increase will be given and confirmation of revised price required.
3. Prices do not included shipping, freight or trucking charges or insurance in transit, all of which will be at customer's expense.
4. Orders approved under this contract are noncancelable.
5. Prices do not include sales or other applicable taxes.
6. No responsibility is assumed for delays occasioned by failure of others to meet commitments or for any other reason or cause beyond our control.
7. Designs, samples, drawings and specifications shall remain Designer's property, whether or not the work for which they are made be executed.
8. Designer does not guarantee any fabric, material or article against wearing, fading or latent defect, but to extent permitted by law. Customer shall have benefit at customer's sole expense in the assertion thereof, of all guarantees and warranties possessed by the Designer against suppliers and manufacturers.
9. Furnishing or installing of any or all materials or articles is subject to Designer's ability to obtain the same and to procure the necessary labor thereof, and is contingent on strikes, accidents or other causes beyond Designer's control.
10. If Designer is required to render services not contemplated by this agreement, or incurs extra drafting or other expenses due to changes ordered by Customer for any other cause, Designer shall be paid for such extra services and expenses the reasonable value of cost thereof.
11. This contract is for custom-made products not subject to return.
12. Design changes, alterations and additions will be subject to further charges to Customer. Such changes, alterations and additions must be submitted in writing and agreed to and signed by both Designer and Customer. Additional deposit may be required.
13. PAYMENT TERMS: 50% Deposit required with all approved contracts. Balance is due on delivery of goods.

ACCEPTANCE OF PROPOSAL:

The above prices, specifications, terms and conditions have been fully explained to me and are satisfactory. I hereby accept this proposal and authorize work to be done as specified. Payment will be noted as above.
Authorized Signature: _____ Date: _____

(Based on a form developed by Pam DeCuir.
Pam recommends printing on three-part paper and having a lawyer approve wording for your state.)

Sample Contract (For a Custom or Bridal Clothing Business)

Your Company Name
Your Company Address
City, State Zip/Postal Code
Phone/Fax Numbers

Date: _____
Wedding/event date: _____
Estimated completion: _____
Policy sheet received: _____

Name: _____
Address: _____
Other: _____

Home Phone: _____
Work Phone: _____
Phone: _____

Description of gown or garment: _____
_____
_____
_____

Materials *(include yardage and estimated cost, if applicable):*
Fabric: _____
Fabric: _____
Lining: _____
Lace: _____
Lace: _____

Labor: _____
_____
_____
_____

Beadwork: _____
_____

Payment schedule: _____
Materials: _____
Labor: _____
Subtotal: _____
Total: _____

Date:	Amount:	Balance Due:

Changes in weight or garment design may necessitate additional charges. Payment in full is required before release of this work.

X _____   X _____

148

(Based on a form developed by Karen Howland.)

Policy Sheet (For a Custom Clothing Business)

Your Company Name
Your Company Address
City, State Zip/Postal Code
Phone/Fax Numbers

Thank you for choosing my company for your project; I look forward to working with you. I take great pride in the quality of my work for all my clients and in providing these services in a timely fashion. To accomplish these goals, I have established certain criteria:

- Clients are scheduled by appointment only. This ensures that all clients will have my undivided attention and will not be inconvenienced by waiting.
- I schedule only those projects that can be successfully completed in a given time period. This policy guarantees that all deadlines are met.
- Clients are asked to please call ahead to cancel appointments. Missed or tardy appointments, without notification, are subject to additional charges.

TYPICAL PROJECT SCHEDULE

Consultation:
This is where we talk, bounce around wants, ideas, needs, desires and estimates, and determine if we should continue. All consultations are billed at the rate of $25 per hour, with a $25 minimum, and are due at the time of consultation. If we decide to work together on a project, the consultation fee is waived.

Design Plan:
At this time we nail down a definite design, determine materials and their purchase and formalize an agreement. Feel free to bring photos and/or patterns or a favorite garment to reproduce. They are extremely helpful in the design process. Please allow 4 to 8 weeks from consultation to final fitting. A 50% deposit on labor and the estimated cost of fabrics and notions are due at this time. These are nonrefundable.

Fittings:
Fittings are a required part of custom sewing. There can be anywhere from two to six fittings per item; three is customary. Come prepared with proper undergarments, shoes and any other accessories necessary for the finished garment, to ensure the perfect fit.

Final Fitting:
This is when we both determine that the fit is good, and all is well . . . at last! We will also "balance the books" at this time. Any credit for an overestimate on materials is applied and a final payment, in cash, is due.

PLEASE REMEMBER:

We are working together. Workmanship only is guaranteed. The proposal you receive is for your weight and measurements as of _____ date. Finished work left for over 30-days is subject to storage fee. After 90 days, the articles will be sold. We pass on to you the $30 returned check fee our bank charges for any returned checks. No work will be released unless paid in full, including such charges. Extra charges may be required when measurements are obtained from an outside source and for fabric you provide. Any changes to the original contract will require additional charges. I understand the above policies:

Signed: _____   _____
         CUSTOMER   *DATE*

Signed: _____   _____
         OWNER   *DATE*

(Based on a form developed by Pam Relitz, Grayslake, Illinois)

Appendix

Professional Associations

American Apparel Manufacturers Association (AAMA), 2500 Wilson Blvd., Suite 301, Arlington, VA 22201, (800) 520-2262.

American Home Sewing and Craft Association (HSA), International Sewing Machine Association (ISMA), 1350 Broadway, Suite 1601, New York, NY 10018, (212) 714-1655.

American Sewing Guild (ASG), 9140 Ward Parkway, Suite 200, Kansas City, MO 64114, (816) 444-3500.

Association of Crafts & Creative Industries (ACCI), 1100-H Brandywine Blvd., P.O. Box 2188, Zanesville, OH 43702-2188, (614) 452-4541.

Custom Tailors and Designers Association of America (CTDA), 17 E. Forty-fifth St., New York, NY 10017, (212) 661-1960.

Embroidery Trade Association International, 745 N. Gilbert Rd., Suite 124-362, Gilbert, AZ 85234, (602) 497-1274.

Fashion Group International, Inc., 597 Fifth Ave., New York, NY 10017.

The Greater Columbia Fantasy Costumer's Guild, P.O. Box 683, Columbia, MD 21045.

Greater Metro Professional Sewing Association (GMPSA), P.O. Box 23382, Richfield, MN 55423.

Hobby Industry Association of America (HIA), 319 E. Fifty-fourth St., P.O. Box 348, Elmwood Park, NJ 07407, (201) 794-1133.

Industrial Fabrics Association International (IFAI), 345 Cedar St., Suite 800, St. Paul, MN 55101-1088, (612) 222-2508.

The International Costumer's Guild, 1444 Arona St., St. Paul, MN 55108.

Iowa Textile and Apparel Association, % Textiles & Clothing Extension, 1055 LeBaron Hall, Iowa State University, Ames, IA 50011-1120, (515) 294-6712.

National Association for Female Executives (NAFE), 30 Irving Place, Fifth Floor, New York, NY 10003, (212) 477-2200.

The National Needlework Association (TNNA), P.O. Box 2188, Zanesville, OH 43702-2188, (203) 431-8226.

Professional Association of Custom Clothiers (PACC), P.O. Box 8071, Medford, OR 97504-0071, (541) 772-4119.

Professional Dressmakers Association, % Kim Baumunk-Kleine, Ultimate Stitch, Inc., 5401 Goethe Ave., St. Louis, MO 63109.

Professional Needle Guild, Inc. (PNG), P.O. Box 40236, Cleveland, OH 44140.

Professional Sewing Association of Ohio, Inc. (PSA), % 944-B Sutton Rd., Cincinnati, OH 45230-2581.

Rhode Island Home Sewing Network, % Cheryl Lepore, 70 New Gardners Neck Rd., Swansea, MA 02777-2524.

Window Coverings Association of America (WCAA), 825 S. Waukegan Rd., Suite A8-111, Lake Forest, IL 60045-2665, (888) 298-WCAA.

Resources

Service Corps of Retired Executives (SCORE). Call your nearest Small Business Administration office for information.

Small Business Development Centers. Call your local Chamber of Commerce to find the nearest one.

State Extension Services. Ask for their catalog of available publications.

Schools

Clemson Apparel Research, Pendelton, SC, (864) 646-8454.

Couture Sewing School, 4600 Breidenbaugh Lane, Glen Arm, MD 21057, (410) 592-5711.

Cheryl Strickland's Professional Drapery Workroom School, P.O. Box 867, Swannanoa, NC 28778, (800) 222-1415.

TC², Manufacturing Research Facility, Cary, NC.

University of Rhode Island Cooperative Extension, Woodward Hall, Kingston, RI 02881-0804, (401) 762-0960.

Patternmaking software

Dress Shop 2.5 Livingsoft, Inc., P.O. Box 819, Susanville, CA 96130-0819, (800) 626-1262.

Fittingly Sew, Knitcraft, 500 N. Dodgian Ave., Independence, MO 64050-3023, (816) 461-1217.

Patternmaker Software, 2029 144th Ave. SE, Bellevue, WA 98007-6216, (206) 644-8161.

Personal Patterns, Water Fountain Software, 13 E. Seventeenth St., Third Floor, New York, NY 10003, (212) 929-6204.

Symmetry, Wild Ginger Software, 4847 Mockingbird Lane, Old Hickory, TN 37138, (888) 929-9453.

Patternmaking system

Cut to the Fit, Karen K. Howland, Kensinger Press, 1316 W. Pine St., Chillicothe, IL 61523, (309) 274-4160.

Business Forms

Contract Forms, Price Lists, and Policy Sheets, Sewstorm Publishing, 944 Sutton Rd., Cincinnati, OH 45230-3581, (513) 232-5403.

Business consultants

Karen Maslowski, SewStorm, 944 Sutton Rd., Cincinnati, OH 45230-3581, (513) 232-5403. http://www.sewstorm.com

Kitty Stein, Workroom Concepts, P.O. Box 283, Clearbrook, VA 22624, (703) 667-5939.

Supplies, including professional pressing equipment

Atlanta Thread & Supply Corp., 695 Red Oak Rd., Stockbridge, GA 30281, (800) 331-7600, (770) 389-9115.

Baer Fabrics, 515 E. Market St., Louisville, KY 40202, (502) 569-7017.

Banasch's Inc., 2810 Highland Ave., Cincinnati, OH 45212, (800) 543-0355.

Brewer Sewing Supplies Co., 3800 W. Forty-second St., Chicago, IL 60632, (800) 444-3111, (773) 247-2121.

Greenberg & Hammer, Inc., 24 W. Fifty-seventh St., New York, NY 10019-3918, (800) 955-5135, (212) 246-2836.

B&G Lieberman Co., 2420 Distribution St., Charlotte, NC 28203, (800) 438-0346, (704) 376-0717.

Sewing Emporium, 1079 Third Ave., Chula Vista, CA 91911, (619) 420-3490.

SouthStar Supply Co., 233 Oceola Ave., P.O. Box 90147, Nashville, TN 37209, (800) 288-6739, (615) 353-7000.

3A Thread & Supply Co., 3216 N. San Gabriel Blvd., Rosemead, CA 91770, (818) 307-9705.

Washington Millinery Supply Inc., P.O. Box 5718, Derwood, MD 20855, (301) 963-4444.

Ely E. Yawitz Co., 1717 Olive St., Seventh Floor, P.O. Box 14325, St. Louis, MO 63103, (800) 325-7915, (314) 231-5729.

Online resources—Web sites

DraperyPros: http://members.aol.com/garbarini/DraperyPro.html
National Craft Association: http://www.craftassoc.com
SewPros Network: http://www.sewstorm.com
Thomas Register: http://www.thomasregister.com
TIMS (Textile, Apparel and Fashion Service): http://www.unicate.com

Periodicals

The Crafts Report: The Business Journal for the Crafts Industry, 300 Water St., P.O. Box 1992, Wilmington, DE 19899, (302) 656-2209.

Draperies & Window Coverings, Clark Publishing, 450 Skokie Blvd., Suite 407, Northbrook, IL 60062, (847) 498-9880.

Embroidery Business News, Virgo Publishing, Inc., 3300 N. Central Ave., Phoenix, AZ 85012-2501, (602) 990-1101.

Embroidery/Monogram Business, P.O. Box 1266, Skokie, IL 60076-8266, (214) 239-3060.

The Independent Patternmaker, 604 Forest Park Blvd., Fort Worth, TX 76102.

Seamstress Network (Drapery Workrooms), LaVelle Pinder Decorating, 9102 Collingwood Dr., Austin, TX 78748-6012, (512) 282-0717.

SewWHAT? The International Newsletter for Professional Drapery Workrooms, Cheryl Strickland, 101 Strickland Terrace, Swannanoa, NC 28778-2457, (888) 4SEWWHAT.

Stitches: The Magazine for the Commercial Embroidery Industry, Intertec Publishing Corporation, 9800 Metcalf Ave., Shawnee Mission, KS 66212-2216, (913) 341-1300.

Window Fashions, G&W McNamara Publishing, Inc., 4225 White Bear Pkwy., Suite 400, St. Paul, MN 55110, (612) 293-1544.

Books

Brabec, Barbara. **Homemade Money.** Cincinnati: Betterway Books, 1997.

Caputo, Kathryn. **How to Start Making Money With Your Crafts.** Cincinnati: Betterway Books, 1995.

Duncan, Beth. **Sewing as a Business.** Meridian, Miss.: Mississippi Cooperative Extension Service, 1967.

Edwards, Paul, and Sarah Edwards. **Working From Home.** New York: Putnam, 1994.

Howland, Karen K. **Unit Pricing for Dressmaking.** Chillicothe, Il.: Kensinger Press, 1995.

Kishel, Gregory, and Patricia Kishel. **Start, Run, and Profit From Your Own Home-Based Business.** New York: John Wiley and Sons, Inc., 1991.

Levinson, Jay C., and Charles Rubin. **Guerrilla Selling.** Boston: Houghton Mifflin Company, 1992.

Long, Steve, and Cindy Long. **You Can Make Money From Your Arts and Crafts.** Scotts Valley, Calif.: Mark Publishing, 1988.

Maslowski, Karen L. **Sew Up a Storm: All the Way to the Bank!** Cincinnati: SewStorm Publishing, 1995.

Ramsey, Dan. **The Crafter's Guide to Pricing Your Work.** Cincinnati: Betterway Books, 1997.

Roehr, Mary A. **Sewing as a Home Business.** Sedona, Ariz.: Mary Roehr Books and Video, 1996.

Shaeffer, Claire. **Price It Right.** Palm Springs, Calif.: La Mode Illustree, 1984.

Spike, Kathleen. **Sew to Success.** Portland, Ore.: Palmer/Pletsch Associates, 1990.

Sykes, Barbara Wright. **The "Business" of Sewing.** Chino Hills, Calif.: Collins Publications, 1992.

No other titles available

Searched sewing FLLS - 295 titles - cool!
looked at first

A House of Tailors? Novel?

Index